BABY-LED BOTTLE FEEDING

The Key to Problem-free Feeding

Rowena Bennett

Your Baby Series

BABY-LED BOTTLE FEEDING

The Key to Problem-free Feeding

Rowena Bennett

Registered nurse
Certified midwife
Certified mental health nurse
Certified child, adolescent, and family health nurse
Graduate Diploma in Health Promotions
International Board Certified Lactation Consultant (IBCLC)

Published by Your Baby Series
PO Box 1260
Maroochydore Qld
AUSTRALIA

www.rowenabennett.com

ISBN 978-0-6480984-2-3

Other books by Rowena Bennett
Your Sleepless Baby (also available in Spanish - **Tu Bebé Desvelado) Your Baby's Bottle-feeding Aversion (**also available in Spanish – **La Aversion Du Su Bebe)**

Available from leading online bookstores, Amazon, and the author's websites.

www.babycareadvice.com

www.rowenabennett.com

Dedicated to the thousands of parents I have seen during my career regarding baby care problems. You have challenged me to learn more about the reasons and solutions to infant feeding and sleeping problems. I have written this book in the hope that babies (and their parents) may be spared from the negative consequences of unrecognized and unresolved bottle-feeding problems.

Contents

Important disclaimer

Baby-led Bottle Feeding: The key to problem-free feeding is designed to help parents and caregivers obtain general information about caring for, and promoting the health of babies and children. Information, opinions, or judgments in this book are not intended as a substitute for medical advice. The content is provided for general use and may be unsuitable for babies or children suffering from certain conditions, diagnosed or otherwise.

Accordingly, no person should rely on the contents of this book without first obtaining appropriate medical advice. This publication is sold entirely on the understanding that the author and/or consultants and/or editors are not responsible for the results of any actions taken on the basis of information in this publication, nor for an error or omission from this publication, and further that the publisher is not engaged in rendering medical, pediatric, or professional or other advice or services. The publisher and author, consultants and editors expressly disclaim all liability to any person, whether a purchaser or reader of this publication or not, in respect to anything and of the consequences of anything done or omitted to be done by any such person in reliance whether wholly or partially upon the whole or any part of the contents of this publication. Without limiting the generality of the above, no author, consultant or editor shall have any responsibility for any act or omission of any other author, consultant, or editor.

About the Author

My husband Bruce and I live on the Sunshine Coast in Queensland, Australia. We have three adult children, Hayden, Jessica, and Caitlin, and five beautiful grandchildren, Elijah ('Eli'), Willow, Harlow, Isla, and Bodhi. All my children and grandchildren were breastfed, but would also bottle-feed when necessary.

Following a 45-year career educating parents on the care of babies, I retired from providing baby care consultations in 2021. I now spend my time writing parenting books and articles. I also train and provide clinical supervision to others to use my methods and provide consultations through my website www.babycareadvice.com.

My other two parenting books are:

- *Your Sleepless Baby: The rescue guide*; and
- *Your Baby's Bottle-feeding Aversion: Reasons and solutions.*

I continue to be passionate about helping parents to prevent and resolve baby care problems and plan to add to this list.

Professional bottle-feeding experience

Throughout my nursing career, I have personally bottle-fed hundreds of babies while working as a pediatric nurse, midwife, and child health nurse.

Australia is one of only a handful of countries that train child health nurses to facilitate well-baby health checks, monitor babies' growth and development and provide health and parenting education. This helps parents better understand their baby's nutritional, physical and emotional needs and behavior, and their responsibility when feeding and caring for their baby.

Where I learned the most about resolving simple and complex infant feeding problems was while working as a child health nurse in an early parenting education center. At these centers the parent(s) and baby or toddler are admitted for four to five days. There they receive 24-hour hands-on support to find Nonmedical solutions to **behavioral** childcare problems, such as those that cause prolonged periods of crying, feeding, sleeping and growth issues. As you can imagine, the demand for admission to these centers is high and waiting lists are long.

Working side-by-side with families for 8-hour shifts in one of these centers afforded me unique learning opportunities that **extremely few** health professionals globally would have when consulted about infant feeding and feeding-related problems during brief health appointments.

I learned from other child health nurses who shared knowledge and experiences. I learned from parents who verbalized their concerns and fears, and shared assumptions made about the reasons for their baby's behavior. Parents relayed the advice they had received before their admission—some of which was good, some unhelpful, and some advice had caused or contributed to an existing feeding problem. Plus I had countless opportunities to observe babies bottle-feeding and learn how babies responded to different infant feeding practices and equipment.

Through these combined experiences I learned what works and what causes or makes infant feeding problems worse.

Why I wrote this book

We would all agree that feeding is one of the most important aspects of caring for a baby. Numerous resources are available to parents who choose to breastfeed, such as support from breastfeeding counsellors, lactation consultants, breastfeeding classes and support groups, and an abundance of books that provide information and advice on how to breastfeed and resolve breastfeeding problems.

By contrast, parents who choose to bottle-feed their baby have access to only a few resources. When it comes to books, those available contain little more than basic bottle-feeding instructions. Seldom are these parents taught about the intricacies of bottle-feeding a baby, for example how to choose feeding equipment to match their baby's sucking abilities, feeding positions that support a baby's latch, sucking and swallowing coordination, or how to interpret and respond to their baby's feeding cues.

The scarcity of bottle-feeding information—in particular that which relates to the causes of, and solutions to, behavioral feeding problems—may be because people in general assume that bottle-feeding is easy. It can appear that way, just as breastfeeding can appear to be effortless for some, but that's not the case for all. Bottle-feeding a baby is more complex than most people realize. And potential problems are plentiful.

Feeding a healthy baby is meant to be an enjoyable experience, and indeed it can be. However, for many parents, it can be filled with uncertainty and self-doubt. During my career, I have witnessed so much suffering related to infant feeding problems (breast, bottle and solids). Babies become so distressed at feeding times, that they choose to go hungry rather than eat. Others are unknowingly prevented from accessing the milk due to equipment and feeding position problems. Feeding battles between parents and their babies (and children) can persist for months or years. Many parents suffer extreme anxiety or depression caused by dealing with prolonged, unresolved infant feeding problems.

In most instances the baby's and parent's suffering could have been avoided. It occurred because of lack of knowledge—their own and that of the healthcare professionals they consulted—related to the reasons and solutions to **behavioral bottle-feeding problems**. ("Behavioral" meaning the baby's feeding difficulties are linked to the parent's infant feeding practices. For example, the parent's choice of infant feeding equipment, the way the parent positions their baby for feeding, and the actions the parent takes, or does not take, in response to their baby's behavioral cues.)

Far too many health professionals and baby care educators advise parents to employ **parent-led** feeding practices, which have the **potential to cause** infant feeding problems. When problems develop, infant crying, fussy and avoidant feeding behavior, poor growth or gastrointestinal symptoms related to behavioral causes are often mistakenly attributed to physical problems or medical conditions.

After such a long career, I have no doubt that **baby-led** feeding—whether this be bottle-feeding, breastfeeding or when eating solid foods—is the best option for **physically well, typically developing babies**. Years of experience specializing in educating parents have confirmed that baby-led feeding is **the most effective** way to prevent and resolve infant feeding problems.

So much of what I have learned about **baby-led** bottle-feeding, and share in this book, is not yet taught to parents in maternity hospitals, or during well-baby health checks. My feeding recommendations differ from **parent-led** feeding practices (the dominant style taught to parents, childcare workers, doctors, midwives, nurses, and other health professionals to this day).

I wrote this book because I want parents to know the reasons behind, and solutions to **behavioral feeding problems**, so that they can appreciate that their baby's enjoyment in feeding is in their hands. My goal is to empower parents to avoid and resolve infant feeding problems and experience joy in this precious time with their baby.

Acknowledgments

I wish to thank Jessica Perini and Candace Johnson for their editing services. I give you credit for helping me to develop as an author and making it appear like I am a better writer than I am.

Introduction

Two things will increase your chances of enjoying problem-free bottle-feeding with your baby: luck and knowledge. The more you know, the less you need to rely on luck.

If you're reading this book, you have made the decision to either exclusively or partially bottle-feed your baby and want to learn more about bottle-feeding in general. Or you might have been unlucky, hence you're looking for answers to a feeding problem that is troubling your baby. Either way, I applaud you for recognizing that there's more to learn.

No one knows your baby as well as you. So, I'm not going to tell you what you should or should not do. Only **you** can decide how to best meet **your baby's** nutritional and emotional needs. I realize that this might initially appear daunting. However, as you learn more, you will gain more confidence about the decisions you make.

What's in this book?

Part A: Feeding Basics

Choosing a parenting style, which includes feeding practices, is one of the most important decisions you can make as a parent. Matching your infant feeding practices to meet the needs of **your baby** is the key to problem-free feeding.

No single method of feeding will universally match the needs of every baby. As the title of this book suggests, I encourage parents of **typically developing babies** to practice baby-led feeding. However, in certain circumstances you may need to take the lead (parent-led feeding). When to lead and when to follow will become clear as you read the pages in this book.

Part A covers:

- How baby-led feeding compares to parent-led feeding.
- Experiences that caused me to question the effectiveness of parent-led feeding strategies.
- What influences an individual baby's milk needs, and why it's not possible for others to know how much milk your baby needs at any given point in time.
- How babies know when and how much to eat. Why you can trust your baby to decide. And how to tell if she's eating enough. (It's not by looking at how many ounces or milliliters she has consumed.)

Part B: Understand your Baby

To understand your role and responsibilities when feeding your baby begins with knowledge of what it means to be a baby, what babies need, how advancements in development change their needs, the way they communicate, and the level of support they require from parents and caregivers.

Part B covers:

- Behaviors linked to infant reflexes and urges, what these are, how they are triggered, and what they mean and don't mean. (They are often misinterpreted.)
- Cues that newborns and babies over three months display when hungry, full, satisfied, frustrated and stressed.
- Why it's helpful to recognize your baby's temperament.
- How to use "timing" and "context" to increase your accuracy in interpreting your baby's behavioral cues.
- What to expect as your baby matures physically, intellectually and emotionally.
- Feeding skills babies acquire at different stages of development.

Part C: Types of Milk and Preparation

We all appreciate how important good quality nutrition is to a baby. Choosing the best milk for your baby might be an easy decision or you could feel overwhelmed by the many options (and opinions) available. The quality of your baby's nutrition is not solely based on your choice of milk or formula. How you prepare, store and transport your baby's milk feeds, and what you add to her milk will all have an effect on the quality.

Part C covers:

- The benefits of breast milk and why it's **rarely** necessary to switch a baby from breast milk to infant formula.
- How an oversupply of breast milk can cause gastrointestinal (GI) symptoms.
- Different types of baby formula, why you might choose one over another and how to tell if your choice of baby formula is the reason for your baby's feeding troubles or GI symptoms.
- How to accurately prepare and store breast milk and baby formula, preparation errors, and how to protect your baby from food poisoning.
- The benefits and risks associated with giving a baby calorie-enhanced feeds, concentrated baby formula, fortified breast milk, oral nutritional supplements or thickened feeds.

Part D: The Act of Feeding

Feeding provides opportunities for your baby to learn when and how much to eat, practice and master new skills, develop a healthy relationship with food, and form a close emotional bond with you.

These are no small things!

How you respond to your baby's behavioral cues while feeding her is the key to harmonious collaboration between you both. However, the many behind-the-scenes decisions you need to make, like feeding equipment and position, will also contribute to her contentment while feeding.

Part D covers:

- How to tell if your choice of infant feeding equipment is suitable, the pros and cons of different styles of nipples and bottles, and whether you can rely on manufacturers' claims about the proposed advantages of their products.
- Good and poor feeding positions.
- How to interpret and respond to your baby's feeding cues.
- What happens to swallowed air, how and when to burp a baby, and whether it matters if she burps or not.

Part E: Combining Breastfeeding and Bottle-feeding

You might be currently breastfeeding your baby, but would like her to occasionally bottle-feed. Or you might have decided to switch from breastfeeding to bottle-feeding, but are facing difficulties getting your baby to feed from a bottle.

Part E covers:

- How breastfeeding and bottle-feeding differ.
- Pros and cons of giving occasional bottle-feeds to a breastfed baby.
- The best time to introduce a bottle to a breastfed baby.
- How to use paced bottle-feeds to minimize the risk of nipple confusion.
- How to successfully combine breastfeeding and bottle-feeding.
- How to switch a baby from breastfeeding to bottle-feeding.
- Steps to take if a breastfed baby refuses to feed from a bottle.

Part F: Nonmedical Feeding Problems

Infant behavioral problems—meaning nonmedical problems—are linked to the decisions we make, and the actions we take or don't take when feeding a baby.

Behavioral feeding (and sleeping) problems are without exception the most common of all reasons for unexplained crying, fussy or avoidant feeding behavior, unusual gastrointestinal symptoms, and poor or rapid growth displayed by physically well, typically developing babies. And yet they are the least well known, and often overlooked or mistakenly attributed to physical problems or medical conditions.

Part F covers:

- Infant feeding strategies that can annoy, frustrate or stress a baby or which may be potentially dangerous.
- How sleep affects feeding and why some babies have trouble sleeping.
- How to recognize and fix feeding equipment problems.
- Unusual feeding patterns—for example snacking, excessive night feedings, and eating more at night than during the day—why this happens and how to remedy the situation.
- Overfeeding causes, signs and symptoms, why overfeeding is often overlooked and misdiagnosed.

- Underfeeding causes, signs and symptoms, and myths associated with underfeeding that cause parents needless anxiety.
- Bottle-feeding aversion, what it is, what causes it, how to recognize it and where to find a solution.
- Top 25 concerning and confusing infant feeding behaviors and potential reasons for each.
- My Infant Feeding Practices Self-Evaluation Checklist to systematically explore causes of behavioral feeding problems.

Part G: Physical and Medical Problems

Your baby will at times surprise or alarm you. Perhaps it's what comes out of her tiny body—top or bottom end—when milk is the only thing that goes in. Or that she fusses and cries for no obvious reason. Or appears to have difficulty sucking and swallowing.

Such occurrences could be normal for a baby, or they could be a sign of a problem that could be relieved by medications, dietary change or feeding therapies. Or it could simply be that you need to change your infant feeding practices.

Part G looks at:

- What a feeding assessment includes, and why you need to be wary of a 5-minute diagnosis. How to avoid the snowball effect of overlooked or misdiagnosed behavioral feeding problems.
- Medical and nonmedical reasons for spitting up, extreme farting, constipation and frequent watery bowel movements, and steps you can take to minimize your baby's discomfort.
- The signs and symptoms of commonly diagnosed medical conditions, such as colic, gastroesophageal reflux disease (GERD), milk protein allergy and intolerance, and others. What else can cause the same signs and symptoms.
- How to tell if your baby has physical reasons for sucking and swallowing problems. Behavioral feeding problems that give the appearance of sucking or swallowing difficulties.

What's not covered in this book?

The information and feeding recommendations included in this book relate to **physically well, typically developing babies** who can safely feed from a bottle. This book **does not** cover:

- feeding recommendations for babies with special needs; or
- treatment recommendations for medical conditions affecting feeding.

Babies born with congenital abnormalities or genetic conditions or syndromes and those who develop acute or chronic illnesses are vulnerable to feeding and growth problems.

If you have a baby with special needs, don't assume that all feeding issues that your baby experiences are related to a previously diagnosed, or yet to be diagnosed, medical condition. If your baby has a medical condition, he can still develop feeding problems related to **behavioral** causes, such as those described in this book. In fact, a physical challenge can increase the risk of a baby developing behavioral feeding problems. So, you may find you can improve the situation through your infant feeding practices.

Note: If your baby with special needs can feed safely from a bottle, then most of the information in this book will be relevant. Discuss any findings with your baby's healthcare professionals before making changes to the infant feeding practices they may have advised.

How to use this book

I developed this book as a **reference book.** It does not need to be read from cover to cover. I have arranged it in an order that I believe might best aid your learning, but you don't need to read chapters in any particular order. You can, of course, skip chapters that don't apply.

Imagine the topics as pieces of a jigsaw puzzle. The more you read, the easier it will be to see the "big picture," the more knowledge you will have and the more confident you will feel when making decisions about your baby's cares.

Some information relates to specific age groups, for example newborns and babies over the age of three months. Regardless of the age of your baby,

I recommend you read about both age groups to better understand your baby's behavior.

Note: The case studies are real but the names have been changed.

Who will find this book helpful?

- **Bottle-fed babies.** Babies enjoy feeding when their parents' infant feeding practices harmonize with their nutritional and emotional needs. Therefore, bottle-fed babies will benefit from their parents reading this book.
- **Parents planning to bottle-feed their baby.** Reading this book will enhance your confidence and your chances of enjoying problem-free bottle-feeding.
- **Child-care workers, nannies, and other caregivers.** You can help the babies in your care by informing their parents of any identified bottle-feeding problems and solutions.
- **Health professionals who care for or teach parents to care for babies.** I hope that by reading this book health professionals will start to question some of the infant feeding practices they have been taught and are teaching parents. A shift from routinely teaching parent-led feeding practices toward baby-led feeding is long overdue.

Part A:
Feeding Basics

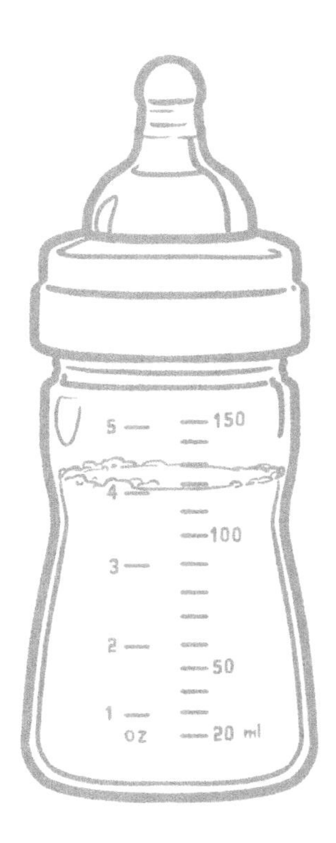

My Journey to Baby-Led Feeding

MY QUEST TO FIND A SOLUTION FOR "FUSSY FEEDERS" • HOW MY VIEWS CHANGED • WHY I PROMOTE BABY-LED FEEDING

When I first started training as a nurse, I was taught that parent-led feeding practices were necessary to ensure a baby's nutritional needs were met. I blindly accepted this. But with each passing year and each move into a new nursing field, I learned more about feeding babies. What I discovered led me to question everything I had been taught and had been teaching others about bottle-feeding babies.

The more I learned, the more convinced I became. Advice that centered on adults controlling a baby's feeding was not only inappropriate but could and indeed did often lead to terrible outcomes for babies and their families. As I gained more knowledge and experience, my recommendations on **how to feed** a bottle-fed baby completely changed.

If you are a parent of a baby or a health professional who is often consulted on baby feeding issues, please take the time to read this chapter and learn from my experience.

Meeting feeding refusal babies

After qualifying as a registered nurse, I worked in pediatric wards for several years. I recall many physically well babies being admitted to the ward where I worked because of "feeding refusal" and poor growth. These babies had a history of feeding well. Hence, they knew how to bottle-feed. And yet, they refused to eat despite displaying visible signs of hunger. They acted as if they would rather starve than eat. Because they were often distressed, health professionals assumed that their feeding refusal was because of pain caused by acid reflux or milk allergy or intolerance.

Once admitted and medically examined, they were given acid-suppressing medications and switched to a hypoallergenic baby formula, which was then thickened with rice flour.

Medical treatments seldom made a difference to feeding-refusal babies' willingness to bottle-feed. It was assumed that their bodies required time to heal now that treatment had been implemented. And that once healed, they would return to willingly feeding when hungry. Until that time, forcing them to drink sufficient volumes of milk was considered necessary, albeit a stressful experience for the baby and parent or nurse.

As a young nurse, I was taught how to force-feed a baby to ensure he consumed the recommended volume. I hated doing it. It felt so wrong! But I was young and inexperienced, and I did what other more experienced nurses instructed me to do. I was also responsible for teaching the parents of feeding-refusal babies how to pressure or force their baby to eat. Once the parent demonstrated that they could make their baby drink sufficient volumes, the baby was discharged. Some babies would be readmitted to the hospital weeks later to have a feeding tube inserted because their parents were no longer able to make them eat enough to support healthy growth.

With hindsight, I've realized that this was my first exposure to babies who had developed a feeding aversion.

After a few years of working in pediatric wards, I wanted a new challenge and decided to become a midwife.

Learning the art of subtle pressure

During my midwifery training, I learned how to bottle-feed sleepy preterm and newly born full-term babies. They often needed coaxing to complete the recommended volume of milk.

Encouraging these tiny tots to finish a feed was not difficult. They would be swaddled for feeding to prevent them from startling, and all that was required to trigger their sucking reflex was some gentle upward pressure under their chin and an occasional jiggle or twisting of the bottle to prevent them from falling asleep and keep them sucking. The parents who chose to bottle-feed their babies were taught these strategies.

I had no idea of the potential ramifications if parents continued to employ these tactics over the long term.

At the time, back in the '80s, the average stay in maternity hospitals was five days after a vaginal delivery and seven to 10 days following a cesarean section. I never worked harder in any field of nursing than I did as a midwife. I can only imagine how hard midwives work today with much shorter admission times resulting in a higher turnover of patients. Most simply don't have time to do more than provide basic feeding instructions to breastfeeding and bottle-feeding mothers. (Hence another good reason to write this book.)

Once my youngest started school, I decided to train as a mental health nurse.

Behavioral theory awareness

At the adult mental health facility where I worked, babies would be admitted to be reunited with their mothers, who were recovering from postpartum depression or puerperal psychosis and were close to being discharged. While I didn't feed many babies during my employment as a mental health nurse, I did learn a lot that would later prove useful concerning bottle-feeding—for example, behavioral and attachment theories and the effect that childcare practices have on a baby's behavior and emotional development.

I loved learning about the psychology involved, but the practical aspect of mental health nursing was not as I expected. After only two years, I decided to move on and train as a child health nurse.

Fussy feeder challenges

When I first decided to apply to train as a child health nurse, in my naivete, I thought, "This will be a piece of cake!" As the mother of three children with years of experience as a midwife and pediatric nurse, how much more could there be to learn about the care of physically well babies? Turns out, **a lot!**

For the next 20 years, I worked alongside other nurses in a government-funded early parenting education center. I finally found my niche as a child health nurse. I loved working with families as well as the autonomy that child health nurses have in planning care and providing parenting education.

As child health nurses, our primary role was to assist parents to resolve **behavioral** (nonmedical) feeding and sleeping problems that commonly trouble healthy babies and toddlers. When solving infant feeding and sleeping problems is your main objective, and it's what you're paid to do, you tend to get good at identifying the cause.

There were very few infant feeding problems that we nurses were unable to solve, with one notable exception: the babies we referred to as "fussy feeders".

Fussy feeders knew how to bottle-feed, but they acted like you were trying to poison them merely by offering a bottle. When awake, they would fuss, cry, and refuse to feed or eat very little even though they were clearly hungry. Some fed well when drowsy or asleep. Before their admission, these babies had already been treated for just about every physical condition known to cause pain or difficulties while feeding. However, treatments had made no difference to their feeding behavior, and so their refusal to eat was then assumed to be "behavioral."

Fussy feeders displayed the **exact same** behavior as the feeding-refusal babies from the pediatric wards where I had worked years earlier. It was now apparent to me that not all the feeding-refusal babies I had cared for in pediatric wards went home to heal and return to enjoy feeding. Many were admitted to early parenting education centers once medical treatments proved ineffective.

From my studies on behavioral theories, I then recognized the behavior of fussy feeders as **aversive** behavior: their distress and resistance to feeding was because they had developed an aversion to (fear of) feeding!

This realization opened the door to a possible solution. An aversion can be solved. There would be **triggers** (these cause the baby to react) and **reinforcements** (these encourage the behavior to repeat). Remove the trigger and reinforcements, and the baby's avoidant feeding behavior would fade (decrease in frequency and intensity) and eventually cease. This sounds simple. But first, you had to identify the trigger and reinforcements. This was the first hurdle. Back then, it was not clear to me what the trigger and reinforcements were. The parents were feeding their baby as was, and still is, generally advised by health professionals, myself included at that time. So nothing stood out as being the cause.

What could cause a hungry baby to fear feeding? It was assumed to be because of pain due to acid reflux or milk protein allergy, or intolerance. But most of these babies did not display other signs associated with these conditions. And so, I was not convinced that these were the trigger. In addition, treatments such as medications and dietary changes often failed to resolve the problem of the baby's avoidant, distressed feeding behavior.

In some cases, the baby only had to be held in a feeding position before he would start to fuss and cry. Medical professionals assumed this avoidant feeding behavior was due to the baby associating the act of feeding with pain before treatments had removed the pain. But I knew behavior must be reinforced to continue, and if the baby no longer experienced pain while feeding, then he would stop trying to avoid feeding within a week or two. I was baffled as to what the cause could be.

Working at the parenting education center enabled me to observe babies feeding. I started to closely watch how the parents and nurses fed fussy feeders. "A battle of wills" is how I would describe the situation. The baby would cry, turn, and arch away in an attempt to avoid feeding. The parent or nurse would restrain the baby's movements and persist in holding the nipple in his mouth, jiggling and twisting the bottle, and manipulating his jaw to try to make him suck. The parent or nurse would only give up once the baby had reluctantly consumed what was considered an "acceptable" volume or when it seemed futile to continue.

The experience was at best unpleasant, but more often than not, stressful for the baby. Some parents relayed that they would spend up to two hours each feed at home, trying to make sure their baby ate "enough." No wonder these babies tried to avoid feeding!

This realization raised more unanswered questions. At this point, all I knew was that these babies should **not** be forced to feed. No baby should be forced to feed. But what was the alternative? If not forced, fussy feeders' milk intake dropped significantly, well below volumes that would support healthy growth. Would they starve themselves? Some say no. Some say yes. They certainly acted like they were prepared to starve. Or would they return to willingly feeding once they were no longer pressured to eat? And, if so, how long would it take?

These babies had not always been pressured or forced to feed. Parents often commented that their fussy feeder had once been a "great feeder." So what caused these babies to become averse to feeding in the first place? How could I be sure that pressuring or forcing them to feed was the only reinforcement of their avoidant feeding behavior?

So began my quest to find a solution for fussy feeders, a.k.a. feeding-averse babies.

Lightbulb moments: "fussy feeding" solutions

In 2002, I decided to branch into private practice and started an internet-based consultation service called Baby Care Advice (www.babycareadvice.com). Years of experience with infant feeding and sleeping problems informed which questions I asked the parents to pinpoint the cause. While I was able to assist parents in finding a solution to **most** infant feeding problems, the dilemma of how to get a fussy feeder to return to being a great feeder continued to evade me. But I eventually figured it out.

I distinctly recall **four lightbulb learning experiences** that gave me new insight and, thus, a new perspective on the fussy feeder conundrum, which enabled me to finally come up with an effective solution.

1. Ellyn Satter's "Division of Responsibility in Feeding" and videos.
2. Learning about dietary regulation.
3. Learning about homeostasis.
4. Lactation consultant education.

Responsibilities of parents and babies

My first realization occurred when I watched a video of Canadian dietitian Ellyn Satter demonstrating the signals babies give when they have had enough to eat (called satiety cues). Once she had pointed out what the behavior meant, it seemed so obvious. Why had I not recognized this before? And why were parents (and health care professionals) not routinely taught to watch for signs that their baby is satisfied?

Ellyn Satter's theory on the "Division of Responsibility" is the cornerstone of baby-led feeding:

Division of Responsibility

- The parent is responsible for what.
- The child is responsible for how much.

Could overlooking a baby's satiety cues be the trigger that eventually turned a great feeder into a fussy feeder? Yes, absolutely.

As enlightening as this revelation was, it didn't help with the dilemma of how to help fussy feeders. Many would **refuse to start** eating even though they were clearly hungry. And when they did eat, it was very little. They didn't display satiety cues, signaling their satisfaction as a result of eating enough, because they did not willingly feed until reaching that point. They stopped in an abrupt and upset manner, turned and arched away, and cried after consuming only a small volume. They were clearly still hungry but refused to eat more. If it was left to fussy feeders to decide how much to eat, they would undoubtedly lose weight.

While I still didn't have a solution for fussy feeders, because of Ellyn Satter's work, I changed how I fed all other babies and taught parents to feed their **non-feeding-averse** babies. I now ended the feed as soon as I recognized the baby wanted to stop and encouraged parents to do the same.

I continued to search for answers for why babies become averse to bottle-feeding and what reinforced their avoidant feeding behavior. I knew the "why" would be an invaluable key to finding a solution.

Healthy babies and dietary balance

My second light bulb moment was when I researched how babies regulate their dietary intake (described in chapters 2 and 3).

As a result, I now understood that **healthy babies** would not starve, provided they were offered sufficient food and were able to freely access the food. However, while feeding-averse babies have the same inborn mechanisms enabling them to regulate their dietary intake, this can be overridden by **an even stronger desire** to avoid the stress of being pressured or forced to feed.

I concluded that while feeding-averse babies might initially resist feeding, consume less than their body needs, and lose some weight, they would eventually come around and self-regulate their dietary intake to meet their growth and energy needs. That is, so long as they were **no longer** pressured to feed.

This conclusion presented even more questions. How could I be sure I had identified all potential reinforcements? How much weight would these babies lose in the process of resolving their aversion? Could weight loss cause the baby harm? I felt confident a small loss wouldn't cause harm. But what if weight loss was substantial?

Parents are often fearful of letting their bottle-fed baby decide how much to eat. This is because of claims they'd heard that their baby could suffer from impaired brain development or stunted growth if he didn't eat enough. I needed to know how much weight loss would be too much.

Homeostasis: internal states of harmony and balance

Learning about dietary regulation naturally led to gaining more knowledge about homeostasis because they are connected. Homeostasis is how our body maintains an internal state of harmony and balance (described in chapters 2 and 3).

Understanding how homeostatic mechanisms maintain blood sugar levels within normal parameters in the absence of food dispelled the widespread myth about a **brief** reduction in milk intake causing impaired brain development.

And as far as a **small temporary weight loss** causing stunted growth, most experienced parents know the truth about that myth. Weight loss is expected when a baby suffers from an infective illness like a cold or flu, or from gastroenteritis. Babies get sick, lose their appetite, eat less, lose a little weight, recover, their appetite returns, they eat very well, and experience "catch-up" growth. If the baby's growth potential isn't harmed when he experiences weight loss during a short-term illness, then it's reasonable to assume that a similar loss experienced while resolving a baby's feeding aversion would have no long-term ill effects on the baby's growth.

This answered my question about how much weight loss would be acceptable, but I still had unanswered questions.

As an additional benefit, learning more about homeostasis helped me better understand so many things about babies, like

- why babies regurgitate milk (a.k.a. gastroesophageal reflux);

- why so many newborns become gassy and suffer because of abdominal discomfort;
- why they have mucous or blood in their stools (it's not solely due to milk allergy);
- why their stools turn green;
- where swallowed air goes;
- what protects babies from aspirating milk into their lungs or choking on food;
- how they digest and absorb nutrients from the foods they eat;
- what causes babies to grow;
- how their body reacts when they are given acid-suppressing medications;
- the importance of healthy gut microbiome (good bacteria in the intestinal tract); and
- so much more.

Breastfeeding: A model for bottle-feeding practices

I found an answer to potential reinforcements of aversive bottle-feeding behavior in an unlikely place: while studying to qualify as an International Board Certified Lactation Consultant (IBCLC) in 2009.

During my breastfeeding studies, I learned more about the biomechanics involved in breastfeeding (plus a lot of other beneficial breastfeeding information). This helped me recognize **serious flaws** in the feeding advice routinely dispensed to **bottle-fed** babies' parents. For example, parents of bottle-fed babies are often taught to

- restrict their baby's arm movements during feeds by swaddling or other means;
- pull down on their baby's lower jaw to cause him to open his mouth or gently push the nipple through clamped lips;
- gently squeeze their baby's cheeks to make him close his mouth around the nipple;
- apply upward pressure under their baby's chin to trigger the sucking reflex;
- twist or jiggle the nipple to trigger the sucking reflex;

- persist with the feed, despite their baby's resistance, to reach a target volume of milk each feed or each day;
- continue the feed for a specified time, for example, 30 or 45 minutes, irrespective of their baby's desire to stop sooner; and
- adhere to rigid, predetermined feeding times, for example, every three or four hours; and
- measure and record the volume of milk consumed.

Not one of the strategies listed would be taught to nursing mothers today. (At least I hope they're not taught!)

I appreciate that health professionals, in general, promote parent-led feeding strategies (listed above) with the intent of "encouraging" and "supporting" bottle-fed babies to feed. However, if a breastfed baby does not require his mother to go to such lengths to encourage and support him to breastfeed, then why do so because he feeds from a bottle instead?

While we may think we're encouraging and supporting a baby to eat by using such strategies, the reality is that these methods involve subtle and not-so-subtle forms of pressure to control when and how much a baby eats. No doubt based on the widely held yet outdated **misperception** that parents and caregivers are responsible for deciding if a bottle-fed baby has had enough to eat. This is simply not possible when a baby is breastfed.

While some of these strategies **might** be necessary for weak and sleepy preterm or newly born full-term babies, or babies experiencing hypoglycemia (low blood sugar levels) or jaundiced babies after birth, I had learned from experience that they are **not necessary and not appropriate** when feeding **healthy, robust** babies. Especially once they reached a stage in their development where they are capable of self-regulating their milk intake (decide for themselves when and how much to eat) and signal when they are satisfied, which is typically around eight weeks of age.

Of course, not all parents try to control how much their baby eats. Many parents disregard advice that promotes timed feedings and target volumes per feed. They take on a more relaxed attitude of "let baby take what he wants and throw out the rest." However, those who continue to employ controlling feeding practices (such as those listed) are more likely to encounter infant feeding problems.

We all know that breastfeeding is the "normal" feeding method for babies. Babies are biologically programmed to breastfeed. And so, how babies breastfeed can be a model for bottle-feeding. Though the sucking action for bottle-feeding is different from breastfeeding, it can be helpful to imitate other aspects that occur when breastfeeding.

The accumulation of what I learned to this point made me realize what a **grave disservice** we health professionals provide to babies by overlooking or misinterpreting their satiety cues, pressuring them to feed against their will to reach target volumes, and teaching their parents to do the same.

I had blindly accepted what I had been taught, as most health professionals and parents do when we don't know any better. I taught parents to use these feeding strategies without realizing that I (and countless other health professionals) were unknowingly setting the stage that would cause some, if not many, of these babies to develop behavioral feeding problems down the road. Problems that would later be mistakenly attributed to physical conditions.

It was only with hindsight that I realized that what we were (and are still) doing by providing or following such bottle-feeding advice was to **work against** a healthy baby's inborn feeding and dietary self-regulatory abilities.

The dilemma of the fussy feeders solved

At last! I had answers as to why a great feeder could become a fussy feeder or feeding refuser.

I could visualize how the situation developed. Parents are taught how to bottle-feed their babies using some or most of the strategies listed with good faith and the best of intentions, but lacking an awareness of the long-term consequences. Parents persisted with the pressure until their baby eventually grew strong enough to object.

The more the parent (or other caregiver) persisted in trying to control how much their baby ate, the more their baby resisted. The more their baby resisted, the more the parent pressured their baby to feed. A vicious cycle developed until their baby became averse to feeding.

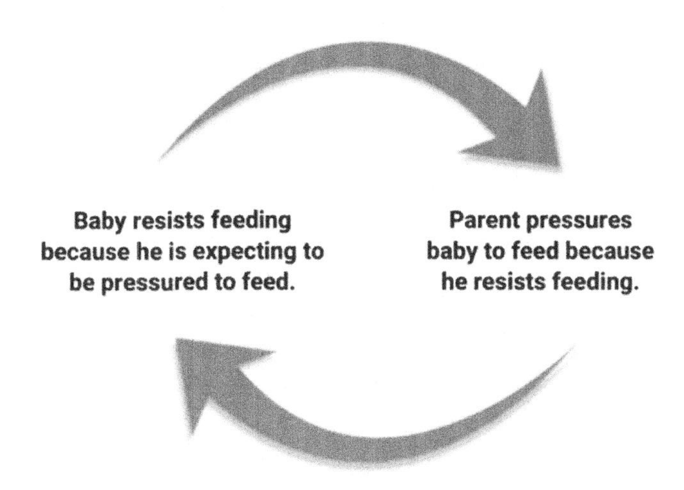

The parents perpetuated this cycle by continuing to try to control when and how much their baby ate—possibly on the advice of the baby's healthcare professional—and by doing so, reinforced their baby's aversion to feeding.

I was now more confident about having identified **direct** reinforcements, which were any strategies that parents employed to "encourage" their baby to accept a feed when he was refusing to do so or "support" him to continue to eat once he indicated that he wanted to stop. For the first time, I felt the stirrings of a plan to enable fussy feeders to enjoy feeding once more.

However, I still didn't know how long it would take a baby to recover from a feeding aversion once all pressure was removed. And little did I know at that time, I was yet to figure out the strategies employed by parents—and recommended by health professionals—that would **indirectly** reinforce an infant feeding aversion. (Other reasons for feeding aversion are described in chapter 27.)

Shifting from parent-led to baby-led feeding

Obvious forms of pressure were the first to go. I provided instruction on baby-led feeding practices (described in chapter 16). Education focused on helping parents interpret their baby's behavioral cues, feed in a way that was responsive to their baby's cues, demonstrate respect and trust in their baby's inborn ability to decide how much to eat, and learn to tell when a baby was well fed without dependence on scales or measuring volumes consumed.

This proved to be far more successful than I had imagined. Around nine out of 10 fussy feeders showed signs of improvement within a matter of days as their aversive-feeding behavior began to "fade." I discovered that it would typically take around two weeks for a feeding-averse baby to switch from acting like he was about to be poisoned to getting excited when offered a bottle and return to being a "great feeder." By two weeks, his milk intake would increase to a level that supported healthy growth. Weight loss was minimal. No worse—in fact, less so—than typically occurs during a bout of illness.

Ninety percent was a good success rate. But not good enough! I felt I was letting down the parents of the remaining 10 percent. I racked my brain trying to figure out why these babies did not make the same improvement. As I supported parents through the process of resolving their baby's feeding aversion, I discovered that **indirect reinforcements,** like feeding a drowsy or sleeping baby during the day, over-offering the bottle, providing extra feeds at night to increase the baby's daily milk intake, giving the baby milk via a spoon, syringe or cup, or curbing the baby's appetite with solid foods were preventing some babies from making progress. Once I figured out what these were, my success rate in resolving feeding aversions rose to around 95 percent.

"Failures" were mostly related to a lack of compliance. Some parents, in particular those suffering from extreme anxiety, admitted that they found it too hard to stop using controlling infant feeding practices. If their baby did not drink what they had been told he needed, their anxiety would skyrocket. They would quickly revert to pressuring their baby to eat the volumes they had been instructed their baby needed. Or feed their baby during sleep or provide milk in other ways. (See chapter 4 for a discussion of the flawed concept of others deciding how much milk an individual baby needs.)

In 2013, I published an article on infant feeding aversions on my Baby Care Advice website. Many of my clients commented that it had struck a chord by describing their baby's distressed feeding behavior. As a result, the number of feeding-aversion consultations I provided dramatically increased.

In 2017, after more than 1,000 successful bottle-feeding aversion cases, I published my book, *Your Baby's Bottle-Feeding Aversion*. By the time I retired from providing consultations in early 2021, I had had more than 3,500 successful cases based on consultations and an unknown number who resolved their baby's feeding aversion by following the recommendations in my book. While written for bottle-fed babies, breastfeeding mothers also found the principles and strategies helpful to resolve a breastfeeding aversion—caused by different pressure tactics.

How my quest for fussy feeders changed my practice

My journey to find a solution for fussy feeders took a total of 10 long years. It led me to learn more about all forms of feeding and about what it means to be a baby, biologically, physically, intellectually, and emotionally. As a result, I no longer feed babies in the way I was taught. I have changed the way I view infant feeding problems, from "what is wrong with the baby?" and "how can we get him to eat enough?" to "what is wrong with the way the baby is fed?" I have changed what I teach, not just to the parents of fussy feeders, but all parents. And not only about bottle-feeding, but all feeding methods.

Fussy feeders made me a better nurse and a more effective parenting educator. So that's my story—and the story of this book! This is how I came to learn so much more about bottle feeding than I had been taught.

But learning never stops, and no matter how much we may think we know, there is always more to learn. Sometimes what we learn will lead us to question what we think we know, which may be the case for you while reading this book.

My feeding advice might differ from what you have read in the past or been told or advised to do. It will go against the advice of many others who advocate for controlling feeding practice—because that's what they were taught. But these people may be unaware of the long-term consequences that such practices can have on a baby's behavior and desire to feed as he matures. So please keep an open mind.

Next

Next, I will describe how baby-led and parent-led feeding practices compare and why I promote baby-led feeding for all healthy, typically developing babies.

1 Choose a Feeding Style

TYPES OF FEEDING STYLES • BABY-LED BOTTLE-FEEDING • HOW IT COMPARES TO PARENT-LED FEEDING PRACTICES • WHY IT'S BENEFICIAL TO CHOOSE A FEEDING STYLE

When I gave birth to my first child, Hayden, in 1979, I was given the standard breastfeeding advice dispensed at that time: to breastfeed for 10 minutes each side and feed every four hours. I disregarded this advice because my mother, who had successfully breastfed nine children, advised me differently. She had a relaxed approach to breastfeeding and taught me to do the same.

Thankfully, a lot has changed since the 1980s. Thanks to the tireless efforts of breastfeeding associations, we are slowly moving away from timed-based feeding toward **baby-led** breastfeeding advice—though some health professionals are still resisting the trend.

Sadly, little progress has been made to move toward **baby-led bottle-feeding**. Many parents of bottle-fed babies continue to be instructed to feed at scheduled times and to ensure their baby consumes a predetermined volume of milk. This is regardless of whether their baby wishes to eat or consume this volume or not.

Feeding styles

Baby feeding styles can be divided broadly into two groups: baby-led and parent-led feeding.

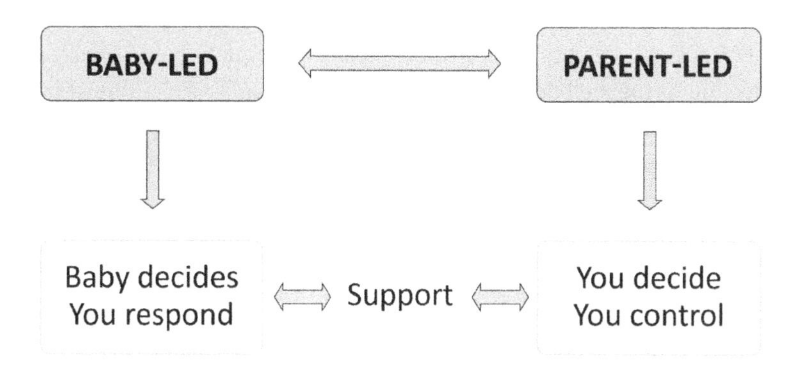

Child-centered feeding can be at either end of the spectrum or anywhere in between depending on your individual baby. It may be a matter of finding the right balance between responsiveness and control to suit your baby's physical abilities and temperament and provide the level of support she requires.

While both feeding styles have their place, the challenge is knowing when to follow and when to lead. To find the right balance, it may help to know what each style looks like.

Baby-led bottle-feeding

Baby-led feeding is often referred to as **responsive feeding**. It involves a **partnership** between the baby and parent.

Basically, you are guided by what your baby wants when it comes to feeding. You allow her to decide for herself when and how much to eat. There is no pushing her to drink more than she wants, and no limitations on her dietary intake. You provide an appropriate response that harmonizes with her behavioral cues—for example, offering a feed when she indicates hunger, allowing her to accept or reject when offered, and pausing the feed when she displays signs of frustration or stress, figuring out and remedying the cause before continuing, and ending the feed when she shows signs of satisfaction or simply that she wishes to stop eating.

I can't emphasize this enough: **your baby's enjoyment in feeding is paramount.** You can promote her enjoyment in feeding by employing baby-led practices. When she receives an appropriate response to her behavioral cues (described in chapter 6), feeding is enjoyable. If she enjoys feeding, she will eat to satisfaction, and good growth will follow.

For normal, healthy babies who can suck and safely bottle-feed, baby-led feeding is the method I recommend. It prevents and resolves **most** infant feeding problems, whether breastfeeding, bottle-feeding, or eating solids. It's also what I advise my children to do when feeding my grandchildren.

Responsive feeding has often been compared to a dance. Both parties are in step, with the baby leading. I was reminded of this comparison while watching a video of Marissa feeding her baby, Ava.

Baby Ava

Marissa originally consulted with me because Ava had become averse to bottle-feeding as a result of Marissa pressuring her to drink the volume recommended by her doctor. The video I originally viewed when Ava was in the midst of a feeding aversion showed a baby and mother who were at odds with each other. Ava was crying and attempting to avoid feeding by arching away and struggling to escape, and Marissa kept restraining Ava's movements while trying to make her continue eating.

During the consultation, I explained to Marissa what Ava's behavior was indicating and how to respond to her behavioral cues. Over time, Marissa regained Ava's trust and her bottle-feeding aversion was resolved. The most recent video, which was two weeks after we spoke, was a stark contrast to the first. Seeing Ava so relaxed and willing to feed was heartwarming. Watching how attuned Marissa now was to Ava's cues reminded me of why responsive feeding is likened to a dance. Ava was now enjoying feeding because her mom was finally in step by providing an appropriate response to her cues.

Table 1.1: Advantages and disadvantages of baby-led feeding

Advantages	Disadvantages
Key to supporting healthy eating habits from birth.[1]	A **much** greater level of parental knowledge is needed compared to parent-led feeding methods.
Supports dietary self-regulation and self-control of food intake.[2]	You must learn to read your baby's hunger and satiety (satisfaction) cues.
Linked with ideal growth (which varies depending on the individual baby), optimal nutrient intake, and long-term regulation of weight, now and into the future.[3]	You must be aware of how your decisions and actions influence your baby's behavior and feeding abilities.
Forms a basis for the **emotional bonding** or **attachment** between baby and parent.[4]	You must learn what your baby needs—physically, intellectually and emotionally—at different stages of development and your responsibilities in providing for her needs.

All reputable feeding therapy programs for typically developing children promote responsive feeding practices. If you do an internet search for "responsive feeding," you will find an abundance of evidence supporting this practice for children of all ages.

Despite strong evidence supporting responsive feeding, not all health professionals promote baby-led feeding. Why? Many health professionals mistakenly believe that babies are too young to self-regulate their dietary intake. Instead, they promote parent-led feeding practices.

Parent-led bottle-feeding

Parent-led feeding involves an **authoritarian** feeding relationship where the parent makes decisions on behalf of the baby. The baby may not be given a chance to decide when and how much to eat—like breastfed babies do. Instead, the parent decides when to offer the feed, according to predetermined time-based intervals. The parent also decides when their baby has had "enough," generally based on the recommendations by a health professional or found on the side of a formula can or a website.

The parent leads, and the baby is expected to follow. This sounds ideal in theory. But … babies often have their own ideas!

Most parents are not so extreme as to ignore their baby's behavioral cues. However, many parents become confused and frustrated when their baby fusses during feeds or outright rejects a feed. Why isn't baby complying with the feeding schedule or reaching the target volume?

Let's go back to the dance metaphor. If baby-feeding is a dance, by not responding to your baby's cues, you will be out of sync, and there's a good chance you'll figuratively be stepping on her toes. She's going to be upset.

Table 1.2: Advantages and disadvantages of parent-led feeding

Advantages	Disadvantages
Removes the need for thinking at a time when we may have no brain space. Your baby's doctor or health nurse or a parenting book or website might instruct you about what you "should" achieve when feeding your baby.	Provides no understanding of the potential short- and long-term consequences of this practice.
Many health professionals promote these practices because it's the only feeding advice they know. Or it may be all they have time to do.	Provides too much control for most babies who don't have health issues. Can negatively impact growth and nutrition and cause issues like underfeeding and overfeeding, bottle refusal, etc.
Provides more guidance for certain babies who need it.	Parent-led feeding practices are the most common reasons for babies' fussy feeding behavior.

Being the opposite of baby-led feeding doesn't make parent-led feeding wrong. Some babies require more guidance and support from parents to successfully feed than others including

- preterm babies prior to reaching their expected date of birth;
- sick and weak babies;
- babies with a neurological impairment who are unable to recognize their internal cues of hunger and satiety; and
- babies with a physical impairment affecting their ability to suck effectively.

These babies may either not give clear signs of their intentions or may require support to consume sufficient volumes of milk. However, for normal, healthy babies, any short-term advantage achieved by parents controlling their baby's milk consumption can be outweighed by disadvantages if the feeding experience is unpleasant or stressful for their baby.

I don't recommend parent-led feeding for healthy babies. When parents believe they must make their baby consume X amount of milk, this can cause them to

- overlook or disregard their baby's hunger cues while rigidly adhering to preset feeding times, and in doing so, keep a hungry baby waiting;
- overlook or ignore behavioral cues that indicate their baby is not interested in eating or is full or wants to stop eating;
- pressure their baby to consume more milk or food than she wants or needs.

When a baby's cues are not respected, the parent is providing **nonresponsive care.** Although well-intentioned, these controlling, coercive, or pressuring feeding tactics are ineffective and **often** counterproductive. Problems arising from this practice include

- overriding the baby's natural self-regulatory behaviors;[5]
- increasing the risk of dietary regulation problems (overfeeding and underfeeding);
- making the feeding experience unpleasant or stressful for the baby; and
- an increased risk of eating disorders, including feeding aversion.[6]

Just because we are bigger and stronger than a baby and thus able to control a baby's milk intake from a bottle (but not breast) doesn't mean that we should.

As you read through this book, you'll understand why healthy babies respond poorly to parent-led feeding practices. You will also find numerous examples of infant feeding problems linked to controlling feeding strategies.

Make a conscious decision

Your infant feeding practices can **positively or negatively** affect your baby's enjoyment in feeding, her relationship with food, her eating behaviors, the amount of food she's willing to consume, her growth, and her relationship with you. Feeding times provide opportunities for you to interact with her in ways that demonstrate love, compassion, and respect. **Feeding your baby should never be a display of dominance.**

The way you respond to your baby's behavioral cues is too important to leave up to chance, so I encourage you to make an informed choice.

For now, I simply wanted to point out the different parenting styles when it comes to feeding babies. Consider whether your current infant feeding practices are baby-led or parent-led. This realization is going to make a **huge** difference to your ability to prevent and resolve any baby feeding problems.

Next

Baby-led feeding involves more than following simplistic advice to "follow your baby's lead." Such advice will be of no benefit unless you understand babies' biological, intellectual, and emotional needs, why they behave as they do, and how they communicate their wants and needs. Next, I will explain how healthy babies know when and how much to eat.

2 When to Feed Baby

CIRCADIAN RHYTHMS • EFFECT ON APPETITE • TYPICAL FEEDING PATTERNS FOR AGE • DEMAND, SEMI-DEMAND AND SCHEDULED FEEDING COMPARISON• HOW TO SUPPORT YOUR BABY TO FOLLOW HIS NATURAL BODY RHYTHMS

You may have bought this book hoping I will tell you exactly when and how much to feed your baby to support healthy growth and development. Instead, I'm going to explain why you can trust your baby to decide when and how much to eat. I know this sounds much scarier and involves a lot of trust. But understanding just how capable your baby is to call the shots for **his body's** energy (caloric) needs might spare you from one of the biggest worries you will have as the parent of a baby, which is how to support him to grow to his full potential.

Neurologically healthy babies are biologically programmed to know when and how much to eat. In this chapter I will explain how your baby's circadian rhythms influences **when** he needs to eat. In chapter 3, I will explain how homeostatic mechanisms enable him to recognize **how much** to eat.

Circadian rhythms

Circadian rhythms (also known as our 24-hour internal body clock) is the natural cycle of physical, emotional, and behavior changes that the body goes through in a 24-hour cycle. Circadian rhythms run in the background to carry out essential bodily functions.

Your baby's circadian rhythms influence when he's alert and playful, when he's tired and ready to sleep, how long he sleeps for, when he's hungry, how hungry he is and how much he eats, how well he digests and absorbs the nutrients in the food he consumes, and when he poops (in addition to countless other bodily functions).[7]

Your baby's circadian rhythms are both internally and externally regulated by

- sleep-wake cycles;
- stage of development; and
- your childcare practices.

Sleep-wake cycles

What's sleep got to do with baby's feeding? Your baby's sleep will have a profound effect on his feeding. His circadian rhythms affect the secretion of hormones such as growth hormone, melatonin, serotonin, cortisol, leptin, and ghrelin.[8] These hormones then affect his energy requirements, appetite, feeding patterns, the volume of milk consumed per feed and over the course of the day, and his growth and mood.

When and how long your baby sleeps are influenced by his stage of development and your childcare practices.

Stage of development

Your baby's circadian rhythm is linked to the development of his nervous, digestive, and endocrine systems. Because these body systems are immature at birth, his feeding and sleeping patterns are likely to be irregular for some time. As his body's systems mature, his feeding and sleeping patterns slowly shift toward a stable, semipredictable daily routine, enabling you to anticipate when he will next want to feed or sleep.

The number, timing, and duration of your baby's naps and how long he can last between feeds before becoming hungry relate to his stage of development. The younger he is, the more often he needs to eat and nap. As he matures, the number of feeds over 24 hours and the amount of sleep he requires during the day slowly decrease.

Some babies fall into a semipredictable feeding and sleeping patterns as early as four to six weeks of age, seemingly without any help from parents. Some babies take a little longer to establish a similar pattern each day and may require guidance and support from parents to do so.

Your childcare practices

Your baby is reliant on you or other caregivers to provide for his needs—**at the time he needs to eat and sleep.** He will signal when he wants or needs something verbally by fussing and crying and by his behavior.

Your childcare practices will influence the development and stability of his circadian rhythms—in positive or negative ways—depending on how closely these cares align with his natural body rhythms. This is particularly true for practices related to feeding and sleeping.

Care provided at times that harmonize with your baby's circadian rhythms—which is more likely when employing baby-led feeding practices—will promote optimal sleep, milk intake, growth, and a feeling of wellbeing. Care that is contrary to what his body is telling him he needs—which can occur when feeds are provided at preset times without regard to a baby's behavioral cues—can disrupt and destabilize his circadian rhythms.

Circadian misalignment

Is your baby sleeping at odd times, experiencing broken sleep, overfeeding or underfeeding, or wanting to feed when he should be sleeping? It could be an issue of circadian misalignment. Misalignment of a baby's sleep-wake cycles with feeding patterns can develop when the care provided does not harmonize with his circadian rhythms.

Knowing what's typical for his age might help, so read on.

What's a typical feeding pattern for age?

During your baby's first year, his circadian rhythms will develop and change more often than at any other time in his life. A feeding regimen that may be perfect for him at one point in time will no longer match his biological rhythms and nutritional needs as he matures.

While it's not possible to accurately predict the circadian rhythms for an individual baby, you may find it helpful to understand a typical pattern for his age.

Typically developing, healthy babies tend to follow similar, though not precisely the same, feeding and sleeping patterns as other babies of a similar age. Knowing in advance what is typical at different ages might help you to anticipate changes in your baby's feeding and sleeping patterns. You can then support him to feed in harmony with his changing body rhythms. Otherwise, your care might not be in keeping with what his body requires at that time.

Birth to 3 months

Babies born full-term generally have not yet developed a "clock" before three to four months of age.[9] Stability of a baby's circadian rhythms can be delayed by nine weeks in preterm babies.[10] This means the timing of newborn babies' feeding and sleeping patterns is generally unpredictable.

Newborn babies have tiny tummies. To consume the volume of milk required for healthy growth, a bottle-fed baby needs to **feed around six to eight times** over a 24-hour period. Newborns generally don't sleep more than four hours at a time, and their sleep is scattered throughout the 24-hour period.

Many healthy, thriving babies begin to demonstrate a subtle difference between their day and night feeding patterns around the age of six to 10 weeks. A baby of this age might sleep for a **single** four-to-five-hour period (once in 24 hours) without waking to feed. A tiny percentage of healthy, thriving newborns will sleep for a longer stretch of time without feeding—for example, eight hours or longer—but these are the exception.

Some newborns have the long stretch of sleeping without eating during the day instead, indicating that their body rhythms are out of sync with a normal day-night pattern. These babies may require guidance from parents to stabilize their circadian rhythms into a day-night pattern.

Three to 6 months

The size of your baby's stomach has grown along with the rest of his body. He's stronger and a more efficient feeder. Hence, he can consume larger volumes in less time than when he was a newborn. Increased calories per feed enable him to last for longer stretches between feeds before he starts to feel hungry again, so the number of times he **bottle-feeds decreases to five or six** over a 24-hour period.

A day-night pattern where a baby has more sleep at night than the day does not generally establish until 12 to 16 weeks.[11] This relates to the secretion of hormones at night. Melatonin (the sleep hormone) and leptin (the appetite-suppressing hormone) secretions occur for longer periods at night, which means he starts to sleep for a longer time at night—possibly between six to nine hours—before waking to demand a feed. This could occur during the first or second half of the night.

Six to 9 months

By now, your baby is eating solid foods in addition to milk feeds. The more calories (energy) he receives from solids, the less milk he needs to consume. Therefore, the number of times he **bottle-feeds drops to four or five times** during the day.

The period of suppressed appetite at night increases, and he might sleep for 10 to 12 hours without waking to eat. A small percentage of babies may achieve this milestone at a younger age.

Ideally, this period of suppressed appetite will be at night, allowing a long stretch of sleep for the baby and parents, but that's not always the case. Some babies continue to demand frequent feeds at night because of an underlying feeding or sleeping problem. Or parents continue to provide night feeds that were **not** requested by their baby—waking their baby to feed or feeding him while he sleeps—in an attempt to increase the volume of milk he receives over a 24-hour period, unaware that by doing so, they could be destabilizing his circadian rhythms.

Nine to 12 months

As your baby learns to master the skills required to eat solids, the calories he receives from eating solid foods will increase, and the volume of milk he consumes decreases. By now, he may be only interested in **bottle-feeding three to four times** per day, plus eating three to five solid meals or snacks.

Feeding patterns and circadian rhythms

We would all agree that any feeding pattern—whether demand, scheduled, or semi-demand feeding—needs to match the baby's needs.

You will find the average number of feeds for age in table 2:1. This can help you determine if you might be misinterpreting your baby's hunger cues and offering feeds too often, causing your newborn baby to overfeed or an older baby to snack feed. Alternatively, identify if you may be trying to make your baby achieve something that most babies of his age can't, by feeding him at predetermined times or withholding feeds.

Average number of feeds for age

The following table depicts the average number of bottle-feeds at different ages. If your baby was born preterm, please use his adjusted age.

Table 2.1: Average number of bottle feeds for age

Age	Average number of feeds in a 24-hour period	Average number of feeds overnight	Period of decreased appetite
Birth to 1 month	6–8	2–3	2.5–4 hours
1–3 months	6–7	2–3	4–7 hours
3–6 months	5–6	1–2	6–9 hours
6–9 months	4–5	0–1	8–12 hours
9–12 months	3–4	0	10–12 hours
Please note: the longer break between feeds at night usually occurs at only one period. It's not the time between each nighttime feed.			

If your baby is generally content and growing well, and the number of times he feeds is similar to those included in the table, this might reassure you that whatever feeding regimen you have chosen to follow is suitable.

If baby is not following a typical pattern

If you discover that your baby's feeding pattern is **not** "typical," it doesn't automatically mean something is wrong. It's important to remember that each baby develops at his own pace.

If your baby is **healthy, growing well, and content,** it doesn't matter when or how often he feeds. His feeding and sleeping patterns are obviously meeting his needs.

If your baby is gaining unusually large amounts of weight or gains poorly, or if he is often gassy, uncomfortable, or cries for long periods of time, or he displays troublesome feeding behavior—and is also feeding more or less often than average for his age—it could indicate **circadian misalignment**. This means his current patterns of feeding or sleeping (or both) or the lack of predictable patterns could be contributing to his distress.

If your baby is not content or not gaining weight as expected, you may need to check if your infant feeding practices match his needs. He may benefit from more guidance or less control from you to help him feed and sleep at times that harmonize with his circadian rhythms. Or you may need to resolve a problem that is preventing him from feeding to the point of feeling satisfied or causing him to overfeed. In Part F, I describe behavioral reasons for feeding and sleeping problems, which will be a good place to start to look for reasons.

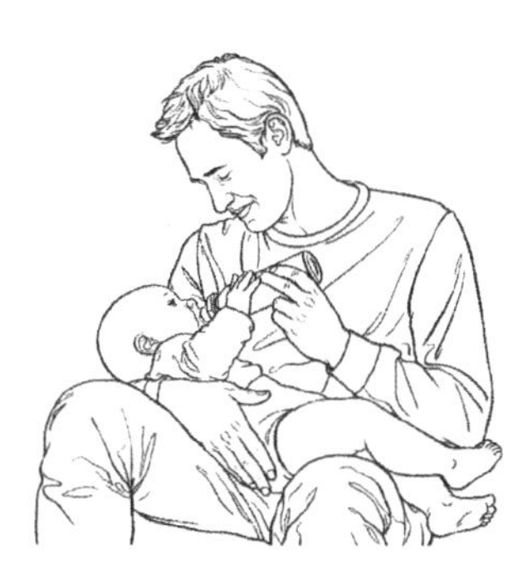

When to offer feeds

> *"When I asked the midwife how often I should feed Hamish, she told me to feed him on demand. For the past two weeks, he has been eating every one to two hours in the day. He keeps throwing up, so I think he's getting too much. His doctor suggested I feed him every three hours. But he screams if I try to make him wait. I am so confused. I don't know what to do." Kirstin*

I am not surprised that Kirstin is feeling confused. She has received simplistic advice without an explanation or understanding of what "demand" entails. And no one explained to her how a time-based feeding regimen might affect her baby. Kirstin may find a semi-demand feeding regimen less confusing and a better fit for Hamish's needs.

It's helpful to think about demand, semi-demand, and scheduled feeding as part of a continuum.

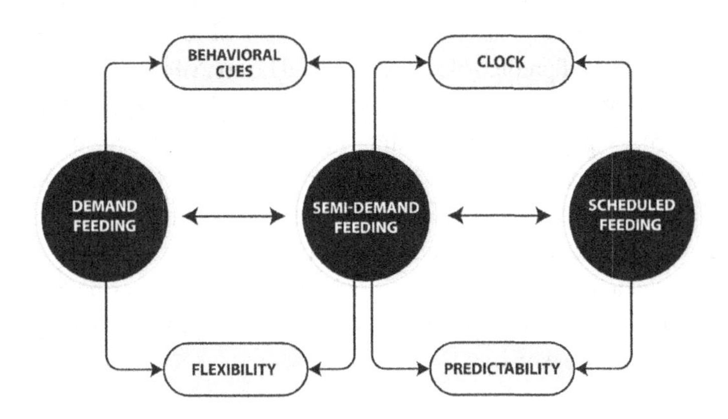

Demand feeding

On the left is demand feeding, also called **cue-based feeding,** where feeds are offered when a baby displays behavioral cues suspected of being caused by hunger. Demand feeding provides the greatest flexibility because there are no set times to offer feeds and no limits on the number of times a baby feeds per day. Demand feeding is based on the principle that healthy babies can decide when and how much to eat. Which is true!

It makes perfect sense to feed a baby when he's hungry. But demand feeding is not as straightforward as it sounds. The main disadvantage of demand feeding is that it relies heavily on parents to **accurately** interpret their baby's behavioral cues. Infant behavioral cues are not easy to interpret, and "feed on demand" is often misinterpreted by parents and others to mean "feed baby every time he fusses, cries, or appears like he wants to suck." For newborns, in particular, **misinterpreting** behavioral cues in partnership with an active sucking reflex significantly increases the risk of overfeeding.

Scheduled feeding

On the right is scheduled feeding, also called **time-based feeding,** where feeds are offered at predetermined times. This might mean the baby is offered a feed at intervals of three, three-and-a-half, or four hours or at set times, for example, at 6:00 a.m., 10:00 a.m., 2:00 p.m., 6:00 p.m., and 10:00 p.m.

There is no onus on parents to interpret their baby's behavioral cues. The clock rather than the baby determines when a feed will be offered.

If a time-based feeding pattern is working for your baby, meaning it matches his biological needs, and he's happy, healthy, thriving, and content to feed at these times, then there's nothing wrong with offering him feeds at predetermined times.

However, you need to remain mindful that your **baby is not a robot** to be calibrated to consume a predetermined number of calories each feed. Nor can he be programmed to cycle at three or four hourly intervals between feeds over a 24-hour period. He has his own body rhythms, which are regulated by his brain for what his body needs at any given point in time at his current stage of development. Keep in mind that his circadian rhythms—and thus his feeding and sleeping patterns—will change multiple times as he matures.

If a time-based feeding schedule **doesn't** match his body's circadian rhythms, this will frustrate or distress him. Circadian misalignment would mean you would then be offering him feeds before he's ready and willing to eat or keeping a hungry baby waiting "until it's time." For these reasons, scheduled feeding patterns are associated with fussy feeding behavior, feeding refusal, and an increased risk of underfeeding.

If you feel compelled to pressure an unwilling baby to accept the feed or continue to eat until he consumes X ounces (or X milliliters) of milk at each feed to "stay on schedule"—irrespective of whether he chooses to consume this volume or not—you may be providing nonresponsive care and risk causing your baby to develop feeding problems.

Demand feeding and scheduled feeding are polar opposites, like black and white. It's at the **extreme ends** of the continuum—where cue-based feeds are offered without consideration of the time or where parents strictly adhere to scheduled times without regard to their baby's behavioral cues—where infant feeding problems are most likely to develop. Rigid and erratic feeding patterns can result in a poor fit with a baby's circadian rhythms.

Semi-demand feeding

A semi-demand feeding pattern sits between demand and scheduled feeding. It provides a mix of flexibility and predictability achieved by using timing and context to determine the most likely reason for a baby's behavioral cues. It's a middle-ground approach and a good starting point for parents who are not confident about their ability to interpret their baby's behavioral cues accurately. From this midpoint, you can determine if your baby is content with a little more flexibility or whether he does better with more structure.

A semi-demand feeding pattern is predictable and yet flexible. The **predictability** of this feeding pattern can support a baby who tends to feed erratically to stabilize his internal body clock. It can also help you anticipate when your baby is likely to get hungry, thereby gaining greater accuracy in recognizing his hunger cues and other reasons for fussing. The **flexibility** of this feeding pattern can accommodate naturally occurring, day-to-day fluctuations in your baby's appetite and sleeping patterns. A semi-demand feeding pattern encourages you to consider reasons (in addition to hunger) for his behavior, and if appropriate, to try other ways to soothe him rather than automatically assuming he's hungry every time he fusses, cries, or wants to suck. (You can learn more about how to use "timing and context" in chapter 7.)

How it works

A semi-demand feeding pattern has similarities with a demand feeding pattern in that the goal is to feed your baby when he's hungry. But unlike demand feeding, a semi-demand feeding pattern provides guidelines to reduce the risk of misinterpreting the baby's behavioral cues.

A semi-demand feeding regimen combines cue- and time-based feeding. It's important to watch for behavioral cues that might indicate hunger but also be guided by minimum and maximum timeframes to help you decide when to offer a feed.

The timeframes vary slightly according to age. The minimum timeframe is a little shorter for newborn babies because they have smaller tummies and need to feed more often compared to older babies.

Newborns

The recommended timeframe is a minimum of two-and-a-half hours and a maximum of four hours during the day. A longer period at night without eating can be normal, due to development of the baby's circadian rhythms (see pages 22-25).

Babies 3 months+

The minimum timeframe is three hours, and the maximum is four hours in the day. Allow the baby to make demand feeds at night.

Note: The timeframes are a guide only; don't follow them rigidly. They apply to healthy, thriving babies and may **not** be suitable for babies with special needs or physical disabilities, or those experiencing feeding difficulties causing them to underfeed. **Feeds are timed from the start of the previous feed.**

During the day

Babies—newborns, in particular—provide similar behavioral cues for all that troubles them. Your initial response to your baby's unsettled behavioral cues could vary depending on the length of time elapsed since he previously fed.

If your baby fusses before the minimum timeframe

The first step is to consider and rule out other potential reasons for your baby's uneasiness. For example, rather than automatically assuming he's hungry, check if he has an unsatisfied sucking urge or is tired, overstimulated, bored, or uncomfortable.

- If he's soothed in other ways—for example, a pacifier, cuddle, entertainment, or an opportunity to sleep—then his fussing, crying, or desire to suck at this point is probably not because of hunger.
- If he's not readily soothed in these or other ways, offer a feed.

If your baby fusses between the minimum and maximum times

- Offer a feed.

If your baby doesn't display signs of hunger by 4 hours

- Offer a feed. Some babies are non-demanding.

What if your baby is hungry outside of the timeframe guidelines?

Your baby might be hungry sooner or later than the suggested minimum or maximum times for a number of reasons. This is why you need to consider the context of what's happening at the time and earlier in the day when deciding whether to feed sooner or later than the suggested timeframe. For example:

- **Sleeping**: Your baby's sleeping patterns will affect when he wants to eat.
  - If your baby **napped only briefly**, he might want to feed sooner than the minimum of two-and-a-half or three hours. If he consistently has brief naps, check if he has a sleep association problem (see pages 292-298). If so, consider resolving this problem because of the many negative effects a sleeping problem can have on a baby's feeding behavior, feeding patterns, growth, and mood.
  - If your baby is having a **long nap,** he might still be sleeping at the four-hour mark. If he's a thriving baby, leave him to sleep **a little** longer, but within reason. Babies can experience circadian rhythm sleeping problems, which means their day and night sleeping pattern is out of sync, and so they sleep excessively long periods during the day and are awake, alert, and wanting attention for hours in the night. If you suspect this may be the case, you may need to wake him to offer a feed during the day and encourage some awake time.
- **Calories consumed**: Healthy babies over the age of eight weeks will regulate their dietary intake according to the calories consumed.
  - If your baby consumed very little volume or calories at the previous feed, he may be hungry sooner than the minimum timeframe. Don't pressure him to consume more than he's willing to take in an attempt to make him go longer between feeds. (If he's snacking, see pages 312-314. If he's underfeeding, see chapter 26.)
  - If your baby has had a big feed or he's given high-energy formula or fortified breast milk, he might be content to go for longer than

four hours between feeds and not be interested in feeding sooner. If he's healthy and thriving, you can let him go for longer between feeds. If you are providing high-energy feeds or adding cereal to your baby's milk, consider if this is necessary (see chapter 11).

If you need to feed your baby sooner or later

You might decide to offer your baby a feed before or after the suggested timeframes. For example, if you anticipate he will soon be ready to settle down for his longest nap of the day or if you're planning on taking him out, you might decide to offer a feed before the minimum timeframe. Alternatively, you might be out longer than expected, and he's content, so you decide to wait until returning home to feed him.

During the night

Babies wake for various reasons during the night. Some reasons are

- hunger;
- missing sleep associations;
- feeling cold or overheated;
- wet or poopy diaper;
- separation anxiety;
- feeling unwell;
- entangled in bed clothing;
- stuck in a position he can't get out of; or
- developmental growth spurts.

Don't assume that your baby is hungry simply because he has woken.

If your baby wakes before the minimum timeframe

First, consider all possible reasons for his waking, and try other means to soothe him back to sleep.

- ➢ If he can be **easily soothed** in other ways—perhaps with a cuddle, patting, returning his pacifier, a diaper change, or more or less bed clothing—and he quickly returns to sleep, his waking was probably not from hunger.
- ➢ If he is **not readily soothed** in these ways, offer a feed.

If your baby feeds more often during the night than expected for a baby of his age, see chapter 24 for possible reasons.

If your baby wakes after the minimum timeframe

A semi-demand feeding pattern will help a baby stabilize his internal body clock, and you may see a pattern emerging where he wakes at similar times each night to feed.

- If he wakes around the time he normally wakes to feed, offer a feed.
- If he wakes unexpectedly, he may be hungry, but don't assume so. He could be waking for one of the reasons previously mentioned. You might first try other means to soothe him back to sleep. But if he's not easily settled back to sleep, then offer a feed.

What if baby is still sleeping beyond 4 hours at night?

From around six weeks of age, many babies will naturally start to go for **one** long stretch at night without eating—provided he does not have a sleep association problem. The period of suppressed appetite **gradually** extends from one stretch of four hours, eventually reaching 10 to 12 hours at around six to nine months of age.

- **If your baby is healthy and thriving,** you can leave him to follow his natural body rhythms.
- **If severely sleep-deprived,** a newborn baby might skip night feeds because he's too exhausted to wake to demand a feed, in which case he may need to be woken and offered a feed or fed while sleeping (called a **"dream feed").** The most effective solution may be to resolve the problem causing him to lack sleep.
- **If your baby is underweight,** it may be necessary to wake and offer a feed or two at night. You might choose to wake him to offer a late evening feed or dream-feed him before you go to bed. And if necessary, offer another feed three to four hours later. However, if this results in him not being interested in eating until many hours after waking in the mornings, he may not require the extra feedings at night.

Like **all** feeding regimens, a semi-demand method works best when a baby has no sleeping problem causing broken or lack of sleep.

Does your baby sleep poorly?

Your baby's sleeping patterns and the quality of his sleep will have a strong influence on his circadian rhythms, which in turn will affect his appetite, mood, feeding patterns, and how well he feeds. If your baby is a "poor sleeper," I recommend resolving his sleeping problem **before** deciding on a feeding regimen. (See chapter 22 for more on sleep and the effect on feeding.)

How to ensure your baby receives what he needs

As parents, we all want the same thing, which is for our children to be happy, healthy, and grow to their full potential. The most effective way to support your baby to achieve **healthy growth** is by supporting him to follow his natural rhythms (circadian rhythms) by employing baby-led feeding practices.

Optimal energy intake means your baby receives **what his body needs**—not more or not less—**at the time he needs to feed**. Your baby is biologically programed to achieve this by following his internal cues of hunger and satisfaction. You can support your baby to achieve healthy growth by 1) providing adequate amounts of good quality, nutritionally balanced food, and 2) supporting him to follow his circadian rhythms by allowing him to decide when and how much to eat.

Receiving an appropriate and timely response to his cues of hunger and satiety (satisfaction) will go a long way towards promoting your baby's **contentment**. But he may also need your support to develop healthy sleep habits (explained in chapter 22).

By the time you have finished reading this book, you will understand how best to support **your baby**—the unique little person that he is—to achieve healthy growth and contentment.

Next

I hope this chapter has helped you understand that neurologically healthy babies can decide when to eat. Next, I will explain how babies know how much to eat.

3 Baby Knows How Much to Eat

HOW YOUR BABY KNOWS HOW MUCH TO EAT • HOMEOSTASIS • APPETITE HORMONES • HOW TO SUPPORT YOUR BABY TO FOLLOW HIS NATURAL BODY RHYTHMS • HOW TO TELL IF YOUR BABY IS EATING ENOUGH

When I recommended to Ryan that he trust his three-month-old baby, Elsa, to decide how much to eat, he commented, "But she's a baby. She doesn't know how much she needs to eat!"

Ryan is not the only person to think babies are too young to know what they need. Like many other parents and health professionals, Ryan believes it's the parent's responsibility to decide for their baby what is "enough." This common misperception is the root cause of many infant feeding problems.

While babies don't know a lot, they can recognize when they're hungry and when they've had enough. This occurs due to homeostasis.

Homeostasis

Homeostasis includes any self-regulating process that enables our bodies to maintain an internal state of stability or equilibrium necessary for survival.

Your baby's brain and body are programmed for survival. Every cell, tissue, organ, and body system is attuned to maintaining different variables within narrow ranges that are compatible with life.

While certain parts of your baby's brain continue to develop long after birth, other parts that control bodily functions required for survival—like heart rate, breathing, body temperature, sleep, thirst, **appetite,** and growth—are developed long before her birth.

Her brain is the control center for all homeostatic mechanisms through a feedback system involving her endocrine system, which produces and releases hormones, and her nervous system, which sends electrical messages between her brain and body via nerve pathways.

Included among the countless homeostatic processes inside your baby's tiny body is the **maintenance of her energy requirements**.

Energy requirements

Energy requirements refers to the number of calories a baby requires to support normal bodily functions (breathing, digestion, etc.), physical activity and growth.

Energy requirements vary among individual babies. They depend on many factors, including gender, the baby's current body size and whether this matches her genetically inherited size, body fat percentage, metabolic rate (how fast she burns calories), physical activity, physical health, and growth rate.

Your baby's energy requirements are constantly changing. The number of calories she needs at each feed or each day will fluctuate depending on her activity levels, rate of growth and state of health. How you can tell if your baby is consuming enough food to meet her growth and energy needs is discussed later in this chapter.

Babies have an inborn ability to regulate their intake of food to consume the number of calories they need.[12] How does your baby know when to eat and when to stop? The same way you do—through appetite regulation. Our energy requirements influence our appetite and food intake.

Three key hormones trigger internal sensations that motivate us to eat and let us know when we have consumed enough food for now. These are

- ghrelin;
- leptin; and
- cholecystokinin.

Ghrelin

Ghrelin—called the "hunger hormone"—stimulates appetite, motivating your baby to eat and take in more energy (calories).[13]

Ghrelin is released mainly in the stomach.[14] Levels typically rise in your baby's bloodstream before a feed or meal, when her stomach is empty and blood glucose levels drop, causing pangs of hunger that motivate her to want to eat. Ghrelin levels drop when her stomach is full[15], removing the motivation to continue eating.

Ghrelin levels are lower in individuals with a higher body fat percentage compared with lean individuals.[16] Thus, a chubby baby might last longer between feeds before feeling hungry again, compared to a lean or underweight baby. A chubby baby might not get the chance to display behavioral cues typically associated with hunger (described on pages 74-76) if she's offered feeds at predetermined times—for example, every three or four hours.

Leptin

Leptin's main role is to regulate fat storage. It also affects appetite and influences how many calories your baby eats.[17] Leptin has the opposite effect of ghrelin in that high levels of leptin in the bloodstream will reduce your baby's appetite.

Leptin is released from fat cells. Levels are directly connected to the percentage of body fat.[18] The more body fat your baby has, the more leptin in her bloodstream. As she adds body fat, leptin levels increase, and she will eat less. Conversely, if she has a low body fat percentage, leptin levels drop, her appetite will increase, and she will eat more. Hence, a chubby baby might not eat as much as a lean baby of the same age and weight.

Basically, the effect of leptin on a baby's appetite is a means to prevent an excessive accumulation of body fat, which is not healthy. However, the effect that leptin has on a baby's appetite regulation won't prevent her from overfeeding or being overfed for reasons that are outside her control (explained in chapter 25), so she could still gain an excessive amount of body fat that places her into an overweight or obese category.

Cholecystokinin

Cholecystokinin (CCK) is another hormone that plays a role in appetite control.[19] It is responsible for the feeling of satisfaction that we get following a meal. CCK is released mainly in the small intestine in response to nutrients, especially fat and protein.[20] Levels rise gradually over 10 to 30 minutes after eating and remain elevated for many hours.[21]

CCK is also responsible for the feeling of drowsiness we sometimes get after eating a big meal.[22] It is a major reason newborn babies become "milk drunk" or fall asleep while feeding.

Have you ever felt full as a result of eating a big meal but thought, "I would really love a piece of cheesecake"? This is because the effects of CCK have not yet kicked in. The delay can be a reason we overeat.

This explains how a baby knows how much to eat. How much milk is required to meet an individual baby's growth and energy needs is explained in chapter 4. The behavior displayed by babies when hungry, full, and satisfied is described in chapter 6.

Dietary intake

You play a critical role in supporting your baby to regulate her dietary intake, not only now but well into the future.[23] Baby-led feeding practices, which encourage parents' responsiveness to their baby's feeding cues, **support appetite self-regulation** and are associated with better health outcomes compared to parent-led feeding practices.

Parent-led feeding practices encourage parents to take over the responsibility to regulate their baby's dietary intake and decide for their baby when it's time to eat and how much is "enough". The use of controlling feeding practices can hamper the development of a baby's appetite self-regulation abilities.

Signs of a well-fed baby

> *"Charlize will happily take a bottle but won't drink much—3 to 5 oz (90–150 ml) when she should be having a lot more each feed, and we are not reaching her daily milk target by a long shot. She is content and putting on weight but not as much as she should be. It's like she just isn't hungry so refuses to drink more." Jacinta*

I only needed to look at Charlize to recognize that she is an active, alert baby who has a healthy layer of body fat. However, I realize that "looking good" doesn't mean she is **currently** consuming enough to meet her needs. Jacinta's comments that Charlize is content and refuses to drink more make me suspect she is getting enough. I ask Jacinta questions to check for signs of a well-fed baby.

Signs of a well-fed baby

- She is energetic and active.
- She demands regular feeds.
- She's content or readily soothed at the end of the feed.
- She's generally content between feeds, except when hungry, tired, bored, or overstimulated.
- She sleeps well.
- She has five or more wet disposable diapers or six or more wet cloth diapers per day.
- Her urine is pale.
- She has regular soft bowel movements.
- She has good skin color and muscle tone.
- She's growing over time.
- She's meeting developmental milestones appropriate for her age.

Charlize checks all of these boxes. Next, I explored the reasons why she's not drinking or gaining as much as Jacinta believes she should be and discovered that her expected weight gain and milk requirements had been overestimated. I encouraged Jacinta to trust Charlize to know what her body needs. And to look at Charlize rather than the markings on a bottle or numbers on the scale to tell if she is getting enough to eat.

If your baby is generally content and growing well, these are indicators that she's getting enough to eat. However, irritability, the appearance of poor growth, and not drinking the volume of milk expected don't automatically point to her not getting enough. There are many variables of "normal" growth, reasons for a baby to not consume the "expected" volume of milk (listed in chapter 4) and causes of irritability or fussy feeding behavior that are unrelated to hunger and underfeeding (described throughout the pages of this book).

Next

I appreciate this chapter may not be enough for you to commit to trusting your baby to decide how much milk she needs, especially if she's not drinking as much milk as you believe she should be. Let's look at milk needs next, and what will influence an individual baby's milk consumption. We'll also look at why a health professional's estimation of your baby's milk needs could be flawed. My underlying message is, as always, trust your baby to decide what her body needs! Her body is biologically programmed to achieve this.

4 How Much Milk Does a Baby Need?

WHAT INFLUENCES BABIES' MILK NEEDS • HOW HEALTH PROFESSIONALS ESTIMATE BABIES' MILK NEEDS • WHY IT'S NOT POSSIBLE FOR OTHERS TO KNOW HOW MUCH MILK A BABY NEEDS

As a loving parent, you're probably wondering how much milk your baby needs. Or you may be looking for confirmation that he's eating enough. Or you're looking for a figure that could help you decide if hunger is causing him to cry unexpectedly or experience broken sleep.

Having a figure in mind can be a source of comfort. However, it can also be a **cause for anxiety** if your baby is not willing to eat the amount you expect.

This chapter should help you understand why it's **not possible** for others to know what your baby needs. It's important that you trust your baby to decide how much to eat. Hopefully, this chapter will help you develop this trust.

Why realistic milk expectations are critical

First, I need to provide a word of warning.

Nothing creates more infant feeding problems than parents being told how much milk (or food) their baby "should have," "must have," or "needs." However, there is one piece of advice that is worse, which is when a health professional tells a parent to "Do whatever you have to do to get your baby to drink X ounces [or milliliters] of milk." Such comments often result in parents using pressure or force to make their baby eat, so I won't be giving you any such advice.

In most cases where parents claim their baby is "not eating enough," their concern is triggered by their baby not eating **the amount they expect.** I make this distinction because not eating the amount expected is **not** proof that a baby is not eating enough.

It's vital you have **realistic expectations** about your baby's milk needs. Having a figure in your head that is higher than the amount he actually needs will cause you needless anxiety when he is unwilling to drink this amount. If you were to pressure or force your baby to consume more milk than he actually needs because you believe it's what he "should have", you risk causing him a great deal of distress.

Overfeeding will lead to gastrointestinal (GI) symptoms, such as vomiting, frequent stools and abdominal discomfort, which may then be misdiagnosed as colic, reflux, or milk protein allergy or intolerance. Babies over the age of three months will object and resist pressure to make them eat more. Repeatedly being pressured to eat more than they are willing to eat is a major reason for babies to develop an aversion to feeding and hence underfeed.

While there is a small percentage of cases where babies are genuinely not eating enough (underfeeding), there are reasons for this, which are described in chapter 26. But for most healthy babies, parents simply need to allow their baby to decide how much he wants to eat.

Babies' milk needs differ depending on many factors. Let's look at these now.

What influences your baby's milk needs?

> *"It's so hard not to compare how much my baby is drinking when my friend's baby is younger and drinking so much more. Especially since mine weighs a lot less." Evelyn*

It's not a good idea to compare one baby against another. There are many possible reasons why Evelyn's baby might require less milk or calories than her friend's baby.

Individual babies vary considerably in their energy requirements and hence milk needs because of a large number of variables, such as

1. gender;
2. genetic endowment;
3. rate of growth;

4. body shape;
5. body fat;
6. metabolic rate;
7. physical activity;
8. quality of sleep;
9. state of health;
10. energy content of milk feeds;
11. feed preparation;
12. solid foods intake;
13. appetite fluctuations; and
14. feeding pattern.

Let's look at how each of these impacts a baby's energy (calorie) requirements. You can decide how many of these might apply to your baby and their impact on the volume of milk he might need to consume before his brain recognizes that he has taken in enough to replenish his energy stores for the time being.

1. Gender

In general, males tend to be larger than females of the same age and thus will likely consume more milk compared to females.

2. Genetic endowment

Your baby's genetic endowment includes everything that he inherited from the genes passed on from his mom and dad, including his growth potential. His size, shape, rate of growth, and metabolic rate (how fast he burns energy) are programmed into his genes at the time of his conception.

Many factors influence his growth in the womb, like his mother's nutrition, her state of health, and blood flow through the placenta, among other factors. This means **a baby could be born smaller or larger than his inherited traits predict.** But that does not mean he will remain smaller or larger.

After birth, his genetic potential will be one of the strongest influences on his rate of growth, which in turn will determine his energy requirements and hence his milk needs.

Smaller than expected at birth

An **intrauterine growth restricted** (IUGR) baby **might** experience **catch-up growth** after birth. His body realigns with the size and shape programmed into his genes. A baby undergoing catch-up growth will gain weight at a faster than average rate. And consequently, he'll have a ravenous appetite and eat more than average based on his age and weight.

Making a baby eat more won't make him grow faster!

If your baby was born IUGR, preterm, small for gestational age, or is currently underweight, it's important to be aware of misperceptions about food and growth; for example, that you can make a baby grow faster by giving more milk or food. **Food supports growth, it does not cause a baby to grow.** Growth hormones are responsible for how fast a baby grows. Growth cannot be forced by making a healthy baby eat more than he's willing to eat.

Larger than expected at birth

At the opposite end of the spectrum, a baby who was born unusually large in relation to the size of his parents might go through a period of **catch-down growth.** In this case, he will grow at a slower rate than average and hence require less than an average amount of milk for his age and weight.

Catch-down growth is a period of slow growth (at a rate below the average based on age) that follows a period of accelerated growth, either in the womb or after birth, where the baby gained more than expected weight.

Catch-down growth is often mistaken as slow growth caused by underfeeding. Babies experiencing catch-down growth display signs of being well-fed (see page 42); whereas babies experiencing poor growth due to underfeeding will display signs of underfeeding (see pages 346-347).

Baby Levi

Levi's birth weight was 9 pounds, 2 ounces (4.14 kilograms), which is around the 90th percentile on an infant growth chart. His length at birth was 19 inches (48.26 centimeters), which is around the 20th percentile. The difference in weight and length percentiles indicated he was a chubby baby at birth.

Following his birth, Levi demanded regular feeds and was allowed to drink until satisfied. His mother, Grace, described him as a happy baby. At his two-month health check, his weight was 12 lb, 2 oz (5.5 kg). His doctor noticed that his weight had dropped to the 50th percentile. He asked Grace how much milk Levi was drinking, which varied between 24 to 28 oz (≈720 to 840 mL) per day. The doctor advised her that Levi needed a minimum of 30 ounces per day.

Grace is 5'2", and Levi's father is 5'6". While Levi was born at a high percentile for weight (but not length), this does not mean his body is meant to maintain his weight at a high percentile. What the doctor assumed was slow growth from not eating enough was, in fact, quite normal because of catch-down growth. Levi was content eating less than average for a baby of his age because his body did not need to gain average weight while going through catch-down growth.

By suggesting that Levi needed a minimum of 30 ounces—which was more than he was willing to eat—his doctor could have unknowingly been setting him up for feeding problems later had Grace tried to pressure or force him to consume this volume. I explained catch-down growth to Grace and encouraged her to continue to trust Levi to decide how much to eat.

3. Rate of growth

Growth does not occur in a linear pattern, where a baby grows a little every day. Babies and children experience periods of accelerated growth, slow growth, and stagnant growth.[24]

- **During periods of rapid or accelerated growth,** which include catch-up growth and growth spurts, your baby's appetite will increase, as will his daily milk intake.
- **During periods of slow or static growth,** for example, catch-down growth and growth plateaus (which occur between growth spurts), his appetite will decrease, and his daily milk intake will drop.

Appetite fluctuations from the normal ebbs and flows of a healthy baby's growth are normal and should be expected.

4. Body shape

Just like the rest of the human population, babies come in different shapes and sizes. A baby's genetic endowment, which includes ethnicity, influences his body shape and length. Different ethnic groups vary in size and shape.

Some babies are naturally more inclined to be leaner and others chubbier compared to an average-size baby because of the traits they inherit from their parents. Your baby's genetically programmed body shape will influence his appetite and the amount of milk he's willing to eat.

5. Body fat

The amount of **body fat** a baby carries is more relevant than weight when estimating milk requirements. For example, three babies of the same age could weigh precisely the same amount, and yet one baby could be overweight, another underweight, and the third a healthy weight. The difference relates to each baby's length. Therefore, despite being the same age and weight, each baby may require different amounts of milk.

Your baby's brain monitors his energy intake and energy stores. The more fat he carries on his body, the more leptin—the appetite-suppressing hormone—his body releases and the less he needs to eat.

A skinny, underweight baby **might** need more food than an average-size or chubby, overweight baby to achieve catch-up growth, provided he is not genetically inclined to be lean. And an overweight baby, who may be going through a period of catch-down growth, might require less milk than an average-size or underweight baby weighing the same.

6. Metabolic rate

Metabolic rate is the speed at which we burn energy (calories) while at rest. This is also influenced by our genetic endowment as well as our percentage of body fat. You possibly have a friend who is stick-thin yet eats like a horse. He or she has a rapid metabolic rate, burns calories quickly, and doesn't tend to gain weight no matter how much they eat. You may have other friends who claim they only need to look at a piece of cake to gain weight. This may be because they have a slow metabolic rate. If they eat more calories than their body needs, they accumulate body fat.

While our metabolic rate is influenced by our level of activity, we are either fortunate or unfortunate to be born with a predisposition toward a faster or slower metabolic rate.

Babies' metabolic rates differ. Two babies may be the same age, weight, length, and yet their energy requirements could differ. Some babies burn calories at a faster or slower rate compared to others in the same way that adults and children do. Hence, a baby with a quicker or slower metabolic rate may require more or fewer calories than another baby of the same age, weight, and length.

7. Physical activity

The more active your baby is, the more calories he burns.

How active a baby is can reflect his temperament type—inborn personality traits. Some babies are highly curious and constantly on the go; you can't get them to sit still. The only time they stop is while they're sleeping. They may require more calories than average to fuel their activities. However, they may be too busy to sit and eat and, in general, tend to be lean babies.

Other babies are chilled observers. They're happy to sit and watch others. They might require fewer calories compared to other babies of the same age and weight because they are less active.

8. Sleep quality

Sleep affects a baby's energy expenditure, appetite, frustration tolerance, feeding patterns, and behavior.

On the one hand, lack of sleep can cause a baby to eat more. Two hormones that help regulate hunger—ghrelin and leptin—are affected by sleep: ghrelin stimulates appetite, while leptin decreases it. When the body is sleep-deprived, the level of ghrelin spikes while the level of leptin falls, leading to an increase in hunger.

On the other hand, sleep deprivation can cause a baby to eat less. A severely sleep-deprived baby is easily frustrated or more likely to reject feeds or fall asleep before the feed is completed.

9. State of health

Some medical issues, such as lung and cardiac conditions, can increase a baby's daily energy requirements. In other words, he might require more calories compared to other babies of his age and size.

If your baby has a cardiac or lung condition, bear in mind that while he has some physical challenges related to his heart or lungs, **if he's neurologically healthy, he is still capable of self-regulating his dietary intake** to meet his needs. He does not require others to decide how many calories his body needs for growth and physical activities.

He might need help to make it easier for him to feed and thus require less effort to receive the calories he needs. For example, high-energy feeds will allow him to receive the calories he needs in smaller volumes. Feeding equipment that matches his sucking abilities will enable him to feed with less effort. A speech-language pathologist (SLP) can provide advice on suitable feeding equipment.

This may be the case for other genetic, metabolic, and chromosomal disorders. **If a baby is neurologically healthy and capable of feeding orally,** he can decide what his body needs. Of course, this does not apply to every physical condition. Some conditions and syndromes are associated with feeding problems and poor growth.

10. Energy content of milk feeds

Normal, healthy babies **over the age of eight weeks** regulate their milk intake according to the energy (calorie) content and not the volume of milk. Increasing the energy content of a healthy baby's feeds will usually mean they consume less volume over 24 hours. Conversely, reducing the energy content will mean they consume a larger volume.

Breast milk

The energy content of breast milk varies between women. The average number of calories is 20 kcal per ounce or 67 kcal per 100 mL. However, some nursing mothers produce milk with a higher or lower fat percentage compared to others.

Average milk estimations cannot be applied to breast milk. The fat content—a major determinant of the energy/calorie content—varies considerably among individuals and changes constantly depending on the mother's milk supply, how full her breasts are at the time of feeding or pumping, the time of day, the age of her baby, and the weather (on hot days, her milk will contain more water).

The constant fluctuations in the fat content and thus calorie content of a mother's milk is not a problem for a healthy breastfed baby because he will eat to satisfaction and stop. If the fat content is higher or lower, he will either eat less or more at each feed or eat less or more often over the day. Whichever way the fluctuation goes, a nursing mother has no idea how much her baby eats.

The same applies when a baby receives breast milk from a bottle. The amount of fat and calories received will fluctuate. Sometimes he will receive more and sometimes fewer calories compared to other feeds. The difference is that when bottle-fed, his mother is aware of how much he consumes. Being aware can cause her needless concern if her baby's milk intake is less than expected because her milk has a higher fat content.

Baby Oliver

Oliver is fed his mother's breast milk from a bottle. However, his mother, Kate, is concerned because he's not drinking the volume recommended by his pediatrician.

Oliver's growth has consistently remained around the 25th percentile since his birth. Kate states he is a happy baby who sleeps well. This tells me his nutritional needs are being met.

If Oliver was breastfed rather than bottle-fed, Kate wouldn't know how much he was drinking. She would see that Oliver was content and following his growth curve and wouldn't be concerned. The only reason she is concerned is because Oliver is not drinking the volume that his pediatrician has recommended. The reason could be because Kate's breast milk has a higher-than-average fat content. Or the pediatrician may have overestimated Oliver's nutritional needs.

Had Oliver been breastfed, the pediatrician would be monitoring his growth to determine if he was getting enough. I encouraged Kate to forget about volumes and look for signs of a well-fed baby instead.

High-energy formula

High-energy formula, also called high-calorie, calorie-enhanced, or fortified formula, basically means the number of calories (kcal) per ounce or milliliter is higher compared to regular strength formula, which provides 20 kcal per ounce or 67 kcal per 100 mL. A baby might be given high-energy formula or fortified breast milk that provides 22, 24, 27, or 30 kcal per ounce (or 75, 82, 90, or 100 kcal per 100 mL).

The purpose of high-energy feeds is for the baby to receive more calories in a smaller volume. As mentioned, the higher the calorie content of a baby's feeds, the less milk he needs to consume across the day. Arjun's mom was not aware of this.

Baby Arjun

For some unknown reason, Ishani was advised to feed her son, Arjun, a commercially produced high-calorie formula, which provided 30 kcal per ounce or 100 kcal per 100 mL, from the time of his birth. Arjun was a tiny baby. Not surprising given that Ishani was 4'10" (147 cm) and Arjun's father was 5'4" (160 cm), but I could find nothing in his history that suggested a medical need for high-energy formula.

Ishani found a website that cited 150 mL per kilogram per day (approximately 2.5 ounces per pound) as the average for a baby of Arjun's age (then 10 weeks). And she tried to force Arjun to drink this volume.

Ishani was trying to do what she thought was best for Arjun, but she was not aware of the bigger picture. For example:

- the estimated volume of 150 mL/kg/day or 2.5 oz/lb/day is based on **regular strength formula** and not high-energy formula.
- Arjun was given a baby formula that provided 50 percent more nutrients and calories compared to regular strength formula, and therefore he would drink less volume because of the higher calorie content.

There are different ways to increase the energy content of a baby's feeds besides a commercially produced high-energy formula that have the same effect on the volume of milk consumed.

Important

Everything you add to your baby's milk—including additional scoops of formula, thickening agents, cereal, carbohydrates, or oils—will add extra calories. For every 20 calories added to the milk given to a healthy baby, you need to expect a volume reduction of approximately one ounce or 30 mL—depending on the caloric concentration of his milk—compared to regular-strength formula that contains no additives. I don't recommend high-energy feeds for **healthy, typically developing** babies. I explain why in chapter 11.

11. Formula preparation

If you're not accurate in measuring scoops of powdered infant formula, you could unknowingly make your baby's formula weaker or stronger, and this would affect the volume he needs to consume. For example, a 20 kcal per ounce formula can vary between 15 and 23 kcal per ounce if you under or overfill the scoop. It may also contain more calories if you add powdered formula to the bottle before water. (Chapter 12 explains how errors in formula preparation occur.)

12. Solid foods

Your baby requires a certain number of calories per day to meet his growth and energy needs. This varies from day to day. The more calories he receives from solid foods, the less he needs to receive from breast milk or infant formula.

The order and timing of bottle feeds to solid foods will affect the number of calories your baby takes from each source. If you were to offer him solid foods directly before or between bottle feeds, he would probably eat more solids. But he then will not be as willing to accept a bottle-feed or will drink less milk. If you were to offer him a bottle-feed first followed by solids 20 to 30 minutes later, he will likely drink more milk but eat fewer solids.

It may be a matter of experimenting with the timing of milk and solids to find the right balance suitable for your baby's stage of development.

13. Appetite fluctuations

As adults, we don't eat at precisely the same time every day. And we don't eat the same number of calories at each meal. This is because our appetite varies over the course of the day and from day to day according to our circadian rhythms. This also applies to babies. **Your baby is not going to willingly consume the same volume of milk at every feed or every day.** There will be times when he eats less and times he eats more.

Day versus night feeds

The volume of milk a baby consumes during the night is influenced by the volume he consumes during the day and vice versa.

Once a baby is developmentally mature enough to no longer require nighttime feeds—typically between six to nine months of age—continued nighttime feeds will dampen his appetite the following day. He might not appear hungry after waking in the morning and may not want to eat for many hours after waking. Or if he accepts a feed, he might take very little. This can be a sign that he's ready to drop a night feed. (See page 320 for suggestions on how to gently encourage this without upsetting your baby.)

Mornings and evenings

As your baby's circadian rhythms mature, he will sleep for progressively longer periods at night. You might notice that he starts to consume larger feeds in the afternoon and evening compared to feeds earlier in the day. This is because ghrelin—the appetite-stimulating hormone—levels rise sharply before the onset of the dark phase of the day.[25] He eats more because he is hungrier at that time. It's his body's way of storing energy to carry him for a longer period of time at night without the need to wake and eat.

The morning feeds are often the smallest of the day. This can be confusing for parents who wonder why their baby is not ravenous when he wakes in the morning after going five to 12 hours at night without eating. In general, most of us tend to eat more in the afternoon and evening, which provides an energy credit to carry us through the night.

Feed to feed

Your baby's **energy expenditure** varies over the course of the day. He will burn more energy when active and less while he's sleeping. Therefore, his **energy requirements,** hence the volume of milk he needs to consume, will fluctuate over the course of the day.

Newborn babies can be coaxed into eating similar or the same volume at every feed. This is because newborns, in general, have limited ability to self-regulate their dietary intake because of an active sucking reflex.

Babies over the age of two months whose parents follow their baby's behavioral cues (baby-led feeding) will eat until satisfied. Hence, the volume consumed at each feed will likely vary.

Day to day

Once a baby has matured enough to eat to satisfaction and stop, the total daily volume of milk he consumes over a 24-hour period will fluctuate from day to day. Some days he will want to drink more, perhaps because it's a hot day or he slept less or he's burned more energy playing. On other days, he'll drink less because he's sleeping more or because he's overtired, feeling unwell, feeling bloated, has a pain in his tummy, or he's grumpy for reasons you can't identify.

Week to week

Your baby's rate of growth will fluctuate. He will experience **growth spurts.** During that time, his appetite will increase to support a brief period of rapid growth. He might appear to be insatiably hungry, wanting bigger bottles or demanding feeds more often, and consequently consumes more than usual over the course of the day.

He will also experience **growth plateaus** between growth spurts. During that time, his appetite wanes because his growth has slowed or temporarily stalled. The volume of milk he consumes over a 24-hour period will be lower than usual. He appears to be content after eating what might appear to be barely enough to keep a sparrow alive.

14. Feeding pattern

The volume of milk a baby consumes per feed is influenced by his feeding pattern. The more often he feeds, the less he needs to consume per feed.

In general, a baby who feeds eight times a day would take less **at each feed** compared to if he ate six times a day. However, **over the entire day,** he receives a similar volume either way.

Any feeding pattern must match your baby's circadian rhythms. You will not make a healthy baby drink larger volumes by stretching the time between feeds **if the timing doesn't match his natural body rhythms.** Equally, you will not make him drink more milk over the course of the day by offering feeds more often than his appetite dictates. Offering feeds before a baby signals hunger won't necessarily be rejected, but it generally results in a healthy baby consuming smaller volumes per feed and may encourage a "snacking" feeding pattern.

When you consider the many variables that affect an individual baby's nutritional needs, it's clear why it's **not possible** for any health professional, infant formula manufacturer, or website to accurately predict how much milk **your** baby "should have" at any given point in time.

Milk consumption recommendations vary by country

When Jane asked her pediatrician how much milk her baby needed, he did not give her a figure; he simply said, "Let Sebastian take whatever he wants, and we'll see how he goes next time he's weighed." When Jane told me what he had said, I was stunned, but not because it was bad advice. On the contrary, it was the first time in years that a parent had relayed such excellent advice. The pediatrician was obviously aware that babies can decide how much they need to eat. It is, after all, what all breastfed babies do. But few doctors seem to know or relay that to parents.

When estimating a baby's milk requirements, many health professionals use mathematical calculations based on age and weight. However, it might surprise you to learn that there is no consensus on what these figures should be. The figures differ between countries—and in some instances between health authorities within the same country! The table below compares standard figures commonly used in Australia, the USA, and the UK.

Table 4.1: Formula calculations according to country

<table>
<tr><th>Age</th><th>Australia: NHMRC Infant Feeding Guidelines: Information for Health Workers 201226</th><th>USA: Merck Manual27</th><th>UK: National Health Service28</th></tr>
<tr><td>Preterm to expected birth date</td><td>180 mL/kg/day
3 oz./lb./day</td><td>180–200 mL/kg/day
3–3.5 oz/lb/day</td><td rowspan="3">150–200 mL/kg/day
2.5–3.5 oz/lb/day</td></tr>
<tr><td>5 days to 3 months</td><td>150–200 mL/kg/day
2.5–3 oz/lb/day</td><td rowspan="2">150 mL/kg/day
2.5 oz/lb/day</td></tr>
<tr><td>3–6 months</td><td>120 mL/kg/day
2 oz/lb/day</td></tr>
<tr><td>7–12 months</td><td>90–100 mL/kg/day
1.3–1.5 oz/lb/day</td><td>100 mL/kg/day
1.5 oz/lb/day</td><td>500–600mL/day[29]
17–20 oz/day</td></tr>
</table>

Note: The above approximations are based on regular-strength infant formula, which provides around 20 kcal per ounce, or 67 kcal per 100 mL. They do not take into account that the fat content, and therefore the number of calories in breast milk, varies. Neither do they consider that the baby might be on high-energy formula or have additional calories added to his milk.

These figures in the table **are estimations only.** They are not "should have" amounts for every baby. They are **based solely on a baby's age and weight** and are, at best, a rough estimation. And as you can see, they vary between countries by as much as 25 percent for babies aged between three and six months.

Others don't know how much milk a baby needs

Estimating a baby's nutritional needs is **not an exact science.** I have observed literally hundreds of mistakes made by health professionals when estimating babies' milk needs. No doubt I made many myself, especially in the early years, because I didn't know then what I know now, which is …

Only baby knows how much his body needs.

The concept that others know how much an individual baby "needs" is inherently flawed.

If healthy breastfed babies don't need others to decide how much they need to eat, neither do healthy bottle-fed babies.

The reality is, **health professionals don't know.** They're guessing.

Overestimations lead to feeding problems

It's not wrong for health professionals to provide parents of bottle-fed babies **with an estimation** of their baby's milk needs. I do! If I don't, parents will look elsewhere for a guide. By providing an estimation, I can clarify that it's a **rough guide only** and reinforce how important it is to trust their baby to decide how much to eat. However, great care needs to be taken to not overestimate a baby's needs because of the potential ramifications this can have.

Overestimating a baby's milk needs can cause the parent to take actions that create infant feeding problems.

If a trusted health professional tells you that your baby is not drinking enough, you might then be tempted to use subtle and obvious forms of pressure to make him drink the recommended amount. Repeatedly pressuring babies to feed against their will is **the** most common cause of infant feeding aversions.

Aaron is just one of countless cases I have encountered where a health professional used a mathematical equation to estimate milk needs to Aaron and his family's detriment.

Baby Aaron

Aaron's mother, Tara, had previously consulted with me regarding sleeping problems that Aaron had at the time. She recently emailed for feeding advice.

"Aaron is still sleeping well, thanks to your advice, and he's such a happy baby. However, I'm worried because he used to be a champion feeder. He would take a full bottle with no problems. Now he'll only take about 120 to 180 mL (4 to 6 oz) at each feed. The total amount is between 700 and 800ml (≈23 to 26 ounces) each day. The doctor said he should be drinking 200 mL (6.75 oz) five times a day. He's not taking anywhere

near this amount. The last couple of days, I've had to force him to try to get him to finish his bottles. I hate doing this. He gets so upset. It breaks my heart. But I'm worried that he won't grow properly if he doesn't eat enough. Please tell me how I can get him to drink more." Tara

I later spoke with Tara, and she relayed what had happened during Aaron's four-month health check. The doctor weighed and measured Aaron and asked if Tara had any concerns. Tara told her she was concerned that Aaron no longer finished his bottles. The doctor asked how much Aaron was drinking. She took out her calculator and informed Tara that Aaron needed to drink 5 x 200 mL bottles each day.

Tara trusted her doctor. She believed that as a health professional, her doctor must know how much Aaron needed to eat, so she had no doubts about the advice she was given. She tried to make Aaron continue eating after he showed signs of wanting to stop. Tara quickly realized that something was seriously wrong when she had to force Aaron to drink.

Even at the point of emailing me, Tara didn't suspect that her doctor might have been mistaken about the volume of milk Aaron needed. She thought I might be able to provide advice on feeding equipment or formula or something else that might enable him to drink the recommended amount without being forced.

Aaron showed signs that he was well fed. He was gaining weight as expected. Tara stated he was happy, healthy, and slept well. Aaron didn't need to drink more. The reason he was no longer finishing his bottles was that he was able to self-regulate his milk intake.

The doctor's assessment was poor. She did not assess whether Aaron was happy with the volume of milk he consumed. She didn't take into consideration that Aaron's growth was fine. Or that not all babies of the same weight require the same volume of milk. Or that Aaron was drinking pumped breast milk and not infant formula. Or that healthy babies don't drink exactly the same amount every feed, every day. Her assessment based on a mathematical equation resulted in her overestimating Aaron's nutritional needs. The advice she provided had the potential for serious ramifications for Aaron and his family.

I was able to reassure Tara that Aaron was regulating his milk intake according to his needs and that Tara's role was to support him to do so and not try to control how much he ate using pressure tactics. Had Tara continued to try to pressure Aaron, the chances of him developing a feeding aversion were high. Tara's once "champion

> feeder" could have turned into a "distressed, avoidant feeder" who was then at risk of underfeeding.

When health professionals use the words "should have," "must have," "needs to have," and "minimum" concerning estimated volumes, this is a real problem. It can cause damage.

If your baby is **genuinely underfeeding,** as opposed to the **assumption of underfeeding** based solely on the fact that he's not drinking the volume of milk estimated, there are reasons (see chapter 26). Pressuring or forcing him to eat against his will is not a solution.

If you're using pressure to "make" your baby drink the recommended amount, stop and think about it. Reassess the situation, starting with how much milk you believe your baby "needs" or "must have" and whether it may be an overestimation.

I am not suggesting that you ignore your health professional's estimation, only that you keep in mind that mistakes are common and that serious negative consequences can be associated with pressuring or forcing a baby to eat more milk than his body actually needs.

Don't get hung up on numbers

Healthy eating habits involve eating when hungry and stopping when satisfied. It's not about eating as much as another person dictates or as much as another baby. If you attempt to make your baby consume a specific volume, this can lead to physical and emotional distress. And it can be detrimental to a baby's relationship with feeding, not just as an infant but well into the future.

If you follow your baby's lead and let him decide how much to eat, in time, you will start to gain a sense of how much to add to the bottle. The amount of milk your baby consumes will fluctuate from feed to feed. His milk intake should not be limited by the volume within the bottle. Equally, he should not be made to empty the bottle. Add what you have learned he generally consumes, plus a little extra to enable him to feed to satisfaction if he wants a little more or leave some milk in the bottle when he's done.

Wow! This is a big chapter with no definitive answer on how much your baby needs. But would you have believed me if I simply said, "Your baby knows what his body needs—trust him!"?

Next

How do you know when your baby is hungry and when he's had enough? There are a few signs to look out for. But infant reflexes—automatic movements babies make—can cause considerable confusion for parents of newborns. For example, the sucking reflex, which is automatically triggered in newborns, is often mistaken as a sign of hunger. I will describe infant reflexes—what they mean and don't mean—next. Even if your baby is past the newborn period, I recommend you read the next chapter as it may help to better understand your baby.

Part B:
Understanding Your Baby

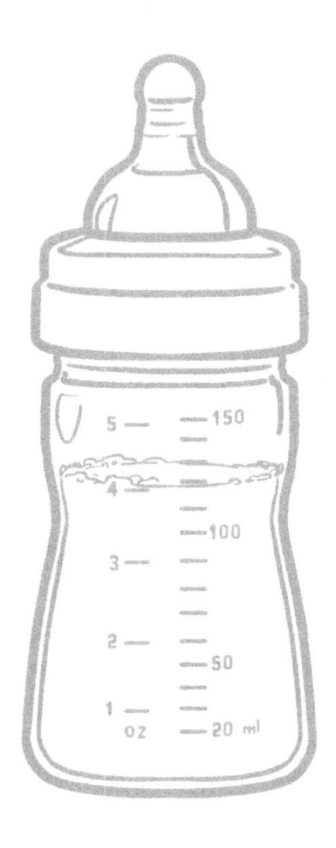

5 Baby Reflexes and Urges

INFANT REFLEXES AND URGES • HOW THESE ARE TRIGGERED • WHY THIS KNOWLEDGE IS IMPORTANT

Knowing about infant reflexes and urges is critical for accurately interpreting newborn baby behavior, but it can be really confusing. When my children were babies, I, like most parents, was unaware of how infant reflexes and urges affect a baby's behavior. I wish I knew then what I know now, as it would have meant fewer mistakes when responding to my babies' behavioral cues.

It's not too late for you to learn about the effect of infant reflexes and how this might affect your baby's milk intake and feeding behavior. Understanding the effect that infant reflexes and urges have on your baby's behavior helps to make the lines of communication much clearer.

What are infantile reflexes?

A **reflex** is an involuntary or automatic action that your body does in response to something—without you even having to think about it—like a knee jerk.

Your baby's "infantile reflexes" are present for only a brief period. Most will have disappeared by the time she is three to four months of age. Other reflexes will remain throughout her entire lifetime.

Most of the movements your newborn baby makes are involuntary and occur as a result of reflexes. Several reflexes related specifically to feeding enable her to breastfeed or bottle-feed from the time of her birth without prior learning. They remain present until she has developed enough, both physically and intellectually, to learn how to feed voluntarily.

Most confusing or concerning to parents and other caregivers include the

- rooting reflex;
- gape reflex;
- extrusion reflex;
- sucking reflex;
- swallow reflex;
- gag reflex;
- gastrocolic reflex; and
- defecation reflex.

Without knowing about these reflexes as well as their triggers, it's easy to misread involuntary body movements as deliberate actions on your baby's part or as a sign of a problem.

Rooting reflex

The rooting reflex, also called the search reflex, is nature's way of helping a baby find food. This reflex is triggered when your newborn baby's cheek is touched, or she's stroked along the corners of her mouth. She will turn her head and open her mouth toward the touch as she seeks something to suck.

The rooting reflex usually disappears by around three to four months of age. It is often interpreted as a sign of hunger, but it can be triggered even when a baby is not hungry.

Gape reflex

Downward stroking of your baby's philtrum (the indented area between the nose and top lip) and across her lips to her chin can trigger a gape reflex. This will cause her mouth to gape open as she drops her lower jaw, keeping her tongue down. The response enables her to latch onto a nipple. The gape reflex disappears around three to four months of age.

Extrusion reflex

The extrusion reflex is also called the tongue thrust reflex. If your baby's lips are touched while this reflex is present, her tongue will automatically move forward. This reflex generally disappears by around four months of age, but it can persist until six months for some babies.

The extrusion reflex will help your baby to successfully latch to her mother's nipple or nipple of a bottle. The presence of her extrusion reflex will prevent her from eating solid foods as it will cause her to push food out of her mouth. This is a good thing because while her extrusion reflex is active, it means that developmentally she's too young to eat solid foods.

Once your baby has effectively latched, sucking and swallowing reflexes take over.

Sucking reflex

The sucking reflex is strongest when the palate (roof of her mouth) is stimulated. Anything that applies pressure to the top of a newborn baby's tongue or roof of her mouth, such as a breast or bottle nipple, pacifier, fist, or finger, could activate her sucking reflex. While the nipple is in her mouth, gentle upward pressure applied under her chin will increase the pressure on her palate and trigger her sucking reflex.

The sucking reflex is an automatic, involuntary response. It enables a baby to suck and feed from the breast or bottle before she has learned how to voluntarily suck. This reflex develops while the baby is in the womb and is present during gestation at around 32 weeks.

A newborn baby doesn't need to be hungry for her sucking reflex to be activated. Once this reflex is triggered in coordination with her swallowing reflex, it can appear like she is hungrily guzzling down a bottle of milk, when, in reality, she might not be hungry. As a newborn, she cannot prevent herself from sucking once this reflex is triggered any more than you can prevent your leg from extending when a doctor checks your knee-jerk reflex.

As your baby matures, her sucking abilities transition from involuntary to voluntary movements. Around **two months** after birth, her sucking reflex has faded. It can still be triggered, but not as easily. By **three to four months** of age (or in the case of a preterm baby, her adjusted age), she will only **voluntarily** suck from a bottle if and when she chooses. But she can be pressured or forced to feed against her will.

Swallowing reflex

As milk pools in your baby's mouth, a swallowing reflex is triggered. Her tongue immediately moves to the back of her mouth. As she swallows, the **phalangeal reflex** is triggered, which causes her larynx (her voice box, which is the opening to her lungs) to close, preventing milk from getting into her airways.

In the early months of life, a baby's swallowing abilities are controlled by reflexes. However, as she matures, she will learn how to swallow voluntarily, enabling her to hold milk or food in her mouth or spit it out.

Provided your baby's head and body is positioned in a way that supports safe swallowing (see chapter 15) and that the flow rate is suitable for her stage of development (see page 184), the coordination of her sucking, swallowing, and phalangeal reflexes will enable her to feed comfortably and safely during the early months of life as she's learning to gain more conscious control over her sucking and swallowing.

Gag reflex

The gag reflex is a natural protective reflex that results in the contraction of the back of the throat to prevent choking and avoid triggering the swallowing reflex. Gagging causes the food or object to be pushed forward on the tongue.

The gag reflex remains with us for life. However, because of their immaturity and limited eating skills, babies are more likely to gag compared to adults.

In the newborn period, anything touching the **midsection** of a baby's tongue could cause her to gag. The trigger point **moves back** in her mouth by around four to six months of age, coinciding with learning to eat solid foods. Around nine months, gagging will be triggered by touch to the **back section** of the tongue.

The gag reflex is a common source of concern for parents, particularly when their baby starts to eat solid foods. The gag reflex is often mistaken for choking, but it's not the same. Unlike choking, which is silent, gagging is very noisy.

Gastrocolic reflex

When your newborn baby sharply pulls away from the breast or bottle, screws up her face, bears down like she's straining to have a bowel movement, and then shortly after, returns to feeding, you've seen the results of the **gastrocolic reflex** (affecting her stomach and large bowel). Sometimes your baby will poop or pass gas, and other times, nothing will come out. This is normal infant behavior!

The gastrocolic reflex occurs in response to the baby's stomach stretching as a result of feeding. This triggers wave-like contractions in her stomach and intestinal tract that move gastrointestinal contents along. It's like her stomach is sending a message to her intestines (via her brain) to get a move on and make more room for the food that's coming in.

When parents observe the behavior associated with the gastrocolic reflex, they often believe that their baby is pulling away from the feed due to abdominal pain or, if there is no bowel movement at the time, that she's straining from constipation. But it's **usually not** an indication of pain or constipation.

This reflex is triggered by the act of eating, but there are other factors that impact **how strong** the intestinal contractions are. The following problems are associated with an increased frequency and intensity of intestinal contractions and abdominal discomfort:

- constipation, in which case your baby will pass hard, firm, pebbly stools;
- functional lactose overload (pages 439-448);
- milk protein allergy (pages 457–458);
- milk protein intolerance (pages 459–464);
- food poisoning (pages 174–178), and
- gastroenteritis.

Except for constipation, all problems listed are associated with frequent, watery, explosive bowel movements.

Defecation reflex

Another related reflex is the defecation reflex, also known as the rectal reflex. This reflex is triggered by the expansion or filling of your baby's rectum (the part of her bowel closest to her anus) with gas or poop.

The combined effect of the gastrocolic and defecation reflexes could cause her to have a bowel movement while feeding or shortly after the feed has ended. Some parents become concerned because they believe the milk is "going straight through" their baby, but that's not the case. What's coming out is **not** the milk the baby has just consumed.

The **average** time it takes for food to transit through the digestive tract (from feeding to pooping) is 8.5 hours for babies aged one to three months and 16 hours aged four to 24 months.[30] The time frame varies considerably from a few hours to many days depending on the type and volume of milk consumed. (See pages 435–437 for more on what is normal frequency of bowel movements for babies.)

Effective emptying of the rectum relies on both the defecation reflex and increased pressure in the abdomen muscles by a "straining" action, which assists to push the gas or stools out. Because babies have weak abdominal muscles, they use their diaphragm (the large muscle that separates the chest and abdominal cavity). This can cause them to go red in the face and grunt. This behavior is often mistaken as a sign of constipation.

Your baby has many other reflexes besides these, some of which will disappear without you ever knowing they existed, and others that will remain present throughout her lifetime. I have only included those that are most commonly misinterpreted by parents.

Next, I will describe the urges babies have that are often mistaken by parents to mean things they don't.

Baby urges

An "urge" relates to a desire or impulse to do something, whereas a reflex is an involuntary action that can be triggered irrespective of a baby's desire.

Babies are in an oral stage of development, which lasts from birth to two years. This means they learn and gain pleasure from their mouth in two ways: sucking and mouthing.

Sucking urge

In general, babies have a strong urge to suck.

New parents are often told that their baby's desire to suck is a sign of hunger, which it can be—but not always. Maybe baby is hungry! Maybe she just wants to suck! More than 80 percent of babies demonstrate a sucking urge **unrelated** to hunger.[31] Most babies want to suck when hungry, tired, frustrated, bored, upset, uncomfortable, and for pleasure.

Sucking provides babies with a sense of comfort and security, aids digestion, and decreases crying. This natural instinct is often soothing and relaxing. It can also help to induce sleep, which is why babies often want to suck as a way to fall asleep.

Newborn babies have limited ability to control their limb and body movements. Their fists are mostly held in a clenched position. If your newborn finds her fist near her mouth by chance, she will try to suck on it—but sucking on her fist is "hit or miss" at this young age. She simply doesn't have the physical capacity to deliberately bring her hand to her mouth and hold it there long enough to satisfy her sucking urge. She might have a short suck but then cry because her hand jerks away.

Without the ability to independently satisfy the urge to suck, a newborn baby has no option other than to cry to have her sucking needs met. She will continue to cry until she's given something to suck on. This could be a breast or bottle nipple, pacifier, or a caregiver's finger.

The combination of a newborn baby's desire to suck, plus an active sucking reflex, and the potential for parents to misinterpret this as a hunger sign (and hence offer a feed), increases the risk of overfeeding in the early months.

By around **three months** of age, a baby will have gained greater voluntary control over her **arm movements.** She can now bring her hand to her mouth and suck on her fist when she chooses. Fist-sucking at this age is just a developmental stage that enables babies to independently satisfy their sucking urge. Without this knowledge, parents often misinterpret their baby's fist-sucking as a sign of hunger or teething.

At this age, your baby's sucking reflex has disappeared or is very close to disappearing. Hence, if she is offered a feed when she simply wants to suck on her fist or a pacifier, she will refuse. Alternatively, she might appear to "fake suck" (make sucking motions without actually sucking or swallowing) and milk might dribble from her mouth.

By the time your baby is **four months** old, she has developed more control over her **hand and fingers.** She may now find sucking her thumb or two fingers to be a more satisfying and reliable means to self-soothe compared to her fist.

Around **five to six months** of age, the inborn urge to suck has faded, but many babies continue to suck because it provides them with a sense of comfort and security. For many children, sucking **up to the age of four**

years is a normal part of their development. Most will stop of their own accord at some point before the age of four, but some continue for longer.

Mouthing

Mouthing means to take in or touch with the mouth.

Around **three to four months of age,** a baby will start to become more curious about the world around her. Her chubby little hands are good at grasping and holding objects, but she doesn't have the dexterity to explore them with her hands. Instead, she uses her mouth. Her lips and mouth are full of sensory nerves that enable her to gain a sense of how something feels. By mouthing an object, she can tell if something is hard or soft, rough or smooth, warm or cool.

As she becomes more mobile, she will start to put all manner of things into her mouth. This could be toys, clothing, leaves, sticks, dog food, keys, or a cell phone, basically anything she's able to pick up or finds within her grasp. In general, this is safe and helps to build a stronger immune system so should not be discouraged. But of course, you can't let her put just anything into her mouth. She has no concept of what might be harmful from a choking or poisoning perspective.

When baby is mouthing her fist, sucking on toys, or chewing the railing on her crib, it is easy to assume these behaviors are a sign of hunger or teething. However, this is not always the case.

As your baby matures, she develops more skills that enable her to poke, squeeze, and stroke objects with her hands. She then becomes less reliant on mouthing as a means to learn, and her desire to mouth diminishes.

Next

As you have now discovered, reflex actions, the sucking urge, and mouthing can mean something very different than what you may have previously thought. Now you will be better equipped to interpret your baby's behavioral cues.

In the next chapter, I will describe behavioral cues babies display when hungry, full, bored, frustrated, or stressed.

6 Is Baby Hungry, Full, Frustrated, or Stressed?

INFANT BEHAVIORAL CUES • NEWBORNS AND OVER THREE MONTHS • EARLY AND LATE SIGNS • TEMPERAMENT TYPES • HOW TEMPERAMENT AFFECTS FEEDING BEHAVIOR

All babies have behaviors that indicate their feelings and needs. Providing an appropriate response to your baby's different behavioral cues is the key to promoting contentment and developing a positive relationship. Knowing you're providing a response that is in sync with your baby's wants and needs can greatly enhance your sense of competency as a parent and enjoyment in caring for your baby.

Decoding your baby's nonverbal cues can seem quite daunting, but it doesn't need to be. By watching and listening, you can develop a heightened sensitivity and understanding of your baby's "language."

Newborns

If you're struggling to understand your newborn baby's cues, you are not alone. Most parents find it challenging. This is because a newborn baby's body movements are mostly controlled by reflex actions—those described in chapter 5, as well as numerous others not included. Consequently, newborns display similar behavior for all troubles, making it difficult to pinpoint the cause based solely on their cries and behavior.

Rest assured, it will get easier at around three months of age. As your baby matures, his behavioral cues will change, reflecting advancements in his development. By then, many infant reflexes will have disappeared, and your baby will begin to use more clearly recognizable signals to express his feelings, wants, and needs. Plus, his feeding and sleeping patterns will become more predictable—provided he doesn't have a sleep-association problem (described in pages 292-298). And you will find it much easier to read his behavioral cues.

Let's look at the behavioral cues occurring at different stages of development that a baby may use to express how he's feeling.

How to tell if your baby may be hungry

As adults, we can appear to morph from mild-mannered Bruce Banner into the angry Hulk when we get desperately hungry. Your baby is the same. The hungrier he is, the more desperate he is to eat and the more upset and impatient he becomes.

Birth to 3 months

You might have been told that the following behaviors are signs that your baby is hungry when he

- licks or smacks his lips;
- sucks on his lip, tongue, fingers, or fist;
- fidgets;
- bobs his head forward and side-to-side with an open mouth;
- opens his mouth wide when touched on the chin, cheek, or lips; or
- fusses and cries.

But these behaviors are not proof of hunger. These signs could be better described as **sucking cues**. While they might indicate a baby's receptiveness to feeding, the same behaviors may be displayed because of his desire to suck when tired, for comfort or pleasure, or simply because the rooting reflex has been triggered.

Clearly, you can't solely rely on the list above to determine when or if your baby is hungry, but don't despair. In the next chapter, I will provide guidance on how to use timing and context to help you to decide.

Three months+

Recognizing when your baby is hungry will get easier at around three months of age. His rooting and sucking reflexes have disappeared or are close to doing so. If he is an experienced bottle-feeder, he has now learned to recognize a bottle and understands it as a means to soothe his hunger.

He has a greater ability to control his body movements and indicate his needs and desires.

You can feel relatively confident that your baby is hungry if you observe **a combination** of the following behaviors

- fussing;
- chewing fists or objects;
- becoming excited at the sight of the bottle;
- leaning toward or reaching for the bottle;
- opening his mouth to accept the nipple; and
- sucking vigorously.

Bear in mind that fussing or chewing on fists or objects are **not** conclusive signs of hunger at this age. Mostly, you need to look for signs of your baby's receptiveness to feeding when offered the bottle to confirm hunger.

Table 6.1: Receptiveness or rejection

Receptiveness	Rejection
looking at the bottle getting excited by the sight of the bottle opening mouth to accept the bottle grabbing the bottle and bringing it to mouth	clamping mouth shut turning head away or from side-to-side pushing the bottle away arching back

If your baby is **not hungry** or not interested in feeding, he will reject your offer to feed him or take very little before stopping. He will become annoyed if you try to place the nipple into his mouth once he has displayed signs of rejection, and he is likely to become upset or angry if you persist.

If your baby is clearly hungry and **occasionally** rejects feeds, confirm that this is not due to overtiredness (see pages 290-292.) If he **often** rejects despite signs of hunger, check whether he has developed an aversion to bottle-feeding (see chapter 27).

Sign language

Once your baby is six months old, you may start to teach him baby sign language. Demonstrate the "hungry" gesture while asking him if he's hungry, and within a couple of months, he will learn to gesture back, at which point, he might gesture "hungry" to you even without being asked. Alternatively, you might teach him the sign for "milk." You could also teach him sign language to indicate when he's tired.

How to tell if your baby is full and satisfied

While it's essential to be able to recognize when your baby is hungry, it's equally vital that you understand when he's full and satisfied. In both instances, you need to respond appropriately by ending the feed.

You might wonder, "Aren't full and satisfied the same?" Not exactly. Satisfaction typically follows fullness. However, your baby can feel satisfied without feeling full, and he can feel full without feeling satisfied.

Think about it. Have you ever felt satisfied after eating something small? Or, if you had eaten a lot and felt full, did you still want some ice cream because you felt unsatisfied?

What causes fullness?

As your baby feeds, his stomach expands, which causes stretch receptors in the stomach wall to send electrical messages to his brain via nerve pathways. His brain registers his stomach as **full,** triggers a decrease in ghrelin and increases leptin secretion (hormones that control appetite), which encourage him to stop eating. He could be feeling full at this point, but he might not be feeling satisfied.

What causes satiety?

The feeling of satisfaction as a result of eating is called **satiety**. This occurs from the release of hormones (cholecystokinin as well as others) into your baby's bloodstream. Hormone release is triggered by the absorption of certain nutrients into his bloodstream. The release of these hormones can also cause drowsiness.

Your baby can experience a lag between the time his brain tells him that he is full and the sensation of satisfaction. Whether your baby is content following a feed largely depends on the length of feeding time. If enough time has passed, his body will have had time to release the hormones that provide the feeling of satisfaction.

So how can you tell if your baby is feeling satisfied?

Birth to 3 months

You might have been told, "Your baby will stop eating when he's had enough." This statement is not right in the case of newborns, especially bottle-fed babies, because they have less control over the flow of milk from a bottle compared to the control they would have while breastfeeding.

A leisurely feed lasting between 20 and 40 minutes generally allows sufficient time for a newborn baby's brain to signal the release of hormones that provide the sense of satisfaction and possibly drowsiness. So, you may find that your baby

- slows down and stops sucking;

- releases the nipple;
- drops his hands in an open and relaxed way;
- has a drunken appearance; or
- falls asleep.

Falling asleep can be a sign of satisfaction. Newborns often fall asleep while feeding. However, it can also be a sign of weariness, such as when lacking sleep; working too hard to feed because of a slow-flowing nipple; struggling because of poor head position (see chapter 13) or a bottle venting problem (see chapter 14). In these instances, a baby could repeatedly fall asleep before becoming satisfied. He might then demand frequent feeds (called "snack-feeding") or experience poor growth due to underfeeding.

Feeding quickly, also called **speed-feeding,** which for a newborn means consuming a full feed in less than 20 minutes, can provide quite different outcomes. He could feel full during this time and stop sucking but may not appear satisfied. If not feeling satisfied, he might fuss following the feed. Despite him having had a "full feed," you may be tempted to give him more. If his sucking reflex is triggered, he might take more and overfeed.

If your newborn baby has already consumed a reasonable volume of milk and is upset following the feed, offer him something else to suck, like your finger or a pacifier, rather than feed him more. Try to slow feeds down in the future by way of a slower nipple.

Three months+

By this age, your baby's sucking reflex has faded or disappeared, and he has full control over his sucking. He has greater control over his body movements and can clearly signal when hunger has been satisfied.

At three months and over, you may find that your baby show signs of fullness or satiety by

- decreasing sucking (and stops sucking when full);
- making little or no attempt to suck;
- pushing the nipple out of his mouth with his tongue;
- clamping his mouth shut;
- pushing the bottle away;
- turning his head or body away from the bottle when offered;
- chewing on the nipple or moving it around his mouth;

- becoming easily distracted; or
- falling asleep.

Babies over the age of three months can fall asleep **while feeding** for a variety of other reasons—for example, overtiredness, chronic sleep deprivation, or a feeding-sleep association (see chapter 22).

What frustrates babies when they're feeding?

Babies, like adults, will feel frustrated when things aren't as expected or when they don't get what they want. A few of the many reasons that a baby could become frustrated before or after the feed include

- waiting when hungry;
- an unexpected change in the flavor of milk;
- milk that is too warm or too cold;
- a nipple that is too fast or slow;
- a blocked nipple;
- taking too long to return to feeding after stopping to burp;
- being pressured or forced to continue feeding;
- ending the feed before he feels satisfied;
- an unsatisfied sucking urge;
- being handled roughly;
- feeling rushed or pressured to feed—for example, jiggling the bottle, touching his face; and

- being prevented from easily accessing the milk, whether from unsuitable or faulty feeding equipment or poor head, body, or bottle positioning.

Chapter 28 describes other reasons for concerning behaviors before, during, and after feeds.

Birth to 3 months

Until around six to eight weeks, a baby will continue to suck while his sucking reflex is triggered. It's hard for him to express frustrations verbally while feeding. However, he can display them through his body and hand movements—for example, appearing tense, squirming, and wiggling. He will be able to express himself verbally by fussing, whining, and crying when the feed is paused to burp him or once the feed has ended.

Three months+

Around three months of age, you will notice that your baby starts to display his "happy" emotions by smiling, laughing, appearing excited, cooing, and playing. He can also show "unhappy" emotions like frustration and anger. If something frustrates or angers him, he's going to let you know.

Over the age of three months, your baby will generally feed contentedly when hungry and undisturbed. He is likely to express frustration by

- squirming or wiggling;
- no longer sucking;
- fussing;
- turning away; and
- pushing the bottle away.

Anger is an extreme form of frustration. When angry, your baby's behavior will be more intense, and he may

- cry or scream;
- claw at his face;
- push the bottle away; and
- arch his back.

How easily and how quickly your baby becomes angry depends on his temperament (described later in this chapter). If he has an "easy" temperament, even major frustrations—like being kept waiting to feed or encountering a blocked nipple—may cause nothing more than a slight annoyance. But if he has a "spirited" temperament, he could react to his milk going cold and other minor frustrations like it's a state of emergency.

What stresses babies?

Your baby might become stressed during feeds for many reasons, which can vary depending on age, but some are the same regardless of age. Common reasons include

- extreme hunger;
- overtiredness;
- speed-feeding, which can cause a newborn to feel panicked as his airways are threatened;
- being pressured or forced to feed against his will;
- becoming distressed by the prospect of feeding—if he has developed a feeding aversion;
- overstimulation—for example, noise, children touching him, and when parents use annoying feeding practices (described on page 279); and
- pain.

As parents, we would all hate to think that our baby reached the point of feeling stressed. Early recognition of stress signals is the key to minimizing the risk. What signs do babies show when they're stressed?

Birth to 3 months

Like all other behavioral cues, newborn babies display signs of stress in ways that differ from older babies. Signs may include

- a frightened expression;
- faster breathing;
- avoiding eye contact;
- a rigid body;
- raising arms toward the bottle or face;
- splayed fingers and toes; and

- gulping, panting, or gasping.

Three months+

Signs of stress in a baby three months or older may include

- a distressed look or wrinkly forehead (sometimes called brow bulge);
- avoiding eye contact;
- clasping hands together;
- ringing hands;
- fussing and turning head from side to side;
- hitting the bottle or trying to push the bottle away with hands or feet;
- crying or screaming; and
- arching his back.

Note: Back arching is often attributed to acid reflux, but a stressed baby will arch back irrespective of the cause.

What happens when we're stressed?

When stressed for any reason, the human body releases stress hormones into the bloodstream. Stress hormones trigger a fight or flight response. These hormones increase alertness, the heart pumps harder, pulse and blood pressure rise, pupils dilate, **appetite is suppressed, and digestion shuts down**.

If you observe signs that your baby is stressed during feeds, you need to stop and calm him. When stressed, he's not going to suck, and attempting to force him to feed will cause further aggravation. Instead, soothe him. Wait until he calms before attempting to feed him again.

Is your baby experiencing pain?

Pain is often blamed when a baby displays signs of stress, especially when other reasons are not obvious. However, babies can be distressed for many reasons unrelated to pain. How can you tell the difference? It's easier than you might think—just assess how your baby responds in other circumstances.

Pain is unlikely the cause if your baby is

- physically well;
- happy when feeding stops;

- readily soothed;
- feeding well in predictable situations—for example, during the night or while in a drowsy state or asleep; and
- content between feeds.

To read more about pain, see pages 409-411.

Is your baby tired?

When a baby is both tired and hungry, tiredness tends to win. Not only will your baby be extra cranky, but he will be more likely to

- reject a feed;
- display "conflicted" feeding behavior (repeatedly swinging between wanting and not wanting to eat); and
- fall asleep while feeding.

Lack of sleep is a major reason for infant distress. In chapter 22, I explain the average amount of sleep for babies at different ages, tiredness cues, signs and reasons for overtiredness, how sleep affects feeding, and ways to minimize the risk of stress and feeding problems caused by lack of sleep.

Is your baby overstimulated or bored?

Sensory stimulation is like fuel for a baby's developing brain—he craves it. But like every craving, the type of stimulation needs to be appropriate for his stage of development: too much will cause **overstimulation** as well as irritation or stress; too little will cause **boredom**.

By carefully observing your baby's behavior and the surrounding circumstances, you will recognize when you need to reduce stimulation or provide more attention.

Birth to 3 months

At this young age, **boredom is not an issue**. Your newborn baby will generally feed smoothly and contentedly if the flow rate is appropriate. Fussing during feeding is likely caused by overstimulation or other frustration and stress-inducing circumstances rather than boredom.

An overstimulated baby will display signs of stress and become increasingly more distressed the more you try to do. A bored baby will soothe when provided with attention and sensory stimulation.

Three months+

You may find your baby attempts to counteract boredom through

- attention-seeking;
- distractibility; or
- self-amusement.

Attention-seeking

While held in your arms, your baby might randomly stop, look at you, smile, babble, and only return to feeding once he has your attention. If he's bored, he might wiggle, fuss, appear disinterested, pause, or stop feeding prematurely.

Distractibility

Around four months of age, your baby goes through an intellectual growth spurt. His long-distance visual acuity and awareness of surroundings are greatly enhanced. It's like his world has suddenly grown much larger. From this time on, he can become easily distracted while feeding.[32] If his surroundings change—for example, if you or someone else in the room moves or speaks, or your phone rings, he will stop sucking and turn toward the distraction.

Certain babies may be more easily distracted than others because of their temperament. Some will feed undisturbed in the chaos of the food court in the mall. Others might stop if they hear a pin drop or see a curtain flutter in the breeze.

Self-amusement

As your baby gains physical strength and ability, he will practice and develop new skills. He will attempt to hold the bottle—at times accidentally knocking it out of his mouth—and practice pushing it out and pulling it back in. He might stick his thumb in his mouth alongside the nipple, grab one of his feet, try to sit up, play with your hair or clothing, chew the nipple, or push it to the side of his mouth with his tongue.

All of these are normal behaviors for a baby. If you're in a hurry for your baby to finish feeding, you might find some of these behaviors mildly annoying. When not in a hurry, take the time to enjoy these precious moments. You may find amusement in your baby's playful antics or feel pride as you observe his sense of achievement and mastery over new skills. You will sit in wonder at just how fast your sweet baby is growing and developing.

How your baby behaves and reacts in various situations partially relates to his temperament.

What's your baby's temperament?

Temperament is the part of your baby's personality that he was born with. Twenty to 60 percent of temperament is determined by genetics (inherited from parents).[33]

A baby's temperament is displayed by the way he consistently behaves in relation to what's happening to him and around him—both inside his body and outside. Individual babies behave in varying ways depending on their temperament traits.

You can support your baby to flourish both physically and emotionally by providing care that harmonizes with his temperament type. Recognizing his personality traits will help you to better understand him and anticipate how he is likely to react in different situations.

American child psychiatrists Alexander Thomas and Stella Chess categorized temperament into types, naming them

- easy;
- slow-to-warm-up; and
- difficult.

Many people, myself included, object to the term "difficult." Some call these babies "high-needs," but I prefer to call them "spirited." Let's look at each category to see if the descriptions resonate with you about your baby's character.

"Easy" babies

Easy babies are the type of baby we all picture when we're pregnant. You'll know an easy baby by his placid or cheerful nature. He'll be easily calmed when crying. He gives clear signals indicating his wants and needs. When you have a baby with an easy temperament, it's easier to feel like a successful, effective parent. The regularity of your baby's feeding and sleeping patterns make it easy for you to predict his needs. His moderate response makes him easy to care for. And if you happen to misinterpret his cues, he's not fazed by delays in having his needs met. You can also manage to find some time for yourself.

Babies with easy temperaments still experience feeding and sleeping problems, but they're less likely to experience problems compared to babies with other temperament types.

"Slow-to-warm-up" babies

A slow-to-warm-up baby tends to be shy or cautious, wary of new situations and new people. He's inclined to be somewhat negative in mood. He doesn't like to be rushed and will withdraw or protest if he feels pressured. He needs more time to adapt to changes compared to an "easy" baby. He might reject or withdraw when first exposed to something new. He might refuse a new food initially but accept it after repeated offers. Instead of being physically active, he's more likely to watch what's going on around him. A slow-to-warm-up baby can quickly become overstimulated, but he can usually be comforted in some way when he cries.

As the parent of a baby with a slow-to-warm-up temperament, you will likely experience some frustrations when he doesn't comply or respond in the ways you expect. Equally, he will feel frustration if you are rushing him or expecting more of him than he's capable of achieving. If you take the time to understand how his temperament affects his reactions and accept that his personality is part of the unique little person he is, you can then adjust your expectations and figure out ways to work with him. If you do, you will experience fewer frustrations on both sides.

"Spirited" babies

A "spirited" baby can be very emotional; he fusses and cries a lot. He's highly strung, easily upset by noise and commotion, and intense when he reacts. He may appear to be demanding and impatient. He has a low frustration tolerance and is prone to temper outbursts. And when he cries, what a racket he makes! He doesn't like to be kept waiting. He'll protest vigorously if he doesn't get what he wants or what he has learned to expect. He can cry for long periods and is often difficult to soothe when crying. When awake, he's very active, engaging in almost constant physical activity. He seems restless and is easily distracted. He resists going to sleep. He tends to develop irregular feeding and sleeping patterns. He's fearful of new people and situations and takes a long time to adjust to new routines and new foods. While a spirited baby can learn to be more patient, it takes time and patience on the parent's part to avoid pushing him into doing something he doesn't wish to do.

If you are the parent of a spirited baby, you will face many challenges. Of all temperament types, spirited babies are the most likely to experience problems in the following three areas:

- **dietary regulation,** in particular overfeeding, plus gastrointestinal symptoms associated with overfeeding such as extreme spitting up, frequent foul-smelling bowel movements, excessive gas, and abdominal pain;
- **sleep regulation,** difficulty falling asleep at night, short or nonexistent naps, irritability from sleep deprivation; and
- **emotional regulation,** evidenced by bouts of inconsolable crying and, in general, requiring a lot of input from parents to regain a state of calm.

Just one of these problems is a challenge. However, babies can experience two or all three problems at the same time. These problems are not exclusive to spirited babies, it's just that babies with a spirited temperament are more susceptible to these problems.

One reason I believe these problems are more prevalent with spirited babies is because their behavioral cues are so difficult to interpret. They are inclined to be "extreme signalers" who make everything seem as if it's urgent and desperate. They can go from quiet to screaming at warp speed. And they find it difficult to calm once they are upset. Consequently, parents don't have much time to figure out what they want, and when they do, it may be too late to stem their baby's cries. The fact that spirited babies struggle to calm when upset can cause parents to second-guess their decisions and take actions that might make the situation worse.

The parents of spirited babies often feel confused, frustrated, stressed, sleep-deprived, and lacking in confidence. When parents make comments to me like, "I'm a bad mother" or "Nothing I do is right," and even "I wish

I never had a baby," I suspect they may be struggling to care for a spirited baby.

You'll recognize the traits of a spirited baby if you have one. If this is the case, it's quite possible that you're already struggling with an infant feeding or sleeping problem, and probably both. Your baby may have even been diagnosed with a medical condition—or two or three, like colic, reflux, or milk protein allergy or intolerance, to explain why the situation is such a mess. Caring for your baby consumes your day. You have little time for self-care. Reading this book is a huge sacrifice of your time, but you're praying it will be worth it. It will!

Please don't despair. Life with a spirited baby can be **much** easier than it is at present. Problems can be solved, frustrations considerably reduced though not completely eliminated, and you can regain confidence in your parenting abilities and enjoyment in caring for your baby by enhancing your knowledge. The information contained in this book will help you to see the light at the end of the tunnel.

Disclaimer: This is just a guide. I'm not an expert in infant temperament. But I do appreciate firsthand, as both a parent and health professional, how temperament affects feeding, sleeping and how babies behave. You may find that learning more about your baby's temperament helps you to feel more confident when making decisions about your baby's concerns.

Next

Many behavioral cues look similar. The confusion this creates can result in a lot of trial and error when attempting to figure out the cause, but there are several ways to improve your accuracy. In the next chapter, I explain how to use timing and context to help you better read your baby's cues.

7 How to Better Read Baby's Cues

HOW TO USE TIMING AND CONTEXT TO INTERPRET YOUR BABY'S CUES • WHAT HAPPENS IF YOU GET IT WRONG

During my career, parents have often asked me to interpret their baby's behaviors. While I could simply tell them what I think, it's more beneficial if I explain how they can enhance their own confidence in identifying reasons for behaviors.

The trick to gaining greater accuracy in decoding your baby's cries and behavior is to use timing and context to determine the most likely cause. **Timing** involves being aware of the age-appropriate "awake windows" and "average time between feedings" to decide when to prepare your baby for sleep or offer a feed. **Context** refers to the circumstances that form the setting for an event. This provides valuable information to help identify the cause of unexpected fussing or crying.

How to use timing and context is something that experienced parents typically learn "on the job," often as a result of a lot of trial and error. I will explain how you can fast track this learning experience.

Why learn to use timing and context?

Deciphering your baby's cues is hard enough when you're not sure whether newborn behaviors are deliberate or involuntary reflexes. Even more confusing, newborns display many of the same behaviors for anything that troubles them. Mostly, only the intensity of the behavior changes. Your baby might cry when hungry, tired, overstimulated, frustrated, stressed, uncomfortable, because of pain, or for reasons you can't identify. The cries just get louder the longer it takes for you to figure out and remedy the situation.

You might be tempted to travel the easy road of giving care prompted by the clock. However, doing so won't help you gain confidence or a sense of competence in your parenting abilities—and it could eventually backfire if time-based care doesn't match your baby's circadian rhythms.

There are ways to improve your accuracy using the following three steps.

1. Anticipate what baby might need next.
2. Know when to act.
3. Use timing and context to pinpoint the cause.

I will describe what these steps involve.

Anticipate what your baby might need

Learning about **circadian rhythms** and typical feeding and sleeping patterns for babies at different stages of development (described in chapter 2) was a game-changer for me when my children were babies. This enabled me to anticipate my baby's next need, whether food or sleep. I would then watch for signs of fussiness, but I already had some idea what to try first.

Know when to act

Though crying is the most obvious form of communication used by newborns, there will be many nonverbal cues that will let you know how your baby is feeling. He will display many subtle forms of communication before he reaches the crying stage. Acting on these subtle behavioral signs to provide care can significantly reduce crying time.

Something I found helpful was to learn about the six states of consciousness of newborns identified by renowned American pediatrician Dr. T. Berry Brazelton.[34] These include deep sleep, active light sleep, drowsiness, awake-alert state, awake-fussy state, and crying. Brazelton explains that all babies will cycle through these states repeatedly throughout the day. He also explains that by watching for these changing states of alertness, you can anticipate when fussiness is likely to occur and understand when it's time to act.

Table 7.1: Six States of Consciousness

	State	What your baby does	What you need to do
1	**Deep sleep**	She lies quietly without moving. Her eyes are closed. Her breathing is deep and regular. She might have brief startles but will not rouse.	Leave your baby to sleep.
2	**Light sleep**	Her eyes are shut, but you can see her pupils moving from side to side under her eyelids. Her body twitches. Her face may move. She might smile, frown, or make sucking movements. Her breathing is shallow.	You might think she is about to wake, which she may be, but not necessarily. She could arouse between sleep cycles but then drop back into another sleep cycle if left. Wait until you're sure she is waking before picking her up.
3	**Drowsy**	Her eyes open and close. She has a dazed appearance. Her arms and legs move smoothly, and she might stretch.	Leave your baby to wake fully and let you know that she wants your attention. If you pick her up, keep things relaxed. No one wants someone to be in their face when they're drowsy.
4	**Quiet alert**	Her body and face are relaxed. She's quiet but interested. She might engage in eye contact with you or observe her surroundings.	You might engage in quiet activities like talking or reading to her. Read or show her things, massage or stroke her.
5	**Active alert or fussy**	This is a transitional state that could lead to crying. She is no longer willing to engage in eye contact. Her movements are tense and jerky. She is indicating something is not quite right. She might be soothed or brought to a quiet alert state by cuddles or entertainment, but it may not last for long.	It's during this state when you need to watch for signs of fussiness. You might be able to prevent your baby's crying by acting as soon as you observe any signs of her becoming tense. Use "timing and context" (described later in this chapter) to help you to decide on the most appropriate course of action.

6	**Crying**	Crying is the most effective way that babies gain the attention of caregivers. Crying is often an indication of mild to moderate stress owing to unmet needs.	Preventing crying depends on whether your response at the active alert/fussy stage matches your baby's needs. The longer it takes for you to pinpoint and provide for her needs, the more her cries will escalate.

When you notice your baby in an active-alert stage, you know it won't be long before she starts to fuss. It's possible for you to reduce the risk of her reaching the point of crying or screaming by acting to provide for her needs, whatever they may be, as soon as she starts to fuss.

The urgency of her needs, stage of development, and temperament will influence how quickly she escalates from being content to fussy, crying, and screaming. If your baby has an "easy" temperament, the transition from fussing to crying will be slow, allowing you plenty of time to figure out what she wants. If she has a "spirited" temperament, it could feel like her mood switches from calm to screaming in the blink of an eye, and you will have less time. But in reality, she will display earlier behavioral cues to indicate her frustration if you watch for them.

Use timing and context

"I am so confused! Liam could be gnawing at his fist like he's starving but then refuses a bottle or drinks 20 mL (0.7 oz) and falls asleep. Other times it's like he's never going to stop eating. I just don't understand him. It's so frustrating. I am his mother. I should know what he wants. I feel like I am a terrible mother. Am I the only one who's just not getting it?" Tahlia

Tahlia might feel like she's the only parent struggling to understand her baby's behavior, but she's not. Most parents find it difficult to interpret their baby's cues—and with good reason. Infant behavioral cues are not easy to read, particularly in the early months and especially in the case of "spirited" babies.

In general, experienced parents are more effective at accurately deciphering their baby's behavioral cues than first-time parents. This is usually because they have previously cared for babies and are aware of the various reasons for babies to fuss and cry. They don't fall for the "crying baby = hunger" trap that often snares first-time parents. Plus, they tend to be more knowledgeable about babies' feeding and sleeping patterns—for example, how long babies tend to be awake before needing to sleep and the average time between bottle-feeds.

Armed with such knowledge, they can use timing to anticipate their baby's changing needs and context to determine reasons for unexpected fussing and crying. But even the most experienced parents or parenting experts won't get it right every time.

If this is not something you're currently doing, I recommend you learn to use timing and context to gain more accuracy when reading your baby's cues.

Timing

Your baby's circadian rhythms will influence when she's hungry and tired, as well as countless other bodily functions. In general, babies of the same age tend to have similar, though not exactly the same, body rhythms. In other words, they have a natural tendency to want to sleep and eat at semipredictable times based on their age.

The more you know about what typical feeding and sleeping patterns for babies at different ages look like, the better you can use timing to anticipate your baby's needs and identify reasons for fussiness.

I recommend you learn about the following

- average number of feeds for age (page 28),
- typical feeding pattern for age (pages 25-27),
- average feeding duration for age (page 184),
- average number of hours of sleep for age (page 288), and
- average awake time for age (page 290).

Of course, not all babies do what is "average." Nevertheless, recognizing what is average is a starting point to identify if your baby is doing something that is typical for babies of her age, or something very different. Different can be perfectly normal, especially if your baby is happy and thriving, but if she is not, different may indicate that you're misinterpreting the reason for her behavioral cues.

Once you're familiar with the relevant information, next time your baby starts to fuss, ask yourself questions that relate to timing, for example

- How long has it been since baby was last fed? Is it reasonable to expect that she would be hungry again at this time? Or is it too soon for hunger?
- How long since she last napped? The younger the baby, the less time she can comfortably tolerate being awake.
- How long does it take for her to complete a feed? Feeding too fast or too slow can be problematic.

There will be many other questions related to timing that could help you to identify potential reasons for your baby's fussiness.

Context

Context includes information about what's happening to and around your baby when she displays particular behavior. When deciding on the reason for your baby's behavior, you can look for possible triggers by considering the following questions.

- What is her environment like? Is the environment supporting her to feed effectively or distracting her? Will it encourage her to fall asleep or stimulate her to remain awake?
- What are you doing while feeding her? Are you attentive while feeding or distracted by your phone or something else? Could you be annoying her by jiggling the bottle, or frustrating or stressing her by pressuring her to continue to eat when she has already shown signs of wanting to stop?
- Has she had enough sleep? Is tiredness affecting her feeding?
- Does she display physical signs that point to a physical condition or problem?

The following scenarios may help you see how timing and context can help you figure out the reasons for your baby's fussing.

Scenario 1: Your baby is fussing. You recall that she last fed one hour ago, at which time she ate a reasonable amount. It's now been two hours since she awoke from a nap. You conclude that tiredness is the most likely cause of her fussing.

Scenario 2: Your baby woke 30 minutes ago after having a two-hour nap. She last fed two and a half hours ago, at which time she didn't eat as much as usual. She's been content lying in her rocker or under her play gym for the past 30 minutes, during which time you have been busy with housework. She's now started to fuss, and likely possibilities include boredom or hunger. You might first try cuddling and attention to rule out boredom, but if she continues to fuss, rule out hunger by offering another feed.

Scenario 3: Your baby is feeding. She's not yet taken her usual amount when she starts to fuss. You remove the nipple from her mouth and attempt to burp her. But nothing comes up. She's now crying. You return the bottle, but she turns away in rejection. You try once again to burp her. And still nothing. You offer the bottle again. She once again rejects it. She has been awake for over three hours. You realize she may still be hungry or perhaps needs to burp, but she's very likely to be overtired. So, you end the feed and try to settle her down for a nap.

There could be countless other scenarios. These are provided simply to demonstrate why it's important to consider timing and context when you need to decide why your baby is fussing.

What is "good enough" care?

Like all parents—even the most experienced ones—you won't always get it right. And that's okay! When you consider that a baby's needs are constantly changing and that infant reflexes are not necessarily as they appear, it's a wonder that any of us figure it out!

The better you understand what's normal and the reasons that babies fuss, cry, and become distressed, the more information you will have to decide on the most logical reasons for your baby's behavior and the greater your accuracy will become. Sometimes, you just need to use a process of elimination and choose the most likely cause first, starting with hunger and tiredness and working your way through other possibilities. If what you're doing is not working, stop and reassess the situation.

Don't feel bad if you get it wrong. The times you get it right will more than compensate for the times you don't. You may feel encouraged to learn that studies show that caregivers only need to get it right 50 percent of the time when responding to their baby's needs to foster a secure emotional attachment.[35] The Circle of Security, an international program teaching parents and health professionals about how secure parent-child relationships can be supported and strengthened, refer to this as **"good enough" parenting.**[36] So, if you get it right more than 50 percent of the time, you're doing great.

Next

Next, we'll look at advancements in your baby's development that will affect her feeding behavior. As your baby matures and continues to develop physically, intellectually, and emotionally, she's going to show countless behaviors for the first time. Recognizing these normal changes is an important part of parenting. You can then adapt your infant feeding practices and provide the support and opportunities she needs to develop new skills.

8 Development and Feeding

WHAT TO EXPECT AS YOUR BABY MATURES • PHYSICAL, INTELLECTUAL AND EMOTIONAL DEVELOPMENT • FEEDING SKILL ADVANCEMENTS

In the first 12 months, your baby will develop more rapidly than at any other stage in life. In the span of just one year, he will transform from a helpless newborn to a cheeky, robust toddler who may refuse to eat if you don't allow him to feed himself. He will grow larger, smarter, and more skilled physically and socially.

Advancements in your baby's development will have a direct effect on his appetite, nutritional needs, feeding patterns, skills, behavior, and communication style. And you will need to adapt your childcare feeding practices accordingly.

Why this is important

"Sawyer (aged eight weeks) has never refused a bottle before. He used to gobble his feeds down and want more. He's not drinking nearly as much as he did last week. He screams if I try to make him finish. I don't understand why all of a sudden he's getting upset. I'm not doing anything different." Melissa

The fact that Melissa is not doing anything different is the problem. She doesn't realize that she needs to adjust her infant feeding practices in ways that match Sawyer's stage of development. Melissa is overlooking Sawyer's satiety cues and pressuring him to eat. She may have done so since his birth, but its only now that Sawyer could display signs of rejection.

I often meet parents who experience anxiety when they observe unexpected changes in their baby's feeding behavior or patterns. They are unaware that the changes relate to advancements in their baby's development. But anxiety is not the only problem associated with a lack of awareness. Like Melissa, they unknowingly frustrate or stress their baby and then think his crying is due to a physical problem or pain.

The following is a **brief overview** of developmental changes related to feeding. Being aware of the changes your baby will go through may help to minimize needless anxiety.

Intellectual development

Massive changes occur in a baby's intellectual development during the first 12 months and beyond in the following areas

- brain and nervous system;
- intelligence and awareness;
- learning;
- memory;
- communication; and
- independence.

We discuss each area below and how it relates to a baby's feeding experiences.

Brain development and nervous system

At birth, your baby's brain is only a quarter of the size it will eventually become as an adult.

Your baby was born with over 100 billion brain cells called **neurons.** After birth, his brain begins to form trillions of connections between the neurons. Genes begin the process of brain development; however, it's the countless experiences he has, all of which stimulate brain development, that take over this process. Every experience helps build and strengthen the connections between neurons, enabling his brain to grow and his intelligence to expand.

By the age of two years, his brain will be three-quarters of the size of an adult brain—three times larger than when he was first born. This massive growth in size correlates with the expansion of neuron connections within his brain. Neuron connections now number around 1,000 trillion.[37]

Intelligence and awareness

According to child development experts Dr. Hetty van de Rijt and Dr. Frans Plooij, babies experience **intellectual growth** spurts roughly around the ages of five, eight, 12, 23, 34, 42, and 51 weeks, which are linked to changes in the baby's developing brain and nervous system.[38] These can be unsettling and may trigger fussy feeding behavior and increased wakefulness for a period of days or weeks. You can learn more about intellectual growth spurts by reading their book *The Wonder Weeks*.[39]

Babies know more than we think

As your baby's brain expands at this rapid rate, it is absorbing, processing, and filing thousands of pieces of information on a daily basis. He notices but does not yet understand everything adults and children around him say and do, as well as changes in his environment and consistencies and inconsistencies in the care he receives. As he matures, his **awareness** of the world expands through these experiences, and the way he interacts with people and his environment will change.

Babies are relatively helpless. They are physically dependent on others to provide for their needs. However, babies understand more than we might give them credit for. For example, they learn to anticipate your actions based on the care you have provided in the past.

Babies cannot manipulate

While many parents underestimate their baby's intelligence, I occasionally meet parents who overestimate their baby's ability to reason. They believe their baby will deliberately cry to annoy or manipulate them.

While babies can sense the mood of others, they have no concept of the cause. Babies **don't** cry or try to annoy or manipulate their parents. They cry, fuss, or refuse to eat because something is wrong. They are merely acting in response to the circumstances.

Learning

Learning is the gaining of knowledge or skills through study, experience, or being taught. Your baby's learning starts even before his birth.[40] Babies learn as a consequence of ongoing interactions between people and their environment. Some learning occurs during random traumatic events—for example, painful or stressful medical procedures, but most learning or skills and knowledge occurs from repeated experiences.

How your baby learns

Babies learn by association. **Associative learning is the process by which a person learns to recognize a link between two things or events.**[41] Repetition is required to make a connection. For example, after repeatedly feeling satisfied after sucking from a bottle, your baby learns that sucking from a bottle containing milk will soothe pangs of hunger. Additionally, if he repeatedly falls asleep while sucking on a bottle (or breast), he learns to link feeding with the act of falling asleep. Your baby will form an ever-increasing number of connections as he has new experiences and these are repeated.

He learns that his cries receive a response and that it feels good to eat and be cuddled and caressed; not-so-good to be stripped in preparation for a bath; good to feel the warmth of the water against his body; not-so-good to be given bitter-tasting medications. Many other experiences from your baby's perspective will feel really good, good, not-so-good, unpleasant, or stressful. All of your baby's experiences will become part of his learning process. All stimulate his brain development, intelligence, and awareness.

Your baby learns what you teach

Parents are their child's first and most influential teachers. Whether you realize it or not, you are teaching your baby from the moment he's first in your care and teaching him through every interaction. You are teaching him

- the steps taken prior to feeding;
- who feeds him and where he feeds;
- how you will respond to his behavioral cues;
- what happens after feeding; and
- where and how he sleeps.

You will also teach him countless other things through his care on a daily basis. Most of us are unaware that we are constantly teaching our babies. I encourage you to remain forever mindful that **your actions** will teach your baby more than your words ever could.

Memory

Because adults rarely remember events before the age of three years and have very few memories of what happened between three and seven years, it was once a common belief that babies are not able to form stable memories. But babies can and do store memories. They're collected in infancy and moved to subconscious areas of the brain and therefore, not readily accessible for recall as adults.

Memory provides the foundation for learning. Without memory, a baby could not learn to drink, eat, roll, sit, crawl or take on innumerable other skills. Babies are not forgetful. At birth, a baby can recognize his mother's voice, which is evidence his memory was developing while still in the womb. He can recognize the smell of his mother's milk as young as six days old.[42]

Each time an experience is repeated, neuron connections strengthen, and it becomes easier for the baby to remember. He draws on the memory of past experiences to predict the future. By **two to three months** of age and as a result of repeated experiences, he learns to link a sequence of events and anticipate the next step. For example, upon laying him in a feeding position, he recognizes he's about to be offered a feed even if there's no bottle within sight.

As his brain continues to develop and his memory expands, he learns more complex sequences—for example, he learns to connect feeding with a bib being placed around his neck. He also learns what to expect will happen during and after the feed. He starts to react in anticipation of what he has learned to expect will happen. If past feeding experiences have been enjoyable and satisfying, he may show signs of excitement in anticipation of feeding. However, if past feeding experiences have been unpleasant or stressful, he may start to fuss and cry.

Communication

Although as a newborn, your baby's communication skills are limited, by three months of age, his ability to communicate has expanded. He is learning to voluntarily move his body. He can move his torso, tummy crunch forward, turn or arch his body, and wave his arms and legs in excitement or distress. He can use facial expressions like smiling or frowning and willingly open his mouth to accept the nipple of a bottle or breast if he wishes to feed or clamp his mouth and turn his head away if he doesn't.

He will still fuss and cry at times, but he has a greater repertoire of vocalizations such as cooing, squealing, screeching, and laughing. He is more sociable and can be engaged in conversation—for example, he will make noise to reciprocate when talked to or may be quieted by the sound of your voice. He can also make sounds that indicate his pleasure or displeasure while feeding.

Between **six and nine months** of age, your baby will babble in syllables, like da-da, and start imitating sounds, such as fake coughing when he hears others coughing. By 12 months, he may start to use his first words and gesture by pointing.

Worth remembering is that babies can understand language long before they can master speech.

Drive toward independence

Imagine attempting a task 100 times and failing each time. Most of us would give up long before that time. But this is not the case for babies and children. They're driven to achieve skills that will ultimately enable independence.

Early signs of your baby's **drive for independence** include trying to hold the bottle and wanting to self-feed solid foods. He will experience frustration if unable to do something due to his own physical limitation or if you prevent him from doing so.

Physical development

While you celebrate when your baby achieves well-known developmental milestones—for example, smiling, rolling, sitting, standing, and walking—he will also achieve many other less apparent skills.

During your baby's first year, his little body will go through many physiological changes that will enable him to slowly transition from sucking to take in liquid foods, such as breast milk or infant formula, to being able to chew and eat a variety of solid foods. His natural drive toward independence will motivate him to develop physical skills that will take him from a completely dependent newborn whose sucking occurs involuntarily to sitting at the table and self-feeding fluids and solids while sharing in family meals.

Sometimes parents become needlessly concerned when their baby displays new and unexpected behaviors while feeding and at other times. This was the case for Beth.

> **Baby Zane**
> Beth sent me a link to view a video of her four-month-old, Zane, feeding. Beth was concerned that Zane was experiencing discomfort, as he had recently started kicking his legs and making sounds that Beth thought were grunting. Upon observing the video, I could see that Zane was an active baby, often kicking his legs, vocalizing with the nipple in his mouth, and easily distracted but content and actively feeding in a disjointed manner. Everything I observed looked like normal behaviors a four-month-old might display while feeding.
>
> Beth accepted my opinion but added that she wished Zane would feed like he had as a newborn, when he had fed calmly and quietly until completing the feed. I explained that she couldn't expect Zane to return to feeding like he once did because he was no longer a newborn. I felt confident that Beth would get used to Zane's new normal feeding behavior. However, as a way to prepare her for the future, I described some other changes in behavior that she might observe as Zane continued to develop new skills.

Skill development

Under the age of three months, your baby is physically limited in his ability to make deliberate body movements. His nervous system is immature, and he lacks muscle development and experience. With each passing day, he becomes bigger, stronger, and smarter. He gains a greater ability to control his body movements.

Your role as a parent is to support your baby's emerging skills, providing "help me to do it on my own" assistance where required.

How do feeding skills progress?

In the following table, I provide a summary that outlines the progression of babies' feeding skill development for their ages.

TABLE 8.1: Feeding skill development

Age	Feeding skills
Preterm baby	• His feeding skills reflect his health and development. • The time of no oral to full oral feedings varies from days to months. • He requires support to regulate his milk intake.
Birth to 2 months	• His feeding skills are controlled by reflexes. • He can signal hunger, but his cues are difficult to interpret. • He has a strong urge to suck, which can be mistaken as hunger. • He does not recognize what a bottle represents and may require coaxing to open his mouth to accept the nipple. • He might continue to fuss until the nipple is in his mouth. • He is unable to support the weight of his head or change his position if uncomfortable or if unable to access the milk. • He requires appropriate support from his parents to safely coordinate his suck-swallow-breathe actions. • While his sucking reflex is activated, he is **unable** to stop or indicate when he has had enough. • He has a tendency to fall asleep while feeding. • He may appear to strain during feeds due to the gastrocolic reflex. • He is vulnerable to experiencing dietary regulation problems such as underfeeding and overfeeding.
2 to 3 months	• He can support his head in an upright position for short periods of time. • He requires appropriate head support when feeding in a reclined position. • His sucking reflex is fading. He is learning to suck voluntarily. • He is able to signal when he's had enough to eat. • He remains susceptible to dietary regulation problems such as underfeeding and overfeeding.
3 to 4 months	• He can recognize the bottle and might stop fussing as soon as he realizes his needs will be met. • He is more socially active and has reciprocal interaction with his parent during feeding, such as stopping and smiling at his parent. • He can move his hand or hands up to the bottle while feeding but is not yet able to hold it. • His sucking reflex has disappeared. • He is now able to indicate when he has had enough. • The risk of overfeeding is reduced. • He begins to go longer stretches between feeds.

4 to 6 months	• He can recognize when he is about to be offered a feed, and he will either get excited or upset—depending on his past feeding experiences. • He learns to hold the bottle with both hands but might require support to steady it at the right angle for feeding. • He might turn away or push the bottle away when he's done. • He is easily distracted during daytime feeds. • His extrusion (tongue thrust) reflex disappears. • He demonstrates signs of readiness to start to eat solid foods.
6 to 8 months	• He can take small volumes of fluids from a sippy cup. • He is able to sit upright without support. • He is eating small amounts of food. • He gags at times while eating solids. • He gives very clear signals of his interest and disinterest in feeding and eating solids. • He begins to display signs of wanting to self-feed. • He might sleep 10 to 12 hours through the night without feeding.
8 to 10 months	• He is gaining competence drinking from a straw cup. • His self-feeding skills are improving. • He can use his thumb and index finger to pick up small pieces of food. • He might show signs of wanting to self-feed from a bottle. • Gagging episodes decrease. • His milk consumption decreases as he starts to eat more solids.
10 to 12 months	• He has become a master at drinking from a straw cup. • He reaches for or points to food when hungry. • He handles finger foods easily. • He wants to self-feed. • He might get upset or reject food if not permitted to self-feed. • He deliberately drops food over the side of a highchair.
Over 12 months	• He continues to gain mastery using a spoon and other feeding utensils. • He shows a strong desire to self-feed solid foods and might refuse to eat if he is prevented. • He can drink independently from a straw cup with handles. • He can drink from an open cup. • He no longer requires bottle-feeding but may have an emotional attachment to it.

Note: The timeframes for the development of these skills can vary between babies, but in general, they tend to occur in a predictable sequence. Babies develop at different paces. Whether your baby achieves a skill sooner or later than other babies is **not** a reflection of intelligence, but it could reflect opportunities to practice and learn.

If your baby displays concerning behavior while feeding, see chapter 28.

Emotional development

> *"I wanted to breastfeed my baby, but it wasn't working. I have now switched him to pumped breast milk from a bottle. He's happy and feeds well, but I am wracked with guilt because I know breastfeeding helps with bonding. How can I make sure my baby bonds with me now that he's bottle-feeding?" Andrea*

As parents, we all want to develop a close, loving relationship with our children. We read that breastfeeding promotes emotional development, and then we worry about whether we can achieve the same bond while bottle-feeding.

Andrea is mindful of the importance of emotional development. But she need not be concerned. She can foster a strong emotional bond with her baby regardless of whether she breast- or bottle-feeds him.

The essential component of emotional development in young children is the relationship between the child and the primary caregiver, which is generally the mother. According to renowned developmental psychologist Dr. Erik Erikson, during the first 12 months of a baby's life, he is **learning to trust** the people caring for him.[43] Learning to trust his primary caregiver is the most important development in a child's life because it shapes his view of the world. Feeding provides perfect opportunities to **earn your baby's trust.**

Dr. Mary Ainsworth, a Canadian psychologist renowned for her work on attachment theory, identified that children develop a close emotional attachment when they receive responsive, nurturing care.[44] Caring experiences that are repeated many times over the course of a day provide the foundation for healthy emotional attachment.

It's not the feeding method that promotes a close emotional bond; rather, it is the care received while feeding and at other times. Breastfeeding supports bonding because the mother must be present and attentive to her baby's feeding cues. The same level of responsiveness can be replicated when a baby bottle-feeds. Below are examples of positive feeding experiences.

Positive emotional feeding experiences

You can nurture a healthy emotional relationship with your baby by accurately interpreting his feeding cues and providing an appropriate response. Positive emotional feeding experiences occur if

- you offer a feed when your baby shows signs of hunger;
- you allow him to set the pace when feeding;
- you pause and try to remedy the cause when he fusses;
- you stop the feed when he indicates he's finished.

The way you look, listen, handle, and react to your baby tells him how you feel about him.

When your baby's nutritional needs are met in a timely and caring manner, and when he receives a fitting response when he's hungry or had enough, he finds feeding satisfying and enjoyable, and he learns to trust that you will provide for his needs. When he receives your undivided attention during feeding times, and he is handled gently and patiently, spoken to in affectionate tones, smiled at, and caressed, he learns he's loved.

When the feeding goes well for baby, it's also enjoyable for you. You gain satisfaction knowing that you're successfully providing for your baby's needs. Your confidence in your parenting abilities grows, and the emotional connection you share with your baby is strengthened.

Other experiences

Feeding is just one of the many ways to demonstrate love and respect. Your baby's emotional well-being and attachment are enriched by all the acts of loving care that you provide on a daily basis, including

- cuddling, stroking, and caressing him;
- holding him when he's upset;
- giving him your attention;
- entertaining him;
- changing his diaper as needed;
- talking to him;
- smiling at him;
- handling him gently and patiently; and
- providing an opportunity for him to sleep when tired.

These are only a few examples. Each day you demonstrate to your baby that he's loved in a thousand different ways.

Next

Next, we move onto the different types of milk a baby might receive starting with breast milk.

Part C:
Types of Milk and Preparation

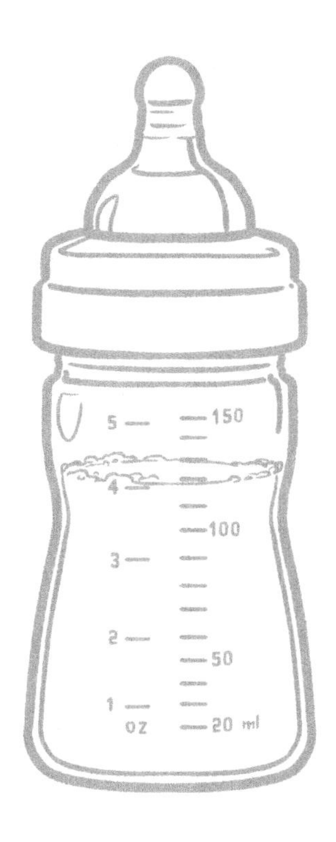

9 Breast Milk

BREAST MILK BENEFITS • WHY IT'S RARELY NECESSARY TO SWITCH TO BABY FORMULA • PROBLEMS LINKED TO OVERSUPPLY

During my career, I have seen hundreds of women who **mistakenly** believed, or were led to believe, that their baby would be better off if given baby formula. Most women were saddened by giving up on their breastfeeding goals.

If you're switching, make sure you're doing so for the right reasons. Babies rarely need to be switched from breastfeeding or breast milk from a bottle to baby formula. After switching over to formula, many parents discover it doesn't solve the baby care problem they hoped it would. Or they later discover that while switching appeared to help, the problem could have been fixed in other ways. In some cases, parents find that switching to baby formula creates new problems.

If you're thinking of giving your baby infant formula in the hope of fixing a baby care problem, I recommend you read this chapter.

I hope to address some of your concerns about low milk supply, maternal dietary restrictions, and milk allergy experienced by breastfed babies and those receiving breast milk from a bottle. It's important that you feel confident about the decisions you make.

The best milk for babies

We all know "breast is best." However, when a baby is unable to breastfeed or the mother is unable or unwilling to breastfeed or she is separated from her baby for long periods, then bottle-feeding is the next best feeding method.

If you have decided it's necessary for your baby to exclusively or partially bottle-feed, the next step is to decide which milk to provide. The best types of milk to provide, starting from the most nutritionally complete option, are

- mother's breast milk;
- donor's breast milk;
- partial breast milk and baby formula; and then
- commercially produced baby formula.

All other types of milk, including homemade baby formula and milk substitutes, are unsuitable forms of nutrition for babies.

Breast milk

Human milk is uniquely suited to human babies. Breast milk is considered the "gold standard for protective nutrients" because it contains hundreds of bioactive components that play a significant role in babies' health and development, including.

- antibodies to protect against illnesses;
- white blood cells that fight infection;
- digestive enzymes that aid in the digestion of protein, carbohydrates, and fats;
- stem cells that may support organ development and repair;
- growth-regulating hormones that have a significant effect on the development of a baby's blood vessels, digestive tract, nervous system, and endocrine system;
- long-chain fatty acids that help develop a baby's brain, nervous system, and eyes;
- hormones that help to regulate the baby's appetite and sleep-wake patterns;
- prebiotics that support the growth of "good" bacteria in the baby's intestinal tract, which not only inhibits the growth of harmful microorganisms (bacteria, viruses, and others) in baby's intestinal tract but actively reduce them; and
- substances that coat the lining of a baby's intestinal wall to prevent microscopic food particles from "leaking" into the baby's bloodstream and causing an allergic reaction.

Formula companies model their baby formulas on breast milk. But even if they worked tirelessly on the development of their baby formulas for 100 years, they could not replicate the numerous health-benefiting components of breast milk.

Should I switch from breast milk to formula?

There is **rarely** a "need" for a baby to receive baby formula. But it's **very** common for nursing mothers to have concerns—most of which are unfounded—about their milk supply or diet.

One of the biggest misperceptions of all is that a well-fed baby will be a content baby.

When a breastfed baby or a baby receiving breast milk displays behavior such as incessant crying, feeding or sleeping difficulties, rashes or eczema, vomiting, frequent watery bowel movements, or blood or mucous in their stools, people in general—including health professionals—are quick to blame the mother's diet or milk supply. They often recommend maternal dietary restrictions, supplementing with baby formula, or switching the baby to a hypoallergenic formula. When these are the first solutions offered, it probably means other potential causes or solutions have not been considered.

Reasons mothers decide to switch their baby to formula

Extremely few medical reasons require switching a baby from breast milk to baby formula. But nursing mothers choose to give their baby formula-feeds for different reasons such as

- uncertainty about milk supply;
- belief that their baby may be more satisfied on formula;
- concern that the taste of breast milk is causing feeding refusal;
- worry about the strength of mother's milk;
- confusion about whether baby is reacting to something eaten by his mother; or
- they were advised to do so by a trusted health professional.

I will explain why most of these worries are often unfounded.

Insufficient supply

Most breastfeeding mothers who worry about low milk supply don't have a low supply, at least not until they start to give their baby an infant formula. These are the three most common reasons I see for mothers to mistakenly believe they're not producing enough breast milk when in reality, they are.

1. They misinterpret their baby's infantile reflexes and desire to suck as hunger (see chapter 5).
2. They are unaware of the effects that a breastfeeding–sleep association—which can occur when a baby learns to associate the act of falling asleep with suckling at his mother's breast—will have on their baby's ability to remain asleep. Or that a feeding-sleep association will cause a baby to act like he's hungry when he's tired.
3. They were told they were not producing sufficient milk, based solely on the fact that their baby did not gain "average" weight—which is something that no baby will consistently achieve.

Other reasons that nursing mothers might mistakenly believe they have insufficient milk supply include; because their breasts do not feel as full or don't leak as occurred in the early weeks, their baby doesn't nurse for as long as he once did, or their baby fusses during or after breastfeeds. In reality, many of these signs and behaviors are either normal or are for other reasons.

Confidence in breastfeeding largely depends on the mother's ability to recognize the signs that indicate her baby is getting enough to eat (described on page 42).

In cases of a **genuinely low supply,** rarely is it a case of a mother not being capable of producing enough breast milk. Mostly, it's because she's making errors in judgment that lead to low milk supply, like a poorly latched or positioned baby, time-based feedings, or giving her baby formula from a bottle.

If you have concerns about your milk production, consult with an International Board-Certified Lactation Consultant (IBCLC) for a **thorough breastfeeding assessment** before taking steps that may inadvertently create a low supply.

Is breast milk "strong enough"?

Sometimes nursing mothers are told their milk might not be strong enough, meaning that it doesn't contain sufficient nutrients to satisfy their baby. This is not true! The nutritional and energy (calorie) content of breast milk varies between women and for the same woman depending on how full her breasts are at the time of the feeding. However, babies over the age of eight weeks or eight weeks adjusted age in the case of healthy preterm babies will regulate the amount they consume according to the energy content of the milk. This means that over the course of the day, your baby will consume more milk if the energy content is lower and less if the energy content is higher.

Nursing mothers often worry about the strength of their milk because of the appearance of human milk, which is very different from baby formula and regular cow's milk (purchased from the store). Non-human milks are heavily processed, which means they always look the same creamy-white color throughout. Milk fresh from a cow doesn't look like the milk you pour from a milk carton.

Human milk is naturally bluish and looks thin when compared to other types of milk. The color can vary, sometimes taking on a green or orange tinge depending on the foods the mother has eaten. Breast milk will separate when left to sit, with a thin layer of fat settling at the top. The milk under the fat layer can have an opaque appearance making it appear "watery." This is normal! You just need to gently swirl it to allow the fat to mix into the milk again.

NOTE: Sick or preterm babies may need fortified breast milk

Babies with high-energy needs, such as preterm babies in the neonatal intensive care unit (NICU), sick babies, and babies with medical conditions that cause them to tire easily or affect their sucking abilities, might benefit from fortified breast milk in the weeks following hospital discharge if unable to breastfeed. (See pages 150-151 for more on the reasons that babies might require fortified breast milk.)

Is formula more satisfying than breast milk?

Babies tend to breastfeed more frequently compared to formula-fed babies. Of course, volume and energy content matter. But whether a baby feels "satisfied" depends on hormones and blood glucose levels.

Breast milk is more easily digestible compared to baby formula. Therefore, it's absorbed into the bloodstream quicker. A breastfed baby may feel satisfied sooner and drink less volume per feed.

Baby formula is harder for a baby to digest and so tends to remain in a baby's stomach and intestinal tract longer. Hence, it can take longer for her to feel satisfied, and she may drink bigger volumes per feed, which then means she can last longer between feeds. It's also easy for parents to make a newborn eat a specific volume of milk from a bottle. For these reasons, bottle-fed babies are more likely to overfeed or be overfed compared to breastfed babies.

Also, a parent can see how much a baby receives from a bottle, and so they may be less inclined to blame hunger as the reason for their baby's **desire to suck** when tired, bored, uncomfortable, and for pleasure.

Could baby dislike the taste of mom's milk?

Most babies prefer the taste of breast milk compared to baby formula, as it has a sweeter taste. The taste of breast milk changes constantly depending on what the mother eats.

A small percentage of breastfeeding mothers produce excess amounts of lipase in their breast milk. (Lipase is an enzyme that breaks down fats in breast milk to help the baby to digest it.) The breakdown of fats by lipase begins soon after the milk is removed from the breast, either by the baby breastfeeding or from pumping. Freshly pumped milk will taste the same as when a baby breastfeeds directly. However, if pumped milk is stored in the refrigerator or freezer, meaning there is more time from when the milk was pumped and offered to the baby, **an excess of lipase** can cause the milk to take on a rancid, soapy, or metallic taste. The milk is safe for the baby to drink, but some babies don't like the taste.

For some women, the milk fats break down enough to alter the taste in only a few hours. For others, it could be 24 hours. Lipase is still active even at low temperatures, like freezing.

If you're offering breast milk **that has been frozen or stored in the refrigerator for many hours,** check the taste. If it tastes fine, then taste is probably not the reason for your baby to fuss or reject bottle-feeds.

Lipase can be inactivated at high temperatures. If the stored milk tastes soapy, rancid, or metallic, scalding the milk **soon after pumping** will prevent lipase from changing the taste. To scald breast milk, heat it in a pot until tiny bubbles form around the edges of the pan (approximately 180°F or 82°C), but don't boil it. Ideally, use a cooking thermometer to check the temperature. Cool, then store in the refrigerator or freezer.

If giving your baby freshly pumped breast milk, there's no need to scald.

Is baby reacting to foods eaten by mom?

Of course, sometimes breastfed babies react to foods eaten by their mother, but this is uncommon.

In many instances, nursing mothers are advised to restrict or eliminate dairy and soy from their diets, **without their baby displaying any evidence** of clearly observable signs and symptoms related to a digestive problem, solely because their baby is irritable, not sleeping, or fussing.

If there are no gastrointestinal (GI) and other allergy signs associated with milk protein allergy (described on pages 457-458), you need to look beyond your diet for reasons for your baby's troubled behavior. I recommend you start with your baby settling (sleep) management (see chapter 22).

When a healthy breastfed baby displays GI signs such as green, watery stools, mucus, or blood in stools, these are automatically—wrongfully so in most cases—blamed on the mother's diet. Gemma was told her baby's green stools were because she ate peas. Erica was told it was because she drank orange juice. Sophie was told it was due to eating cruciferous vegetables such as cauliflower, cabbage, and broccoli. Adrianna was told it was because she was drinking cow's milk in her cereal and coffee. In all of these cases and countless others, the cause was functional lactose overload, a common problem in the newborn period **unrelated** to the mother's diet.

If there are GI symptoms, the first place to start is with a thorough assessment of your milk supply, your ability to **accurately** identify your baby's hunger and satiety cues and responsiveness to these cues, and whether you could be overfeeding your baby.

If you don't consider **all** possible causes and instead assume your baby's troubles are related to your diet—as many nursing mothers and health professionals are inclined to do—there can be unintended consequences. These include

- needlessly depriving yourself of foods you enjoy.
- lack of a well-balanced diet, which can have a negative effect on your health, mood, and energy levels.
- making further restrictions from other food groups if the initial restrictions fail, which further affects your health.
- deciding to switch your baby to formula because severe dietary restrictions become too much to endure long-term—in which case your baby won't receive the benefits that breast milk provides.

What a shame this would be if your baby's troubles had nothing to do with her mother's diet— which is the case for most babies who receive breast milk.

Before going down the path of what could be needless dietary restrictions or switching your baby to formula, I recommend you check out the possibility of

- functional lactose overload (see pages 439-448);
- overtiredness (see pages 290-292);
- overfeeding (see chapter 25);
- oversupply—keep reading.

Oversupply can explain many of the concerns that nursing mothers have about their baby acting hungry, the strength of breast milk, and GI symptoms commonly, but mostly erroneously, attributed to maternal diet.

When mom has an oversupply

Many mothers naturally have an overabundance of breast milk in the early weeks after giving birth. An oversupply can also be created as a result of pumping. Some mothers like to pump more than their baby requires each day to store extra breast milk in the freezer for a future time. Pumping more than the baby needs can create an oversupply.

Producing more milk than your baby needs would appear to be a good thing. However, that's not necessarily the case. Producing a few ounces more than your baby needs doesn't usually cause an issue. However, producing a **lot** more can. Babies can experience mild to severe discomfort due to GI symptoms as a result of functional lactose overload or poor growth due to a lowered fat percentage when a mother produces an abundance of breast milk.

Oversupply (also called hyperlactation) is a frequent yet often unrecognized problem that can present with the baby displaying a variety of distressing symptoms. These are typically misdiagnosed as colic, milk allergy or intolerance, or gastroesophageal reflux.[45]

Why oversupply causes GI symptoms

A breastfeeding mother **with overproduction** tends to have breast milk containing less fat, less protein, and higher lactose.[46]

Fat is the most variable nutrient in breast milk. Fat provides 50 to 65 percent of the total calories. The more full of milk the mother's breast is, the lower the **overall fat** concentration in her milk.[47] The lower the fat content, the more milk her baby needs to consume to receive the calories she needs to feel satisfied. The more milk she consumes, the more lactose she receives.

The fat content affects motility rate (meaning how fast the milk empties from the baby's stomach and moves through her intestinal tract). The **lower the percentage of fat** in the milk, the faster it travels. **The volume of milk** present in a baby's intestinal tract also affects motility rate. The larger the volume, the faster it travels. The greater the volume of low-fat milk, the less time available for lactose to be digested in the small intestine, and the greater the volume of **undigested lactose** that is pushed into the large intestine and the more intense the symptoms of functional lactose overload. (See pages 439-448 for causes and signs and symptoms of functional lactose overload.)

Oversupply can lead to poor growth

In most cases of oversupply, the baby will gain normal or large amounts of weight. However, in a small percentage of cases, as odd as it might sound, an oversupply of breast milk can cause a baby to experience poor growth because of reduced fat percentage and the severity of GI symptoms associated with functional lactose overload.

What to do?

If you are pumping well in excess of what your baby is consuming and requires for healthy growth, you have an oversupply.

If your baby is happy, healthy, and thriving, there's no need to make any changes. However, if she is often crying, has feeding, sleeping, or growth problems, displays GI symptoms suspected to be reflux or milk protein allergy or intolerance, try the following steps.

- **Step 1**. Finish reading all chapters in this book. You might discover the reason for your baby's troubles is not what you expect. If still confused about whether GI symptoms are caused by milk protein allergy or functional lactose overload, or you're concerned about low milk supply, go to step 2.
- **Step 2**. See a lactation consultant holding IBCLC qualifications for individualized breastfeeding or pumping advice.
- **Step 3.** Consult with your baby's doctor.

What can a lactation consultant tell me that a doctor can't?
HEAPS! During their training, a doctor might receive a few hours of lectures specifically related to breastfeeding. The number of hours varies according to the doctor's specialty area. For example, a pediatrician might receive more education related to breastfeeding than a general physician. But both pale in comparison to the months of breastfeeding education and 1,000-plus hours of experience guiding breastfeeding mothers required to qualify as an International Board Certified Lactation Consultant (IBCLC).

A lactation consultant can provide a **thorough breastfeeding assessment**, which includes observing breastfeeding and providing advice on feeding position, latching, pumping, and recognizing your baby's feeding cues.

Should I switch to a hypoallergenic formula?

If you have been advised to switch your baby to a hypoallergenic formula, you need to be aware of a few things.

1. Breast milk reduces the baby's risk of developing food and other allergies now and in the future.[48]
2. Babies are never allergic to their mother's milk but can be allergic to proteins from the foods eaten by their mother. However, this does not occur as often as you might be led to believe. It is estimated that 1 in 200 breastfed babies react to foods eaten by their mothers.[49] That's equivalent to 0.5 percent of all breastfed babies. Babies are more likely to develop allergies if there's a history of eczema, asthma, hay fever, or food allergies in the family.[50]
3. Most breastfeeding mothers can eat foods similar to those eaten during their pregnancy without affecting their babies.[51] Le Leche League International, a leading authority on breastfeeding, states that most mothers can eat whatever they like without it affecting their baby.[52]
4. In the tiny percentage of babies who are allergic to foods eaten by the mother, eliminating the food from the mother's diet will resolve the problem. There is no need to switch to a hypoallergenic formula.
5. Breast milk is hypoallergenic, far superior to any man-made baby formula. Breast milk contains human proteins that are easily digestible. It's made in the mother's breasts from the nutrients carried in her bloodstream. It is **not** made directly from the food she eats. Food eaten by the mother is

    - ➢ first digested (broken down into amino acids) via multiple digestive processes in her mouth, stomach, and intestinal tract;
    - ➢ the digested proteins are then absorbed from her intestines through tiny blood vessels into her bloodstream where it's filtered by her liver to remove harmful chemicals;
    - ➢ then it's filtered again as blood passes through tiny blood vessels in the mother's breasts, where nutrient **molecules** move through the cells that line the **alveoli** (tiny sacs in her breasts that make milk) from her bloodstream and into the milk through a process known as diffusion.

6. Doctors, in general, know very little about breastfeeding. Therefore, they do not understand how the mother's feeding management or excessive production of breast milk can cause the baby's GI symptoms. Without formal breastfeeding qualifications, they may be unable to

conduct a breastfeeding assessment or make recommendations to correct breastfeeding problems such as oversupply, functional lactose overload, poor latch, and others. Some may be unaware of the existence of these problems, so they won't necessarily refer nursing mothers to a lactation consultant for breastfeeding assessment and advice.

7. Most hypoallergenic formulas contain no lactose, so they will resolve symptoms related to lactose overload. Therefore, any misdiagnosis of functional lactose overload as milk protein allergy or intolerance will be believed to be correct.

This does not mean it's impossible for trace elements of food protein to pass into a mother's breast milk and cause an allergic reaction in susceptible babies. But it does explain why the incidence of food allergies is **much** lower when a baby receives breast milk compared to standard baby formula. It also explains why switching to a hypoallergenic formula might **appear** to resolve a baby's GI symptoms.

Next

If you are **mixed feeding**, meaning you're supplementing breastfeeding or breast milk with infant formula, or if you have decided to switch your baby to infant formula, the next chapter describes the different types of formula available, how these differ, and why you might choose one over another.

10 Baby Formula

FORMULA TYPES • HOW BABY FORMULAS DIFFER • SWITCHING FORMULA • MILK TO AVOID

As a loving parent, you want to provide the best nutrition for your baby. If you are not able to breastfeed or provide breast milk, the next best option is baby formula.

Given the huge range of baby formulas available today, choosing a formula to feed your baby can be daunting. It's a task further complicated by misinformation about the reasons for gastrointestinal symptoms and babies' troubled behavior, and the supposed benefits of baby formulas.

As parents, we often doubt our decisions. It's my hope that this chapter will assist you in making an informed and confident decision about the best source of nutrition available for your baby so that there's one less thing for you to worry about.

A note to readers

My area of expertise is behavioral feeding and sleeping problems affecting babies and young children. I am not a dietitian or nutritionist; therefore, I do not profess to be an expert in infant nutrition. However, I do appreciate the impact that nutrition has on babies' health, growth, and behavior, which is why I have more than a passing interest in infant nutrition.

Any information on baby formulas included in this chapter is not intended as a substitute for advice provided by your baby's healthcare professionals. I simply provide information about formulas based on studies I have read (which are referenced), my experience, and feedback received from parents. I hope this helps you to make decisions when choosing a suitable formula for your baby.

Should I switch baby's formula?

Parents change the diet of their **normal, healthy babies** because they attribute their baby's incessant crying, feeding or sleeping problems, or gastrointestinal (GI) symptoms to his diet. In doing so, they risk switching for the wrong reasons.

I'm going to share a lesson I learned based on years of caring for babies. Most problems that affect healthy babies are **unrelated** to the type of formula they are drinking or foods eaten by a mother producing breast milk. So, when I see parents switching formula, some multiple times because they are hoping to fix a baby care problem, I know they will likely be disappointed.

A change in formula will not fix a baby care problem that is unrelated to diet.

If you're thinking about switching from breast milk to baby formula or from one formula to another, read all the chapters in this book first. You may find that the reason for your baby's troubles is not diet-related after all. Alternatively, you may feel more confident that it is.

Who do I trust?

When choosing a baby formula for the first time or looking to switch to another, consider information provided by various sources and their motivations and potential gaps in knowledge.

Formula companies are trying to sell you a product. Don't base any decision solely on the claims made by these companies; not all claims are supported, and some are refuted by leading health authorities. Recommendations made by **individual health professionals** will be based on their depth of knowledge regarding baby formulas plus their professional and personal experiences in dealing with diet-related and other baby care problems, both physical and behavioral.

I tend to place greater trust in independent research and recommendations made by the following health authorities around the globe:

- American Academy of Pediatrics (AAP);
- UK Food Standards Agency (FSA);

- The European Society for Pediatric Gastroenterology, Hepatology and Nutrition (ESPGHAN);
- Health Canada (HC);
- Australia's National Health and Medical Research Council (NHMRC); and
- New Zealand Ministry of Health.

The primary motive of these organizations is to provide evidence-based nutritional advice to support the health of growing babies. The consensus between health authorities on nutritional recommendations for babies instills confidence.

But of course, health authorities can't provide individualized nutritional information for each baby, so consult with your baby's primary healthcare provider or other health professional.

Formula types

Baby formulas can be grouped into the following categories:

1. **standard baby formulas:** suitable for most formula-fed babies;
2. **modified standard baby formulas:** might be helpful for minor tummy troubles; and
3. **specialized baby formulas:** may be necessary for babies who suffer due to digestive disorders, such as cow's milk or soy protein allergy, or babies with high-energy or specific nutritional needs.

Let's look at each category and the different formulas that fit within these categories in more detail.

Standard baby formulas

Standard infant formulas fall into one of three subcategories.

- Cow's milk formula;
- Goat's milk formula; or
- Soy infant formula.

The milk, or milk substitute in the case of soy, is modified to make it a suitable food source to meet the nutritional needs of growing babies. The protein quality is improved, salt levels are reduced, and animal fats are removed and replaced with a range of vegetable fats. The formula is supplemented with essential vitamins and minerals including iron, calcium, and others, and more lactose is added into cow's and goat's milk-based formulas but not to soy infant formula.

All baby formulas available for sale must comply with strict guidelines set by the regulatory board, codes, and administration in each country—for example, the US Food and Drug Administration (FDA); Food Standards Australia New Zealand (FSANZ); and European Food Safety Authority (EFSA).

Cow's milk formula (CMF)

Cow's milk baby formula is the most widely used of all.[53] It is recommended in situations where breastfeeding is not possible, and/or breast milk unavailable, by all leading medical, health, and nutritional authorities.[54] Most, but not all, formula-fed babies will tolerate a standard CMF.

Most CMFs are made from the milk from breeds of cattle that **produce A1 beta-casein proteins.** In recent years, **A2 baby formula** has been advertised as a more natural alternative. A2 milk comes from breeds of cattle that lack A1 beta-casein proteins. The A2 protein is marginally more similar to the human β-casein protein in breast milk, and so it's claimed to be healthier than formulas containing A1 proteins.[55] Independent studies, meaning those not funded by formula companies, have yet to prove this to be the case. A 2009 EFSA scientific review[56] found no supporting evidence to support such claims.

Goat's milk formula (GMF)

Some people believe that goat's milk is healthier than cow's milk, perhaps because it contains A2 protein; therefore, they suspect that GMF is a healthier alternative to CMF. However, no independent evidence supports this claim.

Both goat's and cow's milk need to be modified to provide the right balance of nutrients to make it suitable for babies. The result of these modifications is only a tiny difference in the nutritional content.

Some babies with sensitivity to cow's milk protein might tolerate goat's milk protein, but babies with a true cow's milk allergy usually can't tolerate goat's milk formula either.[57]

Soy infant formula (SIF)

Strictly speaking, soy is not milk because it's produced from soybeans. Several chemical processes are required to extract the protein from soybeans. It's then modified by adding fats, vitamins, minerals, and other nutrients to make it into baby formula.

SIF was once the only vegan baby formula option available. It does not contain animal protein or lactose (the sugar/carbohydrate found in milk). The main carbohydrate source is glucose, corn syrup, or sucrose (from sugar cane).

Fifty to 80 percent of babies who are allergic to cow's milk protein will also react to soy protein.[58]

Soy products contain chemicals called phytoestrogens, which act like the female hormone estrogen. Even though babies have been given SIF from birth for decades with no known ill effects, it's unclear whether phytoestrogens are harmful to babies. Studies report conflicting findings.[59]

Leading medical authorities in the USA, Canada, UK, Australia, and New Zealand **do not** recommend soy infant formula for general use; rather, they recommend it only be given if medically indicated.[60] The European Society for Pediatric Gastroenterology Hepatology and Nutrition (ESPGHAN) recommends that SIF should **not** be given to babies under six months of age.[61]

Modified standard formulas

A modified standard formula is basically a standard formula with **minor variations** in the main nutrients—for example, carbohydrates, proteins, and fats—and micronutrients, which includes everything else.

Baby formula could be subtly altered in hundreds of different ways and remain within the dietary guidelines set forth by the food and drug administration board for a given country. (Any modifications or additions to a formula recipe must receive approval by the country's regulatory board to ensure that these are safe for the tiniest members of our society.)

In the past 30 years, there has been an explosion in the number of modified standard formulas. The range is **huge**, and the number increases every year.

None are essential. Most are unnecessary. But some can be helpful in reducing or relieving GI symptoms associated with **constipation** (hard, pebbly stools) and **functional lactose overload**—a common cause for healthy, thriving newborn babies to have frequent watery or sloppy stools and extreme intestinal gas.

Macronutrient modifications

Macronutrients include carbohydrates (which includes lactose), protein, and fats. The most common of the modified standard formulas involve alteration to the type and amount of **lactose or proteins or both.** These include:

- whey- or casein-dominant formulas;
- lactose-reduced formulas;
- lactose-free formulas; and
- partially hydrolyzed formulas—these also fit into the hypoallergenic category.

Whey- or casein-dominant formula

Whey and casein are two different groups of proteins that are present in breast milk, cow's milk, and goat's milk, but not in soy milk. The ratio of **whey to casein** in baby formulas can vary—for example, 20:80; 60:40, 80:20, or 100 percent whey. If there is more whey than casein, the formula is said to be **whey-dominant**. More casein than whey means the formula is **casein-dominant**.

Whey is a smooth, liquid type of protein. It's believed to be easier to digest than casein. Hence, formulas for babies ages birth to six months tend to be mostly whey-dominant or 100 percent whey.

Casein forms thicker milk curds and takes longer to empty from a baby's stomach and be digested.[62] For this reason, some people believe it might satisfy babies for longer. However, this has not been proven.

Regardless of whether a baby formula is whey- or casein-dominant, it will provide the same number of calories per ounce or milliliter. In relation to growth, after 37 weeks of gestation, healthy babies appear to do equally well on whey- or casein-dominant formulas. Before the 37-week gestation period, preterm babies tend to do better on whey-dominant compared to casein-dominant formulas (if breast milk is unavailable).

Lactose-reduced formula (LR)

Standard cow's and goat's milk baby formula contain around 7 percent lactose—the same percentage as breast milk. Lactose-reduced (also called low-lactose formula) contains 25 to 50 percent less lactose than standard infant formulas.

Lactose-free formula (LF)

Most lactose-free formulas are basically standard cow's milk formulas that have all lactose removed and substituted with other carbohydrates such as glucose, corn syrup, or rice syrup. They are mostly **casein-dominant formulas,** which means they take longer to be digested. A casein-dominant protein formula that contains no lactose could increase a baby's susceptibility to constipation.

Some health professionals recommend lactose-free formula as a **temporary** measure for formula-fed babies who suffer from diarrhea because of gastroenteritis. However, the use of a lactose-free formula for this treatment is considered unnecessary by ESPGHAN.[63]

Lactose-free formulas are **not suitable** for babies who have diarrhea caused by a milk protein allergy because they contain intact milk proteins—meaning the protein has not been predigested.

Some **physically well, thriving babies** exhibit GI symptoms such as frequent watery bowel movements, excessive gas, and abdominal cramping because of incomplete absorption of lactose in the small intestine caused by **functional lactose overload**. Hence, a lactose-reduced formula—and all lactose-free formulas, which include hypoallergenic and soy infant formula—will reduce or relieve GI symptoms related to functional lactose overload. However, I recommend dealing with the cause of lactose overload rather than simply reducing the symptoms.

I don't recommend lactose-free baby formulas because of the uncertainty about their long-term effects on babies' brain development.

Galactose and development

Galactose provides structural elements important to brain and central nervous system development.[64]

The major dietary source of galactose is lactose. **Milk containing lactose is baby's only source of galactose** before starting solids.

It's unethical to conduct scientific studies on babies. Therefore, **no** evidence suggests that lactose-free formula—leading to lack of galactose in a baby's diet—has a negative effect on the baby's development. Equally, **no** studies prove it doesn't.

Don't panic if you have been giving your baby lactose-free formula. Consider whether lactose overload caused by overfeeding or other causes, described on pages 439-448, may have been overlooked. Then, consider other practices you can adopt to relieve your baby's symptoms while providing a formula containing lactose. Of course, this is not possible in all cases—for example, if your baby has a digestive disorder that warrants a hypoallergenic formula.

Micronutrient modifications

Formula manufacturers are also permitted to make minor alterations to the type and number of micronutrients, such as vitamins and minerals, within regulatory guidelines, in their baby formulas. They manipulate the micronutrients to produce **designer formulas**. A designer formula is not an official category but rather a term I use to describe modified formulas that

- target parents' concerns;
- are made for specific age groups; and
- include additives with proposed health benefits.

Formulas that target parents' concerns

As mentioned at the start of this chapter, parents often change formulas because they're concerned that their baby's crying, feeding, sleeping problems, or GI symptoms are connected to the type of milk received or the foods eaten by a breastfeeding mother. Formula companies take advantage of this by producing baby formulas that address common concerns of parents about their baby's health, such as:

- colic;
- reflux;
- constipation;
- diarrhea;
- hunger (a baby who appears to have an insatiable appetite); or
- sleeplessness.

I advise you to remain skeptical about formula companies' claims extolling the benefits of designer formulas. Most baby care problems are unrelated to the type of formula the baby is consuming.

I will describe the most common modifications. Of course, brands will vary, and it's not possible to provide the details for every formula on the market.

Colic or crying baby formulas

Colic is often blamed when physically well newborn babies cry for unknown reasons (see pages 464-465 for more about colic). Hence, formula companies advertise that their brand of hypoallergenic or HA formula—which is partially hydrolyzed or in other words partially predigested—will help to relieve colic or minor tummy troubles. You can identify these formulas by words such as "colic," "comfort," "sensitive," "gentle," or "easy to digest" on the packaging. The modifications in these formulas include

- **reduced lactose:** These formulas generally contain less lactose than a standard formula. Therefore, they might reduce GI symptoms such as intestinal gas and frequent, watery, or sloppy bowel movements related to lactose overload. I recommend you read about functional lactose overload (pages 439-448) before switching your baby to a colic formula.
- **100 percent whey or partially hydrolyzed protein:** This is believed to be "gentler on sensitive little tummies." Some are **whey-dominant or 100 percent whey**, and some are also **partially hydrolyzed**. HA formulas have been shown to cause **softer stools** that more closely resemble the stools of breastfed babies.[65]

Some parents claim these formulas help their baby to feel more comfortable. However, others say their baby appears to be more unsettled after being switched to one of these formulas.

Anti-reflux (AR) or reflux formulas

Formulas advertised as "anti-reflux" (AR) or "anti-regurgitation," or simply "reflux," contain carbohydrates like carob bean gum, rice starch, or corn starch as thickening agents. Some of the lactose is removed to balance the carbohydrate content; hence, AR formulas are technically **lactose-reduced** and mostly **whey-dominant** cow's milk-based formulas.

Thickened feeds are commonly recommended for managing infants with gastroesophageal reflux (GER) despite a lack of supporting evidence.[66] There is no evidence that they reduce acid exposure or aspiration.[67] The use of thickened formulas for the treatment of GER is not supported by ESPGHAN due to lack of information on the potential effects of thickening agents.[68]

I generally find that an AR formula is **not** necessary when parents take appropriate steps to reduce milk regurgitation (described in pages 432-433).

Constipation formulas

Constipation—the passing of hard, pebbly stools—is relatively common for formula-fed babies. So-called "constipation" formulas typically involve various combinations of the following: **partially hydrolyzed, whey-dominant** cow's milk formulas, with the **addition of specific carbohydrates** to increase fluid retention in stools, and **probiotics** to increase the number of lactose-digesting bacteria. Constipation formulas have been shown to soften stools but not increase frequency.[69]

If your baby is prone to constipation, you might consider a constipation or HA formula as a preventive measure. But don't overlook other potential reasons for your baby to become constipated, such as fortified or concentrated formula, the type of solid foods consumed, and side effects of medications given. Also consider ways to improve the health of your baby's intestinal tract—such as providing probiotics and prebiotics.

Diarrhea formulas

"Diarrhea" describes frequent, watery stools associated with a gastrointestinal infection or a digestive or metabolic disorder. Baby formulas advertised as suitable for babies with diarrhea caused by gastrointestinal infection are **lactose-free** or **lactose-reduced** formulas. Some include slightly higher levels of **electrolytes.** Others contain **probiotics.** They are designed for **short-term use only.**

If your baby has diarrhea, seek medical advice.

Note: The frequent, watery stools common for healthy, thriving breastfed babies and babies receiving breast milk from a bottle are **often mistaken as diarrhea.** (See pages 435-439 for normal and abnormal bowel movements for breast- and formula-fed babies.)

Hungry baby formulas

Some newborn babies seem to be insatiably hungry. They guzzle down feeds quickly but then appear like they're hungry again much sooner than expected and guzzle down another bottle. They drink volumes that are much greater than expected for their age and size. As a result, they may gain large amounts of weight or spit up or poop a lot.

Some formula companies produce a "hungry baby" formula. This is a casein-dominant CMF. Casein is believed to take longer to digest than whey protein, and therefore, it is believed to sustain a baby for longer. Some hungry baby formulas also contain carbohydrates that take longer to digest.

However, there is no evidence that babies are more content or sleep better when given casein-dominant formulas.[70] There is also no evidence to support claims that babies sleep longer when fed this type of formula.[71] The higher ratio of casein protein can increase the risk of constipation.

I don't recommend hungry baby formulas because, in most cases, the baby is **not** excessively hungry. The parent just thinks he is because they mistake behavioral cues, in particular tiredness cues or a desire to suck, as a sign of hunger.

Sleep formulas

Twenty-five to 50 percent of babies over the age of six months continue to wake during the night.[72] Formulas advertised to promote babies' sleep, and entice sleep-deprived parents, include words such as "good night" or "sweet dreams" on the label. "Sleep" baby formulas are mostly **casein-dominant** with slow-to-digest carbohydrates. Basically, they are the same as hungry baby formulas. Some sleep baby formulas contain a small amount of rice cereal.

So-called sleep formulas should not be given to babies under six months of age because they are not nutritionally suitable. They are not necessary for any baby, and no independent evidence supports the claim that they help babies to sleep better.[73]

How well your baby sleeps is related to his stage of development, as well as the conditions he has learned to associate with the act of falling asleep—in other words, his sleep associations. Learn about what babies need to sleep well (described in page 287) before reaching for a quick-fix formula.

Formulas for age

Many companies produce formulas for different age groups.

Birth to 6 months

Formulas designed for babies from newborn to six months use names such as "Stage 1," "Starter," "newborn," and "suitable from birth." They are generally **whey-dominant** formulas—for example, they have a whey-to-casein ratio of 80:20 or 60:40.

Six months+

Formulas for babies six months and older, labeled as "Stage 2" or "Follow-on" formulas, are mostly casein-dominant. Some claim to include additional iron.

Most babies don't need the additional iron contained in these formulas because they can eat solid foods containing iron.

All leading health authorities concur that switching babies from a Stage 1 or Starter baby formula to a Stage 2 or Follow-on formula has no proven benefits. It's okay to continue to provide a Stage 1 or Starter formula for your baby until he's 12 months or older.[74]

Toddler milk

Toddler milk is not the same as baby formula. The ingredients include powdered milk, corn syrup and other added sugars, vegetable oils, and salt. It's often advertised as a healthier alternative to regular cow's milk. **Such claims are misleading.**

Toddler milks are expensive, unnecessary, and even unhealthy. Research shows toddler formulas are less nutritious because they contain more sugar, less protein, and less calcium compared to regular cow's milk.[75] Toddler milk is **not** something that is recommended by any health authority or medical or dietary association.

Critics have argued that Stage 2 and toddler formulas were introduced so that formula companies could continue to advertise their brand of formula while bypassing regulations that restrict the advertisement of infant formula.[76]

Additives

Formula companies strive to continually improve the quality of their baby formulas by adding nutrients and biological factors that mimic those found in breast milk. The more commonly advertised inclusions are long-chain polyunsaturated fatty acids, nucleotides, lutein, prebiotics, and probiotics.

Proposed health benefits

- **Long-chain polyunsaturated fatty acids (LCPUFAs)** are found in formulas labeled "gold" or "neuro" or "AA and DHA". LCPUFAs found in breast milk are believed to support vision and brain development. However, several independent studies have reported that their addition to baby formula had no beneficial effect on the eye or brain development for full-term formula-fed babies. Researchers claimed that LCPUFAs are generally not included in standard formulas because **full-term babies** can make AA (arachidonic acid) and DHA (docosahexaenoic acid) from the fats in regular formula.[77]
- **Nucleotides** found in breast milk are associated with beneficial gastrointestinal and immunological effects and are a permitted additive in infant formula. However, the findings on their benefits when added to **baby formula** have been inconsistent.[78]
- **Lutein** found in breast milk is believed to enhance brain and eye development. The European Food Safety Authority (EFSA) claims lutein-fortified baby formula is safe, but that it has not been shown to help visual function.[79]
- **Probiotics** are live microorganisms, usually lactose-digesting bacteria considered to be "friendly bacteria." Probiotics have been shown to help to normalize stools by reducing symptoms of diarrhea[80] and constipation.[81] They can be purchased separately and either given separately or mixed with the baby's regular formula.
- **Prebiotics** are types of carbohydrates that promote the growth of good bacteria, including probiotics, that assist with digestion. The jury is out regarding the benefits of adding them into baby formula.[82]

Specialized formulas

Specialized infant formulas are available for

- babies allergic to proteins in standard infant formulas;
- babies with high-energy needs; and
- babies requiring special diets because of genetic or metabolic disorders that affect their ability to digest, absorb, or tolerate the nutrients in standard infant formulas.

Specialized formulas include

- partially hydrolyzed formulas;
- extensively hydrolyzed formulas;
- amino acid-based formulas;
- high-energy formulas; and
- formulas for specific medical conditions.

We'll look at each of these subgroups.

Hypoallergenic and nonallergenic formula

First, I would like to demonstrate how formulas prescribed for babies with milk allergies compare to regular formula and partially hydrolyzed formula.

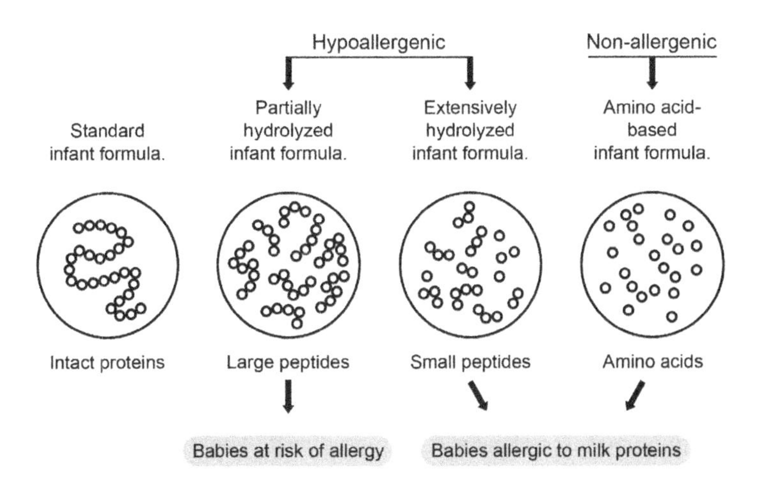

A hydrolyzed protein is simply a protein that has already been broken down into smaller parts. Hypoallergenic formula is classified according to the degree of protein hydrolysis as "partially" or "extensively" hydrolyzed protein products. **Amino acid formulas** are nonallergenic because they are **not** made from milk. These have been developed for babies who don't tolerate cow's milk or soy-based formulas.

Let's look at the types of problems each of these formulas might help.

Partially hydrolyzed formula (HA)

While HA formulas are classified as hypoallergenic, they contain **cow's milk** protein **partially** broken down into large peptides. This means the protein is more readily absorbed in the baby's intestinal tract. They may be helpful for **minor** tummy troubles like gassiness, constipation, and diarrhea experienced by healthy, thriving babies. However, the proteins are not broken down enough to be suitable for babies with **major** tummy troubles such as milk protein allergy.

According to the Australasian Society of Clinical Immunology and Allergy (ASCIA), HA formulas are not recommended for babies with suspected or confirmed milk protein allergy. [83] Such babies require an extensively hydrolyzed or amino acid-based formula.

HA formula is sometimes recommended for formula-fed babies who are **at risk** for developing an allergic reaction to milk protein because of their family history—meaning if mom/dad/brother/sister have an allergic condition such as eczema, asthma, or a food allergy. However, this has not been proven to be an effective means to reduce the risk of a baby developing cow's milk protein allergy.[84]

Extensively hydrolyzed formula (EHF)

EHFs include brands such as Nutramigen®, Progestimil®, Alimentum® Alfare® and Pepti-Junior®. EHFs are made from **cow's milk protein or soy protein,** but the protein has been broken down into small peptides. A newcomer to the market is a **rice-based** EHF—not yet available in every country.

In simple terms, EHFs have been predigested **before** the baby receives the milk. By breaking the protein down to small peptides, EHFs are of **low risk** for triggering a milk protein allergy.

EHFs are usually the first choice for babies with suspected cow's milk protein allergy (CMPA), cow's milk protein intolerance (CMPI), or milk or soy protein intolerance (MSPI).[85] They are only available by medical prescription in some countries.

Ninety to 95 percent of babies with CMPA, CMPI and MSPI will tolerate this type of formula.[86] The remaining five to 10 percent of babies who continue to experience symptoms like vomiting, diarrhea, eczema, and poor growth while on an EHF can be given an amino acid formula.

Amino acid formula (AAF)

AAFs are sometimes called elemental or ultrahydrolyzed formulas. AAFs are not made from milk. They are synthetically produced from amino acids, the nonallergenic building blocks for all proteins. These lactose-free formulas are balanced to meet the nutritional needs of babies and children.

Brand names include Neocate®, Elecare®, Puramino® and Alfamino®. AAFs are generally reserved for babies with CMPA, CMPI, MSPI who continue to experience symptoms when given an EHF. A reduction of symptoms is usually seen in two to four weeks of switching the baby to an AAF.

AAFs tend to be thin formulas; this means the milk will flow faster through the hole at the end of the nipple. You might need to provide a slower nipple if your baby appears to have trouble coping with the flow rate. If he often coughs, splutters, or aspirates while drinking, his doctor or speech-language pathologist might recommend adding a food thickener to the formula.

High-energy infant formula (HEIF)

HEIFs are high-calorie, nutrient-dense formulas developed for babies who have increased energy requirements and babies who fail to gain sufficient weight on regular strength formula, as well as babies requiring restricted fluids due to specific medical conditions, for example

- preterm and low birth weight;
- chronic lung and cardiac conditions; and
- "failure to thrive."

Another way to increase the caloric content of a baby's feeds is through concentrated formula, fortified breast milk, or the addition of oral nutritional supplements. These are described in chapter 11.

Note: High-energy feeds are helpful for **only some** babies who underfeed or fail to gain sufficient weight (see page 150-151 for examples).

Formulas for babies with specific medical needs

Various types and brands of specialized baby formulas are available, such as those for babies with malabsorption and metabolic disorders, renal conditions, and other medical conditions. These are available by a doctor's prescription only.

Switching formula

There are few reasons to switch from one formula to another and even less to swap breast milk for infant formula. Consider it in the following situations:

- if you are unable to breastfeed or provide breast milk;
- if your baby displays clearly observable symptoms associated with milk protein allergies (see pages 457-458);
- if your baby's healthcare professional has recommended switching formula;
- if your baby suffers from chronic constipation—he often passes hard, dry pebbles;
- if a certain brand of formula is easier to find or better suits your budget; or
- to provide a better-tasting formula for your baby.

How to switch formula

In the early weeks after birth, most hungry babies will accept almost any type of milk—breast milk or baby formula. After eight weeks of age, some will fuss and object in mild ways if switched from breast milk to infant formula or between a standard and modified formula. They often strongly reject the bitter taste of hypoallergenic formulas, in particular EHFs and AAFs, if switched after eight weeks of age.

To minimize the risk of rejection, I recommend switching your baby over to the new formula gradually.

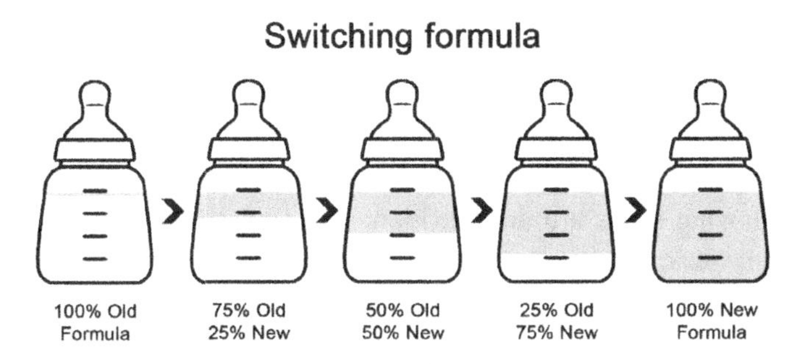

To minimize the risk of causing a **feeding aversion**, avoid pressuring your baby to feed against his will. Be prepared for rejections and reduced milk intake in the short term. He will come around to accepting the new formula within days—provided he's not pressured to feed or not already averse to bottle-feeding.

Note: Be aware that the scoop size and number of scoops per ounce or milliliter can vary between brands, as can preparation instructions, so read any new instructions carefully.

What to avoid

The nutrition a baby received in the womb and receives after birth will not only affect his health and growth now but also into adulthood and old age.[87] Conditions such as allergies, cholesterol, heart disease, obesity, diabetes, and immunologic issues, including celiac disease, can all be linked back to infant nutrition.[88] It's not the sole reason for these conditions, but it is a contributing factor.

All leading medical and dietetic organizations recommend offering baby formula for at least 12 months in cases where breastfeeding is not possible or where pumped breast milk is not available.[89] Starting from around the age of four to six months, solid food is nutritionally acceptable in **addition to** breast milk or baby formula—but **not as a substitute** for breast milk or formula.

Other types of milk are **not** suitable for babies. Avoid

- regular cow's milk or milk substitutes;
- homemade baby formula; and
- sweetened beverages from a bottle.

Note: Nutritional recommendations for babies are constantly changing based on scientific evidence and ongoing research. Therefore, nutritional advice given today will be very different from that provided to your parents.

Regular milk or milk substitutes

The following milks are **not** nutritionally adequate for babies under the age of one year:

- **cow's milk** in any form, including fresh, full cream, reduced fat, low fat, skim, evaporated, powdered, sweetened condensed, UHT/long-life. Cow's milk-based infant formula is suitable;
- **sheep's or goat's milk,** though goat's milk-based baby formula is fine;
- **plant-based milk**, such as rice, oat, almond, coconut, or soy milk. Soy baby formula is acceptable though not generally recommended.

Each of these milk types has excesses and deficiencies in levels of nutrients—including fats, carbohydrates, and protein—and in vitamins and minerals. None provide the right balance of nutrients to meet the **nutritional needs**—which are different from caloric needs—of babies younger than 12 months of age. A baby could appear to gain adequate weight as a result of receiving these milks and yet be malnourished due to nutrient, vitamin or mineral deficiencies or excesses.

Babies over six months of age can have **small** amounts of fresh full-cream pasteurized cow's or goat's milk added to cereal or mashed vegetables, but not as their main source of milk.[90] When a baby is over 12 months old, it's generally acceptable to cease baby formula and switch to reduced-fat or full-cream cow's milk.

Homemade baby formula

Homemade formulas are dangerous[91] and can lead to serious health problems for your baby. The U.S. Food and Drug Administration (FDA) and the American Academy of Pediatrics (AAP) warn against using homemade infant formula.[92]

Makers of commercial formulas add precise amounts of vitamins and minerals and alter the ratios of proteins and fats to achieve nutritional value that approaches that of breast milk. You can't achieve this as effectively as formula companies can.

If you're not able to breastfeed and can't afford baby formula, see your healthcare provider. They will direct you to health organizations that provide baby formula free or at a reduced rate for struggling families.

Sweetened beverages fed from a bottle

Babies should **never** be given sweetened beverages—such as soda, fruit juice, sweetened teas—because they are associated with a higher risk of dental cavities and childhood obesity.

I don't recommend giving babies **diluted juice,** except as a treatment, and not prevention, for constipation. Potential problems include

- **excess calories.** Once the pulp is removed, it's easy to overconsume juice.
- **malabsorption.** Symptoms include diarrhea, bloating, gassiness, and abdominal cramps.
- **nutritional shortage.** The more calories a baby receives from drinking juice, the less he will receive from other foods, including breast milk or infant formula.
- **preference for sweetened fluids.** A baby could become accustomed to drinking sweetened fluids, which may result in refusal to drink plain water.

When your baby is old enough to eat solid foods, rather than giving him fruit juice, encourage him to eat fruit and drink milk and water.

Next

Anything you add to your baby's formula can affect the quality of the nutrition he receives. In the next chapter, I describe reasons to give babies calorie-enhanced and thickened feeds and how these milk additives impact upon the nutritional balance of breast milk and infant formula.

11 Calorie-Enhanced and Thickened Feeds

HIGH-CALORIE FEEDS • FOOD THICKENING AGENTS • ADVANTAGES AND DISADVANTAGES • DO BABIES BENEFIT?

If your baby is exhibiting certain symptoms—such as not eating as much as expected, appearing to be hungry, suffering from reflux, trouble sleeping, not gaining enough weight, or appearing to choke when feeding—you might be instructed by a health professional to mix extra scoops of formula, nutritional supplements, food thickener, or baby cereal into her milk to increase the calories or thickness of her feeds.

In theory, this sounds simple and logical. In practical terms, it's not always effective. Such strategies can benefit a tiny percentage of babies with physical disabilities affecting their feeding abilities. But for most babies, increasing the calories or thickness of their feeds can cause more harm than good.

Whether you're currently giving your baby high-calorie or thickened feeds or thinking about doing so, for the sake of your baby's health, it's important that you understand the advantages, disadvantages, and associated risks.

As with all chapters in this book, the information provided is not intended as a substitute for medical advice. Please consult with your baby's doctor if you have concerns regarding her diet or diet-related problems.

Why I don't recommend such feeds

Parents often consult with me about baby care problems, such as tiny newborns who cry incessantly and babies with feeding or sleeping problems. Many of these babies were given **enhanced-calorie or thickened feeds** or both as part of a treatment plan or as part of a process that involved checking off a list of things to try to remedy a problem.

But in a disproportionate number of cases, such strategies have failed.

When calorie-enhanced or thickened feeds are given to typically, developing babies who are physically capable of feeding orally but who underfeed because of other issues, these types of feeds fail to solve feeding or sleeping problems. Usually, the underlying problem of underfeeding or broken sleep is behavioral and not always recognized by health professionals. Behavioral feeding and sleeping problems require long-term solutions, not quick fixes. The solution often lies in parents making appropriate changes to their infant feeding or sleep-settling practices.

Similarly, food thickeners may be given to babies who genuinely benefit; however, they are also often recommended for babies experiencing problems believed to be caused by "reflux" or "silent reflux," which in reality have nothing to do with reflux.

Therefore, calorie-enhanced or thickened feeds **should not be the first strategy** employed to resolve such problems. The first step should be a thorough assessment of **all** issues, including behavioral reasons, for the problem in question.

The further a baby's diet is removed from what's natural, the greater the risk of negative or unintended consequences.

This applies to adding substances into pumped breast milk or baby formula that would **not** normally be present. All components naturally found in breast milk—which is the model for baby formula—benefit babies. If a substance is not present or not in the same ratio as in breast milk, you need to be cautious.

An unbalanced diet can cause problems ranging from minor tummy upsets to life-threatening complications. The take-home message is to

never add anything to your baby's milk that has not been recommended by a health professional.

Oversights

The two most common oversights specific to calorie-enhanced and thickened feeds include

- forgetting to take into account the extra calories when estimating a baby's milk needs and using calculations based on normal-strength formula; and
- expecting a baby to consume the same volume of milk despite the additional calories. That's not how a baby's body works.

Such oversights can cause parents to pressure their baby to eat and may create additional problems as a result.

What you need to know

If you have been advised to give your baby calorie-enhanced or thickened feeds, or are thinking about doing so, consider the following questions.

- **What is the goal?** Is the goal that your baby will receive more calories from the milk she is drinking? Or that she will not need to work as hard to receive sufficient calories? Or to improve her growth? Or to reduce spitting up, vomiting, or aspiration?
- **Is it helping?** If you know the goal, it's easy to tell if the recommended dietary changes are helping. For example, has your baby's total caloric intake increased, or is she now drinking less in response to the additional calories? Is she more content and feeding or growing better as a result of reducing spit-ups? If the additional calories or food thickener is not achieving the intended goal, then explore alternative strategies.
- **How many calories will it add?** To tell if it's working, you also need to know the total calories provided. All additional calories count—don't forget any. For example, you might provide a 22 kilocalorie (kcal) commercially produced formula designed for preterm babies and have been advised to add a food thickener. You need to know the total

calories to determine if additional calories from the food thickener is negatively impacting on your baby's total formula intake.

- **Will the nutritional balance be changed?** Oral nutritional supplements and thickeners will change the nutritional balance—the percentage of carbohydrates, fats, and protein. Do additives change the nutritional balance of your baby's feeds in an unhealthy way? (This will be explained further in this chapter.)
- **What is the potential for complications?** Are there risks involved in altering the nutritional balance or reducing the percentage of water in relation to the number of calories? What might these be? You need to know about the risks to weigh these against the anticipated benefits.
- **When is it enough?** If the extra calories are not achieving the intended goal, it might be tempting to further increase the caloric content of your baby's feeds, which will further increase the risk of adverse effects. You may need to decide when it's time to change direction.

Baby Mia

Mia was born at 37 weeks' gestation. She was induced early because of growth concerns. Her weight and length at birth were at the 3rd percentile. Both parents were only a little below average height, and so her tiny size was not considered to be genetic. Mia was perfect, but petite. No reason was identified for her small size.

Her mother, Sarah, consulted with me for Mia's avoidant feeding behavior when she was four months old. Despite obvious signs of hunger, Mia would scream when placed into a feeding position and refuse to eat. Sarah felt the only way to make her feed was through force. But even then, she could only manage to get Mia to eat around 10 oz (≈300 mL) per day. Sarah had been advised by Mia's pediatrician that she needed to drink 25 oz (739 mL) per day. Sarah was worried sick at not being able to get Mia to drink even close to that figure. She was also worried because for the previous two weeks, Mia had only three wet diapers per day. This situation could not continue. A consultation with me was a last-ditch effort to see if Mia's feeding could be improved. If not, the plan was for her to be tube fed.

Based on Sarah's admission of long-standing force-feeding and my observation of her feeding Mia, I suspected a feeding aversion. Mia looked good physically. Her weight and length were still around the 3rd percentile, and her body mass index (BMI) indicated her weight in relation to her length was in a healthy range. I asked about Mia's diet;

she was given a commercially produced high-energy infant formula that provides 30 kcal per ounce (or 100 kcal per 100 mL), which was then thickened with rice cereal, adding a further 5 kcal to each ounce of milk, plus 1 mL of MCT (medium chain triglyceride) oil per ounce of milk, which added another 8 kcal to every ounce of milk she consumed. The total calories now added up to a massive 43 kcal per oz or 143 kcal per 100 mL, which was 2.13 times the normal number of calories in regular-strength infant formula.

Ten ounces provided 430 kcal. This was within the normal range of calories per pound per day for a baby of Mia's age and petite size. She was receiving sufficient calories to meet her caloric needs. However, three wet diapers per day showed her fluid needs were not met. Twenty-five ounces of formula which contained 43 kcal per ounce (or 143 kcal per 100 mL)—which is what the pediatrician had told Sarah that Mia needed to consume each day—would be a gross overestimation of her caloric needs.

Wanting to understand how a health professional could allow such a dangerous situation to occur, I asked Sarah to describe the circumstances that led to Mia receiving ultrahigh-calorie feeds. It turned out that not one but multiple health professionals were advising Sarah about Mia's diet. I can only assume that the pediatrician, who was the primary healthcare provide—and therefore, ultimately responsible for monitoring Mia's diet—was unaware of just how extreme the calorie content of her feeds were. By quoting 25 ounces per day, which is the average for Mia's age and weight based on **normal-strength formula,** I wondered if he remembered that she was given high-energy formula. Either way, this oversight had serious consequences for Mia, who was now mildly dehydrated and traumatized by force-feeding.

I knew it was going to take time for Mia to get over her feeding aversion and consume a healthy volume of milk. This would not happen while she continued to be offered such dangerous, ultra-high-calorie feeds. I made recommendations to continue the high energy formula but cease the MCT oil and switch from rice cereal to a carob bean food thickener. This reduced the calories to around 30 kcal per oz (100 kcal per 100 mL). Reducing the calorie content of her feeds would motivate her to drink larger volumes and receive more fluids. I also recommended **baby-led feeding practices** to regain her trust.

The first day of being fed 30 kcal formula without pressure, Mia took 12.5 ounces and had four wet diapers. The second day, she took 14 ounces with five wet diapers. Volumes fluctuated for a few days. By day seven, she consumed 17 ounces—which at 30 kcal per ounce provided the same number of calories as 25.5 ounces based on regular-strength milk. However, it took two weeks before she enjoyed feeding and before her milk volumes increased further.

It soon became clear Mia did not require a thickening agent. Once she was no longer forced to eat in a distressed state, her sucking was perfectly coordinated. To further reduce the risk of complications associated with high-energy feeds, she was returned to a normal-strength formula. Within three days, her volumes increased in response to fewer calories. Mia was now consuming an average of 27 ounces of regular strength formula. Sarah got to experience the pleasure of feeding a willing baby and avoid ending up with a feeding tube.

Mia's story was the most extreme I had seen with respect to the calorie content; however, it is a classic example of the sequence of events that start with overestimation of a baby's milk needs and end with the baby becoming feeding averse.

Calorie-enhanced milk feeds

Calorie-enhanced (also called calorie-dense or high-energy) feeds include any breast milk or infant formula given to a baby that provides more energy (calories or kilojoules) than a regular infant formula, which is 20 kcal per ounce or 67 kcal per 100 mL.

Increasing the energy content of a baby's milk feeds can be achieved in a number of ways, including

- concentrated infant formula and fortified breast milk (FBM);
- oral nutritional supplements (ONS); or
- commercially produced high-energy infant formula (HEIF).

Concentrated infant formula and fortified breast milk (FBM)

To **concentrate infant formula** means adding more scoops of powdered infant formula (PIF) to water or less water to liquid concentrate formula than recommended, in the instructions on the side of the formula can. To **fortify breast milk** involves mixing either PIF or human milk fortifier (concentrated heat-treated donor breast milk with additional protein vitamins and minerals) into breast milk.

The degree of concentration or fortification varies. Some parents are advised to concentrate their baby's formula or fortify breast milk to a caloric density ranging from 22 to 30 kcal per ounce or 75 to 100 kcal per 100 mL and anything in between. This increases the calorie and nutrient content of the baby's milk by 10 to 50 percent.

Oral nutritional supplements (ONS)

Oral nutritional supplements may be recommended as another way to increase a baby's nutritional intake. Examples of nutritional supplements commonly recommended for babies who are not gaining weight as expected are included in the following table.

Table 11.1: Oral nutritional supplements—nutrients and calories

Brand/type	Main nutrients	Calories
Duocal®	Carbohydrates and fats	5 grams = 25 kcal
Polycal®	Carbohydrates	5 grams = 20 kcal
Energivit ®	Carbohydrates, fats, vitamins, minerals and trace elements	5 grams = 25 kcal
Maltodextrin	Carbohydrates	5 grams = 20 kcal
MCT Oil (Medium chain triglyceride)	Fats	1 mL = 8.55 kcal
Liquigen®	Fats	1 mL = 4.5 kcal
Calogen®	Fats	1 mL = 4.5 kcal
Vegetable oils (coconut, olive, avocado, and sunflower)	Fats	1 mL = 8 kcal
Baby cereal (rice, oat, barley, or mixed)	Mostly carbohydrates	1 teaspoon = 5 kcal 1 tablespoon* = 15 kcal
*Based on USA-sized tablespoon (15 mL). A tablespoon is 1.35 percent larger in Australia (20 mL). Teaspoon sizes are the same. You may need to check on the standard tablespoon size in your country.		

All calories count, no matter the source. If you are adding nutritional supplements into your baby's feeds, be aware of how many calories it adds because it will affect how much milk your baby consumes.

Commercially produced high-energy infant formula (HEIF)

Energy and nutrient dense infant formulas are available commercially. The concentration level, which ranges from 22 to 36 kcal per ounce (75 to 120 kcal per 100 mL), is displayed on the label. All you need to do is follow the manufacturer's instructions when preparing feeds.

While being calorie-dense and providing more nutrients in a smaller volume, commercially produced HEIF are not concentrated feeds. While containing less water in relation to nutrients, the ratio of nutrients and micronutrients are finely balanced.

Reasons parents concentrate formula

As parents, we might be tempted to make our baby's formula stronger or we may be advised to do so. This practice should be avoided as it can have serious consequences related to incorrect fluid balance. The following are examples of what can go wrong.

- At birth, when Luca was classified as intrauterine growth restricted (IUGR), his doctor advised his mother to add an extra scoop of formula to help him grow faster. It didn't work! Growth cannot be forced by packing more calories and nutrients into a smaller volume of water.
- Geraldine believed that her baby's insatiable appetite meant her formula was not strong enough for her. Geraldine had been misinterpreting her baby's tiredness cues as hunger. Her baby would guzzle down the feed because of her sucking reflex, but then suffer tummy discomfort due to functional lactose overload.
- Gianna was a very large baby at birth, over the 97th percentile for weight and length. She would often cry, and she barely slept longer than 30 minutes three times during the day. Her mother thought that because she was a big baby, she might need stronger milk. Large babies might require **more milk** compared to small babies if they are genetically inclined to be large, but they don't need stronger milk. If

a "large at birth" baby is not genetically inclined to be large, she may go through catch-down growth, in which case she will drink less milk than expected for a baby of her age and size.

- Henry was not drinking the volume of milk recommended based on his age and weight, so his dietitian recommended that his mother add five scoops instead of the usual four into the same volume of water. In response to the additional calories the volume he was willing to consume dropped.
- Jake's father thought that adding an extra scoop of powdered formula to his baby's bedtime feed might help him to sleep longer at night. It didn't. Jake's wakefulness at night was because of a sleep association problem and not hunger.
- Josie overfilled the scoop when preparing her baby's formula because she thought a little extra formula powder "wouldn't hurt." It's unlikely to help! And could be harmful if Josie is not aware that it will reduce the volume of milk her baby consumes over 24 hours.

If you have been adding extra formula to water without the approval of a health professional, thinking it might make your baby more content, **please stop.** You are more likely to create problems that lead to discontentment or worse.

Which babies might benefit from calorie-enhanced feeds?

Calorie-enhanced feeds are typically recommended by health professionals to improve babies' growth or to restrict fluids. It's a very effective means of restricting fluids, but not always effective in improving growth. When deciding if high-calorie feeds might help your baby to achieve better growth, first consider the reasons why his growth might be poor.

There are several reasons for babies to consume less than sufficient calories to support healthy growth (giving high-energy feeds will **not** be an effective solution for them all). For example:

- **Baby has high caloric needs,** such as a very immature or ill baby challenged by the need for a high caloric intake, but who is unable to tolerate large fluid volumes—these babies often benefit from enhanced-calorie feeds;

- **Baby is too weak to feed effectively**—for example, babies with chronic lung disease or cardiac conditions—in which case, calorie-enhanced feeds can help to increase caloric intake and support healthy growth;
- **Baby is spitting up large volumes of milk** and unable to keep down sufficient volumes of normal-strength formula to maintain healthy growth. (Check if the baby is overfeeding—see chapter 25—because in some cases, overfeeding can lead to poor growth.);
- **Baby is prevented from eating because of a physical disability** affecting her sucking ability;
- **Baby is prevented from eating to satisfaction** because of equipment problems, errors in preparation, poor feeding position, or chronic sleep deprivation. (See chapter 26 for other behavioral causes for underfeeding);
- **Baby is unwilling to eat unless ravenous or asleep** as a result of having developed a feeding aversion, in which case, calorie-enhanced feeds will simply result in her drinking less volume but receiving similar calories either way. (See chapter 27); and
- **Baby is eating sufficient calories for healthy growth.** It's been mistakenly assumed she's not eating or gaining enough because of unrealistic expectations; in such cases, giving calorie-enhanced feeds will result in her drinking less.

> The problem of poor growth does not occur because infant formula or breast milk is too weak. It occurs because the baby is too weak to consume sufficient quantities of regular strength milk. If the baby is not too weak to feed effectively, the cause of poor growth, and hence the solution, lies elsewhere.

In summary, calorie-enhanced feeds can be helpful for babies with physical or medical conditions affecting feeding or who require fluid restriction. However, they are not usually helpful for normal, healthy babies troubled by behavioral feeding problems that make it hard for them to eat, cause them to become unwilling to eat, or when it's mistakenly believed they are not eating enough.

Can calorie-enhanced feeds cause harm?

You would be forgiven for assuming that mixing extra scoops of formula, or nutritional supplements, or baby cereal into your baby's breast milk or infant formula would be harmless. After all, it's food that a baby might otherwise eat! But there are problems associated with this practice; some minor, and others far more serious. These include

- **overnutrition**. Very young babies can be more easily tricked or forced to consume excess calories when given enhanced-calorie feeds. This can cause overnutrition (an overconsumption of nutrients). Symptoms include indigestion, vomiting, diarrhea, irritability, sleeplessness, or wakefulness from abdominal discomfort (see chapter 25);
- **reduced milk intake.** In the case of healthy babies who can self-regulate their milk consumption, calorie-enhanced feeds often result in a reduction in total daily milk intake; and
- **behavioral feeding aversion.** If you try to pressure or force your baby to drink similar volumes of calorie-enhanced milk feeds compared to normal-strength breast milk or infant formula, this may cause or reinforce a behavioral feeding aversion.

  Note: Adding more calories simply allows a feeding-averse baby to resist feeding for longer periods of time. In response to decreased milk intake, you might be advised to further increase the calories, setting up a self-perpetuating negative cycle.

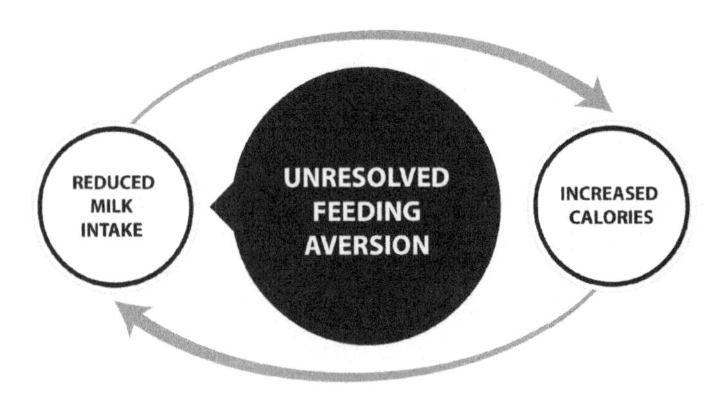

Adding more calories is generally not helpful in the case of a feeding aversion because it targets the symptom of a feeding aversion, which is reduced milk intake, but does nothing to resolve the cause of the baby's feeding refusal.

The cyclical pattern of reduced intake and progressively adding further calories increases the risk of much more serious problems, such as

- **protein dilution.** The energy source in regular strength formula is modelled on breast milk. The approximate percentage of total calories from nutrients is fats 50 percent, carbohydrates 41 percent, and proteins 9 percent.[93] Concentrated formula and HEIF maintain the proportions but with a lower water percentage. The addition of **nutritional supplements** doesn't!

  Nutritional supplements, which are mostly carbohydrates and fats, dilute the percentage of protein and micronutrients (vitamins and minerals). Protein plays a very important part in a baby's growth and development. Fat should not exceed 60 percent, and protein should be **greater** than 7 percent of the total energy.[94]

  The long-term impact of providing babies with a low-protein diet at a time when they're growing at a rapid rate—the average is double their birth weight by four months and triple by 12 months—is unclear because it has not been studied.[95] However, it's reasonable to assume that deviations from the ratio of protein, fats, carbohydrates, and vitamins and minerals found in breast milk have the potential to impair growth, which is the very thing they are given to prevent.
- **fluid restriction**. Concentrated formula, fortified breast milk, and HEIFs involve packing in more nutrients—and therefore, more calories—into a smaller volume of water. It's a strategy that is used to intentionally restrict fluids for babies with specific medical conditions. It will also restrict fluids for healthy babies because they too will consume less volume in response to higher calories. The more calories you add to your baby's feeds, the more you may be unintentionally restricting her fluid intake.

  Take care to prevent your baby's total fluids from dropping too low. Babies on calorie-enhanced feeds need to be monitored closely to ensure adequate hydration. If your baby has fewer than five wet diapers per day, have her seen by a doctor.

- **increased renal solute load.** Your baby's renal (kidney) function will not be fully mature until around two years of age. The younger your baby, the more immature her renal function, and the more limited her kidneys are in concentrating urine and retaining bodily fluids.
- **electrolyte imbalance.** Electrolytes—minerals like sodium, calcium, potassium, magnesium, bicarbonate, and phosphate—are involved in many essential processes in your baby's body. A risk for all babies receiving insufficient fluids (or with fluid loss) includes electrolyte imbalance. Electrolyte imbalance can cause dehydration, muscle weakness, cardiac arrhythmias (irregular heart beat), and loss of consciousness.[96]

The higher the concentration of calories and nutrients, the greater the risk. The younger the baby, the greater the risk.

The seriousness of these problems, some of which are life-threatening, is why you should **never** alter the concentration of your baby's formula or add anything into her milk, like cereal, vegetable oil, or nutritional supplements, unless advised to do so by a doctor, nutritionist, or dietitian.

I'll now discuss the pros and cons of thickened feeds.

Thickened feeds

You might have decided or been advised to thicken your baby's milk to reduce gastroesophageal reflux (the backward flow of milk from the stomach, also called regurgitation) or to improve feeding coordination.

Reduce gastroesophageal reflux

Reflux (meaning baby spits up or projectile vomits) or **silent reflux** (meaning baby doesn't spit up) is often believed to be the cause of infant crying and sleeping problems and the cause of feeding refusal or distressed feeding behavior linked to poor growth. However, it's **rarely** the cause of such problems in the case of typically developing, healthy babies.

There is evidence that thickened feeds will reduce the number of regurgitations.[97] The increased viscosity (thickness) of thickened feeds makes the stomach contents heavier and harder to regurgitate, which means the milk is less likely to come back up.

Improve feeding coordination

Thickened feeds are commonly recommended for babies who exhibit **dysphagia** (trouble or difficulty swallowing), **aspiration** (when fluid or food gets into the lungs), or both.[98]

Thickening liquids slows the flow rate, thereby allowing more time for the baby to coordinate swallowing.[99] On the flip side, using thickened feeds as a long-term solution impedes babies' oral and swallowing development.[100] Basically, the baby gets used to drinking thickened fluids and doesn't develop the skills to swallow the normal consistency of milk and water.

While some studies have shown that thickened baby formulas will reduce vomiting and spitting up—and thus reduce the laundry load for parents—thickened formulas don't appear to reduce measurable regurgitation in a baby's esophagus (silent reflux).[101] There is no evidence that they reduce acid exposure or aspiration.[102] For more on dysphagia and aspiration, see chapter 33.

Thickening products

Multiple products can be used to thicken a baby's milk. Food thickeners fall into three basic groups:

- **vegetable gums**—such as carob bean (also called locust bean), xanthan gum, and sodium alginate;
- **starch**—for example, cereals, arrowroot, rice, maize, corn starch, oatmeal, tapioca, and wheat; and
- **mixed**—some commercially produced food thickeners contain a combination of starch- and gum-based thickeners.

Table 11.2: Popular food thickening products

Product	Main thickening ingredients	Calories
Baby cereal	Rice, barley, oatmeal, or mixed starch	1 tablespoon (15g) = 15kcal 1 teaspoon (5g) = 5kcal
Gelmix®	Maltodextrin, carob bean gum	1 scoop (1.2g) = 5kcal
Cow & Gate Instant Carobel®	Maltodextrin, carob bean gum	1 scoop (1.7g) = 5kcal
Karicare/Aptamil food thickener®	Maltodextrin, starch (from maize), carob bean gum	1 scoop (4g) = 15.5kcal
Thick-it®	Corn starch and maltodextrin	1 packet (5g) = 20kcal
Infant Gaviscon® sachet	Sodium alginate and magnesium alginate	Calories not specified. Assumed to be negligible
Maltodextrin is a white powder made from corn, rice, potato starch, or wheat. It's added into many foods to improve their flavor, thickness, or shelf life.		

There are many more brands and combinations. To help you to make an informed decision, I have included some of the advantages and disadvantages of gum- and starch-based thickeners below.

Gum-based thickeners

Commercially produced anti-reflux (AR) infant formulas mostly contain carob bean thickening agents or similar vegetable gum thickeners. Using them has specific **advantages,** including that they

- are effective in reducing the regurgitation of stomach contents;
- do not increase the calories or alter the nutritional value of the milk;
- are gluten and carbohydrate free;
- are suitable to be added to breast milk; and
- can soften stools.[103]

Using these thickening agents also has specific **disadvantages.**

- Carob bean thickening agents slow gastric emptying time (how quickly food passes from the stomach into the intestines). Delayed gastric emptying can increase the risk of spitting up.[104]
- The thickening agent is only slightly thicker when prepared and heated compared to regular formula. However, it will thicken to 10 times that of regular formula in the stomach,[105] but only when in **contact with stomach acid.**[106] Therefore, an AR formula will **not** thicken to the full extent when a baby is given acid-suppressing medications.
- Carob bean thickening is indigestible but fermentable by bacteria in the large intestine.[107] Because of this fermentable characteristic, some babies may react with abdominal pain, crying, and diarrhea.
- Changes the microbiome (the balance of bacteria) in a baby's intestinal tract.[108]
- The fermentation by bacteria in the large intestine (colon) can create colic-like symptoms.[109]
- Carob bean thickeners can cause diarrhea, constipation, and allergies.[110]
- Infant Gaviscon® is not recommended for babies under one year of age except under medical advice. It should not be given within two hours of providing other medications as it may compromise the effectiveness of other medications.[111]

Starch-based thickeners

I don't recommend starch-based thickeners, which include all types of baby cereal, because of the large number of disadvantages and potential complications.

These include

- **increased calories.** Baby cereal and other starch-based thickeners that have similar caloric content (see Table 11.2), can significantly increase the caloric content of the feed. For example:
- **1 teaspoon** of rice cereal (5 kcal) added to **one** ounce of milk (20 kcal) will increase the calorie content of your baby's feeds by 25 percent.
- **1 tablespoon** (15 kcal) added to **one** ounce of milk (20 kcal) adds a massive 75 percent extra calories.
- **1 tablespoon** (15 kcal) added to **two** ounces of milk (40 kcal) equals a 37.5 percent kcal increase.

- **ineffective in breast milk.** Breast milk contains digestive enzymes that break down the starch in baby cereal. Adding cereal to breast milk **as a thickening agent** is largely ineffective, as after several minutes, the breast milk is no longer thickened—but it still carries the same risks associated with increased calories and reduced protein.
- **significant increase in weight gain.** These thickeners can cause excessive weight gain if used for extended periods.[112] I have seen many overweight and obese babies who have been given thickened feeds.
- **increased risk of obesity in later life.**[113] A high-carbohydrate diet can increase body fat without improving skeletal and muscle growth. In other words, high calories make the baby grow fatter rather than grow longer. Consuming cereal in a bottle is associated with obesity in later life.[114]
- **inconsistent flow rate.** Starch particles keep absorbing more liquid and get thicker **after** they are prepared. The longer the milk sits, the thicker it gets, the harder it is for the baby to feed. As a result, the feed may be too thick within 20 minutes of being prepared.
- **taking longer to complete the feed.** As the feed thickens, it becomes increasingly more difficult for the baby to suck the milk through the nipple.
- **clogging the nipple.** Starch can clump and block the nipple.
- **choking risk.** The American Academy of Pediatrics advises that it can pose a choking hazard.[115] Rice starch is associated with an increased risk of coughing.[116]
- **increased risk of food allergies.** Giving solids before the age of four months by spoon or in a bottle is associated with an increased risk of food allergies. [117]
- **increased risk of diabetes.** Receiving cereal before three months of age is associated with an increased risk for type 1 insulin-dependent diabetes.[118]
- **increased risk of constipation.** Adding cereal can cause **constipation**.[119] This is more likely to occur when the concentration is high—for example, one tablespoon of rice cereal to one ounce of milk.

Remember, if something is not naturally found in breast milk, you need to be cautious about adding it to your baby's milk feeds. Don't add cereal to your baby's bottle unless advised to do so by your baby's healthcare professional.

If your baby has problems, explore all options

If your baby suffers from uncoordinated sucking, aspiration, spitting up, projectile vomiting, irritability, feeding or sleeping problems, or genuine—rather than the mistaken perception of—poor growth, she requires a thorough investigation into **physical and behavioral** causes first. Behavioral reasons are described within the pages of this book. The use of calorie-enhanced or thickened feeds should only be considered **after** behavioral causes have been ruled out.

Failure to assess **behavioral reasons** for baby care problems can result in a series of misdiagnoses. Alicia's case provides an example of what can happen.

Baby Alicia

When Alicia was three months old, her mother Gaby consulted with me regarding concerns about poor growth and not eating enough. During my assessment process, Gaby related the following series of events.

Gaby described Alicia as a "dream baby" during the first two weeks after her birth. Around two weeks of age, Alicia started to cry a lot. She appeared to demand feeds every 1.5 to two hours and slept for around 20 minutes, four times a day. Although she slept well at night, she woke every three to four hours to demand a feed and return to sleep. She would spit up after most feeds. Sometimes she would have huge vomits, losing most of the feed. At these times, Gaby would feed her once again.

When Alicia was four weeks old, Gaby had already tried every recommendation made by her family and friends. She was emotionally and physically exhausted. She discussed her concerns with Alicia's pediatrician. He diagnosed reflux and advised Gaby to thicken Alicia's feeds by adding a teaspoon of rice cereal to each ounce of milk. This increased the calorie concentration of her feeds by 25 percent to 25 kcal per ounce (84 kcal per 100 mL). This was effective in preventing vomiting and minimizing the size and frequency of spit-ups. But it did not reduce her crying or encourage longer sleep. She was then prescribed Pepcid (an acid-suppressing medication). This had no effect on reducing crying or increasing sleeping times.

Between four and eight weeks of age, Alicia gained large amounts of weight each week, well in excess of average. Gaby was delighted to see her gaining so well. Alicia's weight percentile climbed from the 35th

to the 75th percentile in only four weeks. She was now a chubby baby—something most parents and health professionals love to see. However, her crying and sleeping problems became worse during that time.

Around eight weeks of age, Alicia started to fuss during feeds and leave milk in her bottle. She had always drained her bottle prior, so Gaby was confused. She tried many changes in equipment, but it made no difference. Alicia's weekly weight gains dropped significantly and were now below average. Her doctor recommended that she be switched to a hypoallergenic formula to rule out the possibility of a milk allergy, but Alicia hated the taste and refused to drink any. So, she was switched back to her usual formula.

Concerned about poor growth, which was attributed to her not drinking enough, her doctor then advised Gaby to add five rather than four scoops of PIF into her bottles. This increased the calorie content of her feed by an additional 25 percent compared to regular strength formula. Her feeds now contained 30 kcal per ounce (100 kcal per 100 mL). This is 50 percent more calories than regular-strength formula. In response to the additional calories, Alicia's milk intake dropped even further. She was then diagnosed with gastroparesis (delayed gastric emptying) and given Domperidone (a medication which causes the contents of the stomach to empty into the intestinal tract faster). This also had no noticeable effect on her feeding or milk intake, which prompted Gaby to start to look for non-medical solutions—and hence, book a consultation with me.

My assessment of the situation was that the original reason for Alicia's distress, sleeplessness and spitting up, was because she was chronically sleep-deprived. Plus, she was also overfeeding, both problems due to her having developed a feeding-sleep association (see pages 297-298). Alicia was offered feeds 1.5 to 2 hourly because Gaby misinterpreted her tiredness cues as hunger. Gaby would encourage her to empty the bottle using **parent-led feeding practices** taught to her when Alicia was born. Hyper-expansion of her stomach from overfeeding was the reason she would often spit up or projectile vomit.

While the addition of rice cereal was effective in reducing the incidence of vomiting, it did not resolve the problem of overfeeding. It made it even easier for Alicia to be overfed. The additional calories further increased the calories Alicia retained. Hence, she gained excessive amounts of weight. By eight weeks of age, her body mass index (BMI) had tipped into the overweight category.

Fading of her sucking reflex around eight weeks of age meant she was now in a better position to decide how much to eat based on the energy content of her feeds. She could stop feeding when satisfied; hence, she left milk in the bottle. She cried and resisted Gaby's efforts to make her consume the volume she had taken previously, because she did not need the volume she consumed previously. Not now, and not before. The addition of cereal minimized vomiting—that had occurred due to overfeeding—resulted in her gaining excessive weight before the age of eight weeks. If her weight continued to follow the same trajectory, she would eventually become obese.

Once Alicia's sucking reflex had faded, she was able to stop eating when she had had enough and consequently her milk intake dropped and weight gain slowed. What was mistakenly perceived as poor growth due to not eating enough was catch-down growth. Alicia's body was doing what it needed to do to correct the imbalance and get her growth back on track in keeping with her genetically programmed size and shape.

Gaby followed my recommendations to resolve Alicia's behavioral feeding and sleeping problems. The thickener and extra calories were removed. Alicia's sleeping problem was resolved. Her body now received the amount of sleep it needed. No longer distressed due to sleep deprivation, she was generally content between feeds. To resolve her distress during feeds, I encouraged Gaby to trust Alicia to know what her body needed and employ **baby-led feeding practices**.

Unable to rely on the scales or average milk volumes to confirm if Alicia was getting enough to eat—because a baby going through catch-down growth does not gain average weight or consume an average volume of milk based on age and weight—Gaby simply needed to look for signs of Alicia being a well-fed baby. I also encouraged her to allow Alicia's body to realign to her natural state, which may involve weight percentiles dropping. She would now be using some of the extra stores of body fat accumulated when she was too young to resist overfeeding.

Adding more calories and/or thickening baby's feeds for the **wrong reasons** will provide no benefit and risks further complicating the situation or creating new problems.

Next

Next, we look at how to prepare, store and transport your baby's milk, which can have an effect on the quality of milk she receives.

12 Preparing Bottle-Feeds

HOW TO PREPARE AND STORE BREAST MILK AND INFANT FORMULA • COMMON ERRORS • DANGERS OF DILUTED AND CONCENTRATED FORMULA

When preparing, heating, storing, and transporting milk that will be fed to a baby, it's so important to carefully follow the manufacturer's instructions for formula and safety guidelines for breast milk. If you make adjustments to the water or nutritional content of your baby's feeds without fully understanding the consequences, this can lead to many problems and can even be harmful.

When it comes to your baby's health, prevention is better than a cure. Being aware of the causes can help you to prevent a problem. Read this chapter to confirm that you're ensuring your baby gets safe feeds of the highest quality.

Preparing pumped breast milk

Breast milk is not sterile, but when it comes direct from a healthy mom, as in the case of breastfeeding, it's fresh and highly unlikely to contain harmful microorganisms. However, breast milk given from a bottle can become contaminated from inadequately cleaned pumping or feeding equipment or from incorrect storage practices or offering leftovers.

Freshly pumped breast milk is preferable to breast milk that has been refrigerated, and refrigerated is better than frozen. Freshly pumped breast milk has the best antibacterial properties and is higher in antioxidants and vitamins than milk that has been refrigerated or frozen.[120]

Warming breast milk

A major difference between breast milk and infant formula is that breast milk contains antibodies and other living cells that restrict the growth of harmful microorganisms, but these can be destroyed by overheating. To warm breast milk, place the bottle in a jug of lukewarm water—**not** boiling water.

Freezing breast milk

Some mothers like to keep a small store of breast milk in the freezer for emergencies. Others may try to accumulate stock for when mom returns to work. In such cases, use single-use storage bags or reusable containers designed for breast milk storage. Label the bag or container with the date and time collected. Use the oldest bag or container of breast milk first.

Thawing frozen breast milk

Breast milk can be defrosted in around 12 hours in the refrigerator or about 30 minutes in a bowl of lukewarm water. The fastest way to defrost breast milk is to hold it under a faucet of warm running water. Depending on the volume to be defrosted, this will take around 15 minutes. It helps to plan in advance, so you don't keep your hungry baby waiting. Once thawed, use it straight away. Also,

- don't refreeze milk once it's thawed;
- don't leave frozen breast milk to defrost at room temperature; and
- don't thaw breast milk in the microwave or in boiling water.

Storing breast milk

How to store breast milk depends on how soon you plan to use it. If you are not planning on feeding freshly pumped breast milk to your baby in the next few hours, refrigerate it as soon as possible. If you plan to use it within a few days, refrigeration is better than freezing.

You can mix breast milk pumped on separate occasions on the same day. However, it needs to be cooled in the refrigerator first for at least one hour before mixing the two batches.

How long does breast milk last?

Advice on how long breast milk can be stored varies. Below are the most commonly recommended time frames.

Table 12.1 How long does breast milk last?

Stored in ...	Discard after ...
Room temperature	Up to 6 hours if freshly prepared 4 hours if the room is warm
Insulated cooler with ice packs	Up to 24 hours
Refrigerator—in back, not in the doors	Up to 5 days Previously frozen breast milk can be stored in a refrigerator for 24 hours after it has been thawed.
Refrigerator freezer or deep freezer—in the back	2 weeks Up to 12 months Within 6 months is optimal

Breast milk's antibacterial properties help it stay fresh. Live cells and antibodies guard against bacterial growth in breast milk, which is why it can be stored longer than baby formula.

Preparing baby formula

You have chosen a suitable baby formula; the next step is preparing a feed. Baby formula needs to be prepared accurately and hygienically, according to the manufacturer's instructions, to minimize the risk of food poisoning or problems associated with concentrated or diluted formula.

Three types of baby formula preparations are commercially available.

1. Ready-to-feed;
2. Liquid concentrate; and
3. Powdered infant formula.

Ready-to-feed

Ready-to-feed (also called ready-to-use) formula is a premixed liquid formula ready to be poured into a bottle and fed to the baby. It's available in 2 oz, 6 oz, or 8 oz (60 mL, 180 mL or 240 mL) containers. These formulas are sterile and are recommended for very young babies and babies with very low immunity. Ready-to-feed formula is generally the most expensive option.

For optimal preparation,

1. Shake before opening.
2. Separate the amount you believe your baby might require, plus a little extra to allow him to feed to satisfaction and leave some milk in the bottle when he's done.
3. Don't add water.
4. Once opened, unused portions can be covered and refrigerated for up to 48 hours.

Liquid concentrate

Liquid concentrate infant formula is cheaper than ready-to-feed but more expensive than powdered infant formula. Preparation typically requires mixing equal parts of the formula concentrate and water. Like ready-to-feed products, liquid concentrate formula is commercially sterile. However, water, previously boiled or otherwise, is not.

Once you have added the correct amount of formula concentrate and water to your baby's bottle, shake. You can prepare just enough for a single feed or mix an entire can of concentrate with an equal amount of water and store it in the refrigerator to be used over the next 24 hours.

Powdered infant formula

Powdered infant formula (PIF) comes in a can or box with a measuring scoop. It's also available in single-use sachets. Most parents opt for PIF because it is less expensive than ready-to-feed and liquid concentrate.

PIF requires more time to prepare compared to other types of formula. Preparation varies between brands, which is why it's important to read and follow the instructions provided on the side of the can or box. If you switch formula brands, don't assume that preparation will be the same. Formula instructions differ in various ways. For example:

- **The number of scoops to water volume.** The ratio of water and number of scoops can vary between brands. For example, one scoop to two ounces (60 mL), one scoop to one ounce (30 mL), or one scoop to 50mL (1.66 ounces).
- **Scoops are not interchangeable**. Use the scoop provided with the formula to measure the amount of powder. A scoop from another brand could be larger or smaller. Don't try to add half a scoop as this can be inaccurate. When the can of formula is empty, also discard the scoop to avoid mix-ups.
- **Anti-reflux (AR) formula.** AR formulas contain a food thickener that will begin to thicken when heated. Some formula manufacturers recommend that the powder of their AR formula be mixed into cool rather than warm water to prevent clumps from forming, then shaken or stirred and warmed.
- **Unpacked level scoop**. Most, but not all, formula manufacturers recommend measurements be via an "unpacked level scoop." But what does that mean? Fill the scoop with powder, gently tap the handle of the scoop on the side of the can just once to allow the powder to settle, and then push off any overfill with the edge of a knife.

What to measure

Adding PIF to water will increase the total volume. This is called displacement. Displacement after mixing PIF is around half an ounce increase in total volume to every four ounces of water. For example, if you add four ounces (120 mL) of water to your baby's bottle and then add the recommended number of scoops of PIF, the total volume of the **prepared formula** is now 4.5 ounces (135 mL).

Regular strength formula provides 20 kcal per ounce or 67 kcal per 100 mL **based on the prepared volume and not the water volume.** Formula companies allow for the fact that the prepared volume will be higher than the water volume. In the example above, the total volume of the prepared formula is 4.5 ounces (135 mL), hence the total number of calories is 90.

When deciding how much milk their baby has consumed, parents often ask if they should subtract the volume their baby drinks from the volume of water added during preparation or the total volume once the feed is prepared. If your goal is to measure **how much milk** your baby has received, subtract the volume consumed from the prepared volume. It's not "milk" until you have added and mixed the PIF into the water.

Water + infant formula powder = milk

Warming baby formula

There is no medical reason for a baby to require warm milk. Mostly, we warm babies' bottles because the milk they receive when breastfeeding is warm. Your baby may prefer his milk warm, at room temperature, or directly from the refrigerator. All of these options are fine.

If you decide to warm your baby's bottles, you have a few options.

- **When heating in hot water,** place the bottle into a jug containing hot water for around 10 minutes, give or take, depending on the volume. Swirl the formula after heating to ensure the heat is evenly distributed.
- **Bottle warmers** designed specifically for warming baby bottles are convenient and safe as long as they have a thermostat control. Warm directly before use. Don't leave the bottle in the warmer for more than 20 minutes before feeding your baby.

- **Heating formula in the microwave is not recommended** because the milk can heat unevenly, and there can be hot spots that reach very high temperatures. While it's not something I encourage, I know many parents will microwave rather than have a hungry baby crying for 10 minutes or longer while they boil the kettle and wait for the bottle to warm. If you decide to warm your baby's formula using a microwave, exercise **extreme caution**. Shake or swirl the formula well and let it stand for a minute, then shake or swirl again before testing. **Do not put the nipple or nipple ring in the microwave**, as these could heat up and burn your baby's mouth. Be aware that **heating baby formula in this way can destroy probiotics** that may have been added to the PIF.
- **To test the temperature,** drip a little milk from the end of the nipple onto the inside of your wrist. You will know you have it right if you hardly notice the milk as it touches your skin. This means it's body temperature. If your baby is using a nipple with a crosscut, you might find the milk does not drip out the end like a nipple with a hole does.

Cooling overheated milk

We have all done it at some point. We got distracted and left the bottle warming for too long, and now the milk is too hot to give to baby. The quickest way to cool it down is to run cold water from the faucet over the outside of the bottle. Shake the bottle frequently. The next fastest is to sit the bottle in a container of cold water.

Storing formula

When storing baby formula, you need to be careful. Don't risk bacteria growing in the milk or formula powder and making your baby sick.

Prepared formula

The temperature of the milk affects safety. The temperature range between 41 degrees Fahrenheit (41°F) or five degrees Celsius (5°C) and 140°F (60°C) is known as the "temperature danger zone."[121] Bacteria will grow rapidly in this range, doubling in number in as little as 20 minutes. Prepared formula has a very short shelf life outside the refrigerator.

Table 12.2: When to discard prepared formula

Stored in ...	Discard after ...
Refrigerator (in the back, not door)	24 hours
Warmed	1 hour
Room temperature	2 hours if unused 1 hour if used
Insulated cooler —with ice packs —without ice packs	2 hours 1 hour—sooner if cooler is left in a hot car

Previously boiled water

If not using fresh water from the faucet, you can add cooled, previously boiled water into sterilized bottles and store them sealed with a nipple ring and cap in the back of the refrigerator until needed. Use these bottles within 24 hours.

Powdered formula

Avoid extreme temperatures when storing powdered formula. Keep the opened can of formula in a cool, dry place with the lid securely in place. Don't store it in the refrigerator because the humidity can cause the powder to clump. Cans of infant formula generally have a one-month shelf life after being opened. Check the date on the can to ensure the formula has not passed its use-by date.

Traveling with formula

When you and your baby are out and about, you need to take extra care with his formula. Without access to a refrigerator, the risk of spoiling is increased, but it can be minimized with some planning. Here are your options.

- **Prepared formula.** Prepared formula is unsafe after two hours at room temperature and less in a warm environment. If you place the bottles in an insulated bag with an ice pack, the prepared formula is safe for consumption for approximately two hours after removal from the refrigerator. It will just need to be safely heated up.

- **Separate components.** Keep the water and powder separate until your baby needs a feed. Measure the required number of scoops for a single feed into a formula dispenser. Carry the required volume of cooled boiled water in the bottle. When your baby is ready to feed, add the powder to the water and shake or stir. This means you don't need to carry ice packs, and if your baby drinks milk at room temperature, you won't need to heat it. If your baby prefers warmed formula, you can heat the water only and carry it in an insulated bag until required.
- **Ready-to-feed.** You can switch between forms of the same formula type, for example, PIF for everyday use and ready-to-feed for convenience when traveling. No refrigeration is necessary. But keep it in a cool place until ready for use.

Concentrated formula

Chapter 11 describes the ways calories and nutrients in baby formula might be **deliberately** increased and the associated advantages and disadvantages.

How accidental concentration occurs

Errors in preparation could mean you are **accidentally and unknowingly** increasing the concentration of your baby's formula. Some ways this occurs include

- **adding PIF to the bottle before adding water.** Most formula manufacturers recommend adding water first, then PIF. Adding PIF first can decrease the total water volume of the baby's feed by around one-ninth, which in turn increases the calorie content by approximately 10 percent.
- **compressing PIF in the scoop.** Most formula companies recommend "unpacked" scoops. Compressing the powder by pushing the powder into the scoop can increase the calorie concentration by around one-sixth or more. So instead of it being 20 calories per ounce, it's now around 23.3 calories per ounce. **Note:** A tiny number of formula companies recommend packed scoops, so read the instructions and follow them carefully.
- **overfilling the scoop**. The scoop should not be overfilled. Removing the mound of formula on the top of the scoop by pushing the excess off with a knife prevents overfilling.

- **using a scoop meant for a different brand.** Scoop size varies between brands. If you're using a larger scoop meant for a different formula, you might accidentally concentrate your baby's formula.

If you're tempted to deliberately add extra PIF to your baby's bottles, carefully weigh up the hoped-for benefits against potential risks (see chapter 11).

Diluted formula

Adding extra water or insufficient scoops of PIF to the volume of water recommended by the manufacturer can mean you are providing diluted or watered-down formula.

When a baby receives diluted formula, it's usually because the parent has **accidentally and unknowingly** made mistakes during preparation. It's easier than you might think. You might accidentally

- omit reading the preparation instructions when switching formula brands;
- use the wrong scoop;
- lose count and add fewer scoops of PIF than recommended;
- not fill the scoop; or
- not accurately measure the water.

Sometimes parents might **knowingly dilute** their baby's formula, unaware of the risk of serious harm that this can cause. Here are a few examples.

- Chelsea watered down her baby's formula because she thought the formula was too strong for him, and that made him "colicky."
- Lindsay suspected her baby was overfeeding. She had already tried restricting the volume she offered, but he was not happy when she did this, so she added extra water (diluting the formula) to help make him feel full.
- Georgia progressively watered down her three-month-old baby's nighttime bottles in the hope of encouraging him to stop waking to demand feeds during the night.
- Francis ran out of money to buy more formula and diluted it to make it last until she could afford to buy more.

The formula strength is not the reason for colic, and it's not a solution to overfeeding. If you cannot afford infant formula, consult with your baby's healthcare professional. A number of programs provide free or subsidized infant formula for families under financial strain.

Problems linked to diluted formula

Diluting formula or breast milk, whether accidentally or intentionally, can cause underfeeding and the risk of water intoxication. An underfed baby does not receive the number of nutrients, vitamins, minerals, and essential electrolytes that he needs for his growth and energy.

Insufficient calories and nutrients

While diluted milk might fill a baby's stomach, it will not provide the sense of satisfaction that occurs when receiving regular strength formula or breast milk. A healthy baby will let you know if he's hungry. Upon receiving diluted milk, he might fuss as soon as, or shortly after, the feed has ended. If denied sufficient nourishment, he will be fussy, demand attention, and have difficulty falling and staying asleep. His growth may stagnate, or he could gain very little or possibly lose weight.

A severely undernourished baby will be undemanding and sleep excessively as his body tries to reserve energy.

Water intoxication

We all need water, so it's hard to believe that it could cause a baby harm. However, drinking too much water is potentially harmful.

Water intoxication is rare. When it does occur, it's the result of the baby drinking too much water, typically when a baby drinks large volumes of water.

Overconsumption of water without the right balance of electrolytes causes dangerously low levels of sodium in the blood. Low sodium can affect brain activity. Water intoxication can result in seizures, brain damage, coma, or death.

Breast milk or formula is all babies under the age of six months need for hydration. They don't need additional water until they start eating solid foods.

Never water down your baby's breast milk or infant formula. Only give additional water to a baby less than six months of age if instructed to do so by your baby's healthcare professional. When a baby is ill and refusing to drink milk, you might be advised to give him fluids that contain electrolytes.

Next

Next, we're going to look at how to best avoid food poisoning. Though no one sets out to provide contaminated milk for their baby, it does happen, but it can be easily avoided in a few simple steps.

13 Food Poisoning Prevention

HOW FOOD POISONING OCCURS • HOW TO PREVENT FOOD POISONING • WATER QUALITY

Food poisoning is a type of gastroenteritis. We all recognize that food can be contaminated with harmful microorganisms (bacteria, viruses, parasites, protozoa) and cause food poisoning. You may have personally experienced food poisoning at some point and can fully appreciate how bad it makes you feel. However, you may not be aware that it's possible for a baby's milk to become contaminated and cause food poisoning.

There are steps you can take to protect your baby from suffering food poisoning.

Symptoms

The symptoms of food poisoning vary in severity. They include

- vomiting;
- diarrhea;
- fever;
- nausea—demonstrated by baby not wanting to eat;
- tummy cramps;
- diaper rash—a scalded little bottom from acidic stools;
- irritability; and
- sleep disturbance.

The symptoms associated with food poisoning can develop within one to 24 hours of consuming spoiled food. In most cases of food poisoning, the symptoms are fleeting and cause no serious harm to healthy babies. Provided the baby is no longer exposed to contaminated milk, food or water, symptoms generally resolve in a day or two. However, if the baby is repeatedly exposed, symptoms will continue and could negatively impact her health, growth, and development. **In rare cases**, severe complications such as dehydration, coma, and death can occur without medical treatment. Any unusual gastrointestinal (GI) symptoms, such as vomiting or diarrhea, require a medical assessment.

Serious complications resulting in death are rare in Western societies where clean water is available, hygiene practices are generally good, and high-quality medical treatment is easily accessible. However, hundreds of thousands of bottle-fed babies in developing countries die every year as a result of food poisoning from contaminated milk, usually caused by unclean water, poor hygiene, and the absence of refrigeration and medical care.

The severity of symptoms, the speed at which food poisoning develops, and the duration of symptoms depends on a number of things, such as:

1. **the type and the number of bacteria ingested.** There are bad microorganisms and really nasty ones, like salmonella, which is particularly dangerous and multiplies quickly.
2. **the efficiency of your baby's immune system.** The younger your baby, the more immature his immune system.

Who is at risk?

We can all suffer from food poisoning. However, babies are especially vulnerable because their immune systems are not fully matured. Plus, they don't have as much stomach acid, which not only breaks down foods but can also kill germs. Their little bodies **cannot** destroy harmful microorganisms like our bodies can. As a general guide, the younger the baby, the more vulnerable he is, but other factors increase vulnerability. Babies under the age of two months, preterm and low weight babies, and babies with weakened immune systems are at the greatest risk.[122]

You don't need to be paranoid about your healthy baby experiencing food poisoning. Millions of babies worldwide are fed powdered infant formula (PIF) every day without any ill effects. But you do need to remain mindful of the possibility of food poisoning and take precautions.

How milk becomes contaminated

So how does a baby's milk—infant formula or pumped breast milk—become contaminated? Common reasons for babies to receive tainted milk include

- contamination during manufacture of PIF, but this is rare;
- insufficient cleaning of pumping or feeding equipment;
- inadequate handwashing when preparing baby's feed;
- improper or prolonged storage of PIF or pumped breast milk;
- reoffering unused milk leftover from one feed at the next feed; and
- contaminated water.

During manufacture

Unlike liquid concentrate and ready-to-feed infant formulas, PIF is not a sterile product. PIF contains many strains of bacteria at the point of sale.[123] Contamination by such bacteria is not usually associated with illness in healthy, full-term babies. However, in preterm or immunocompromised infants in neonatal units, there have been rare cases of serious illness and, occasionally, death.[124]

Hastily cleaned equipment

Remnants of milk can stick to the walls and crevices of the bottle and inside the nipple or pumping equipment following use. Rinsing with water, hot or otherwise, is not sufficient to remove this. Whether you sterilize pumping or bottle-feeding equipment or not, all surfaces in contact with the milk need to be thoroughly cleaned using dishwashing detergent and a bottle brush after use. Dishwashers can be used. Use a fresh bottle for every feed.

During the preparation process

Formula could become contaminated during the preparation process because of unwashed hands or unclean preparation area. So remember to

- wash your hands thoroughly using soap before preparing your baby's formula;
- wash the lid of the formula can before opening it for the first time, and
- avoid touching any pumping or feeding equipment with your hands as much as possible.

Improper storage

Microorganisms require three things to flourish: **moisture, food, and warmth.** A baby's bottle containing milk provides all three. Incorrect storage of baby formula and pumped breast milk is where the greatest risk of food contamination lies. Parents make errors about storage primarily because of a lack of awareness.

Microorganisms grow and multiply most rapidly in temperatures between 41°F (5°C) and 140°F (60°C). Basically, this means any temperature outside the refrigerator unless close to boiling. The longer **prepared formula** remains in this temperature range, the greater the number of bacteria within the milk. Here are some examples that could lead to food contamination:

- Ebony would prepare all of her baby's feeds for the day and leave them sitting on the counter, ready for use. She was not aware that room temperature was warm enough for the bacteria to grow rapidly in prepared formula.
- Gillian would place her baby's prepared bottle in a bottle warmer ready for nighttime feeds. The bottle could remain in the warmer for two to four hours before her baby woke to demand a feed. Leaving an electric bottle warmer on overnight may appear convenient since the bottle is already warm when your baby wakes, but it's just not worth the risk. This might cause bacteria to breed in the formula or breast milk, similar to leaving a bottle of milk in a hot car for hours.
- Sandra would carry her baby's prepared and prewarmed formula in an insulated bottle carrier when going out for the day. The bottles could be in this warm state for a number of hours before her baby was ready to eat.

While doing these things won't necessarily cause food poisoning, it's a little like playing Russian roulette with your baby's health.

It's generally recommended to make up the feed **directly before use**, preparing only one bottle at a time. For storage times for breast milk, see page 164.

Offering leftovers

Another way that babies suffer from food poisoning is when they are given leftover milk from a previous feed.

Leftover milk will contain bacteria from your baby's mouth. It may have already been warmed once and will potentially be rewarmed. This makes the perfect breeding ground for bacteria to flourish, which they can do very quickly. Here are examples.

- Alana's baby is fed expensive hypoallergenic formula. To avoid waste and save money, she refrigerates leftover formula and adds this to her baby's bottle at the next feed.
- Michaela hates to throw away pumped breast milk, so she keeps the leftover and reheats it at the next feed.

Contaminated water

Water contains microorganisms. Town water is treated to reduce the number. Most microorganisms cannot survive in very high temperatures, and so boiling water that was fresh from the faucet will further reduce the number of harmful microorganisms. (**Note:** A water temperature of over 158 degrees Fahrenheit or 70 degrees Celsius will also kill any bacteria present in the formula powder.)[125]

While boiling significantly reduces the number of bacteria, it does not sterilize the water. When water is left to sit at room temperature, bacteria in the water will multiply, but growth is limited with the absence of food. However, once you have added PIF, the rate of bacterial growth rapidly increases.

Water quality

When preparing infant formula, the water quality matters! Water quality and safety vary greatly depending on the source. Some water sources can be safe for an adult to drink but not for babies. Others are unfit for human consumption.

Table 13.1: Water safety according to source

Water source	Safety	Comments
Tap water	Safe in most developed countries	Your baby's doctor will be aware if town water supplies are safe to use for your baby's bottles. If you live in an old building, there may be lead in the pipes that can leach into the water. Run the faucet for one to two minutes before taking water for your baby's feeds. Use cold water, not hot water. Cold water picks up less of the lead than hot water. Boil for extra safety. According to the American Dental Association, it is safe to use fluoridated water to mix baby formula.[126]
Rain or tank water	Maybe	Tank and roof quality can affect the water quality. Be sure to have the water tested. If using tank water, it's recommended that it be boiled until your baby is 18 months old.
Well water	Maybe	Wells can contain toxins and microorganisms. Well water should be used with caution when mixing baby formula, and only after it has been tested and confirmed to be safe.
Bore water	Not safe	Bore water can contain minerals, heavy metals, pesticides, viruses, and protozoa that could make your baby very sick after short- or long-term exposure.
Nursery water	Safe	Nursery water is purified bottled water marketed for preparation of baby formula.
Springwater	Maybe	Springwater that has been purified is usually safe to use. However, it is advisable to boil it.
Mineral water	Not safe	Mineral water can contain dangerously high levels of calcium.
Sparkling water	Not suitable	Sparkling water and soda water are carbonated and may make your baby uncomfortable.
Filtered water	Safe	May require boiling. The filter needs to be changed regularly.

Purified or distilled water	Safe	Distilled water removes nasty chemicals but also removes beneficial minerals from the water. It's fine for use when preparing baby formula because baby formula contains essential minerals; however, it shouldn't be the only water a child drinks.
Softened water	Not safe	Softened water contains high levels of sodium and is not safe to be used for preparation of baby formula.
Electrolyte-enhanced water	Not safe	Infant formula contains the right balance of electrolytes. Electrolyte-enhanced water should not be **used to mix baby formula**. But it is safe to be given (without PIF) for hydration when a baby suffers from gastroenteritis. Consult with your baby's doctor for recommendations.

Be sure to discuss the water source you are using to prepare your baby's feeds with your baby's healthcare professional for confirmation regarding safety.

Does water need to be boiled?

The idea behind boiling is to minimize babies' exposure to bacteria present in water.

Whether water used for formula preparation needs to be boiled depends on the source, whether it's fresh or has been stored, plus your baby's age and state of health. Your baby's doctor will know about the water quality in your local area and your baby's history and will be the best person to advise you about whether you need to boil water or not.

If you have been advised to boil water before use, only boil for 60 seconds; prolonged boiling will increase the level of impurities due to evaporation.

Next

You have chosen the best milk you can for your baby. You have prepared it accurately and hygienically. The next step is to confirm that her feeding equipment enables her to freely access the milk at a pace that complements her sucking abilities. The next chapter describes what to look for in bottles and nipples and the tactics the equipment manufacturers use to get you to purchase their products.

Part D:
The Act of Feeding

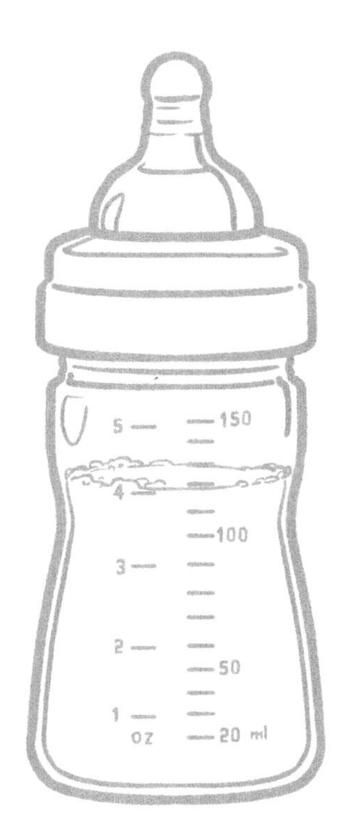

14 Nipples and Bottles

HOW TO TELL IF EQUIPMENT IS SUITABLE • PROS AND CONS OF DIFFERENT NIPPLES AND BOTTLES • ARE MANUFACTURER'S CLAIMS RELIABLE?

Bottles and nipples come in a confounding variety of sizes, shapes, materials, and features. Whether you're looking at equipment for the first time or are unsure about the choices you've already made, this chapter should help. I will describe the features of different nipples and bottles and the effect these may have on a baby's ability to feed effectively. Hopefully, you'll feel more confident about your choices by the end of the chapter.

Is baby's feeding equipment suitable?

The following checklist might help you to identify if your baby's feeding equipment enables him to freely access milk from a bottle at a pace he finds comfortable.

Equipment suitability checklist

- ☐ The duration of the feed is within the recommended timeframe (see page 184).
- ☐ Baby appears to be comfortable with the flow rate.
- ☐ Baby is drinking sufficient volumes of milk to support healthy growth.
- ☐ Baby makes minimal clicking sounds and does not gag or cough while he feeds.
- ☐ There are **no** bubbles flooding into the bottle **after** he releases suction. (Bubbles **while** feeding is okay.)

If you have checked all the boxes above, the equipment your baby is using is functioning well. If you left any boxes unticked, read the top five equipment problems described in chapter 23.

Nipples

The nipple is the most important piece of bottle-feeding equipment. When selecting a nipple for your baby, consider a number of features, such as

- flow rate;
- shaft length;
- material;
- cut; and
- shape.

I find that infant feeding problems are more likely to relate to the flow rate and the length of the nipple shaft than any other feature. However, some nipple features could provide an advantage depending on an individual baby's circumstances.

Flow rate

The size of the hole in the nipple determines how fast milk can be drawn from the bottle as the baby sucks. As a general guide, the younger the baby, the slower he needs to feed. Manufacturers usually provide a guide on different flow rates by labeling nipples as

- **Preterm:** for babies before reaching what was their expected date of birth.
- **Slow, Newborn, or Level 1:** for babies aged birth to three months.
- **Medium or Level 2:** for babies three to six months.
- **Fast or Level 3:** for babies over six months.
- **Level 4, X or Y cut***:* for babies over nine months or when a younger baby is given thickened feeds.

Consider the labeling as a **guide only.** Choosing a nipple recommended for your baby's age—adjusted age in the case of preterm babies—doesn't guarantee the nipple flow rate will be right for him. Babies of the same age vary in size, strength, sucking ability, and stamina, so it's possible that a flow rate that matches his age could be too fast or too slow for him.

Note: The length of the nipple increases along with the flow rate to accommodate the fact that a baby's face and mouth are getting bigger as he ages.

The speed at which your baby completes what might be considered a "full feed" for a baby of his age and weight will help you decide if the flow rate is suitable. Table 14.1 provides a guide on the average feeding time for healthy bottle-fed babies at different ages.

Table 14.1: Ideal feed duration

Birth–3 months	20–40 minutes
3–6 months	10–20 minutes
Over 6 months	5–10 minutes

If you think your baby may be feeding too slowly or too quickly, see chapter 23 for other potential reasons before switching your baby's nipples to a different flow rate.

Shaft length

The shaft is the part of the nipple that sits inside your baby's mouth, not the entire length of the nipple. Ideally, the tip of the nipple sits close to the junction of your baby's hard and soft palate while he's sucking. If the nipple shaft is too long it can cause gagging and vomiting. If too short it can cause clicking due to loss of suction.

Material

Nipples come in silicone and latex. Regardless of the type you choose, make sure you replace nipples regularly because they can become sticky or cracked with age. Let's look at the advantages and disadvantages of each type below.

Silicone

Silicone nipples—mostly clear but sometimes also colored—are usually quite stiff. Silicone is the most widely used material for nipples today because it's durable and relatively long lasting.

Latex (rubber)

Latex nipples are usually brown in color. Latex nipples are softer and cheaper than silicone nipples, but they are also harder to find. Being softer, latex nipples may be helpful for a baby with a weak suck. In rare cases, babies can be allergic to latex.

Latex doesn't last as long as silicone, especially if you use sterilization methods that involve heat. Using a chemical sterilization method will maintain latex nipples longer.

Cut

The cut is the opening at the end of the nipple through which the baby sucks and draws fluids from the bottle. The type and size of the cut affect the flow rate.

Single hole

Most nipples have a **single hole** at the tip or slightly offset in the case of orthodontic nipples. The hole of an orthodontic nipple needs to be **facing toward the roof** of the baby's mouth and **not** his tongue.

Sometimes, the hole can become clogged by a clump of poorly dissolved formula powder. It's a good idea to check just prior to feeding by holding the bottle upside down when it's filled with milk. The milk should drip steadily through the hole in the nipple. If not, it could be clogged.

X and Y cut

X and Y cut nipples are mostly used for thickened feeds. With these types of nipples, the edges of the cut can stick together. Before feeding your baby and with freshly washed hands, try squeezing the nipple tip open to make sure the edges are not sticking together.

If you are thickening your baby's milk because he often spits up, check that he's not feeding too quickly (see page 184) or overfeeding (see chapter 25).

Variable flow

Variable flow nipples allow you to adjust the flow rate by turning the bottle. These might be worth trying if you have a baby who sucks vigorously at the start of the feed but then slows down as the feed progresses. You could slow him down a little at the start of the feed and then turn the bottle—which changes the flow rate—to make sucking easier as he becomes more relaxed or tires.

Sucking vigorously at the start of the feed can occur if a baby becomes ravenous. If this is occurring because you're trying to stick to a rigid feeding schedule, consider a semi-demand feeding pattern instead, which allows for more flexibility. (See chapter 2 for more on when to feed a baby.)

Shape

The shape, and in particular, slope, are important features when choosing a nipple. The **slope** is the angle from tip to base. As you can see from the illustrations to follow, the slope varies depending on the shape of the nipple. Both affect a baby's gape. **Gape** means how wide your baby needs to open his mouth to accommodate the nipple.

The most common nipple shapes include

- narrow-based;
- medium-wide-based;
- wide-based; and
- orthodontic.

Narrow-based

Also called narrow-necked nipples, narrow-based nipples have a bell shape. An advantage of this nipple shape is that the shaft is usually a good length. Narrow-based nipples encourage a narrow gape, which is okay for an exclusively bottle-fed baby. However, this could be a disadvantage for a breastfed baby who occasionally bottle-feeds, as it might encourage the baby to use a narrow gape when latching to his mother's breast, resulting in a poor latch and poor milk transfer when breastfeeding. Best to be on the safe side and steer clear of these if your baby also breastfeeds.

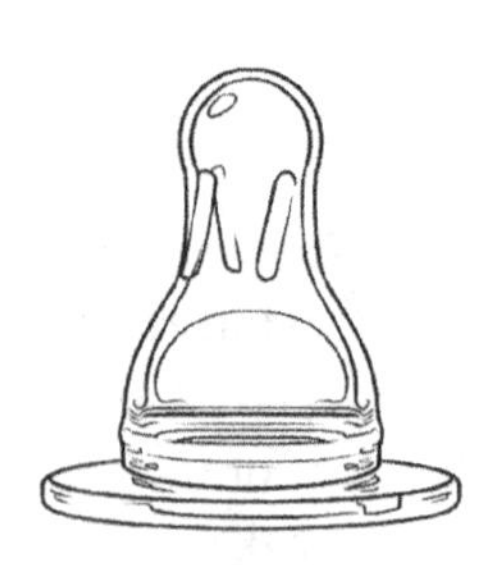

Medium-wide-based

A medium-wide-based nipple encourages a wide gape without baby slipping to the tip. If you are bottle-feeding a breastfed baby, I recommend a nipple with a medium-wide base.

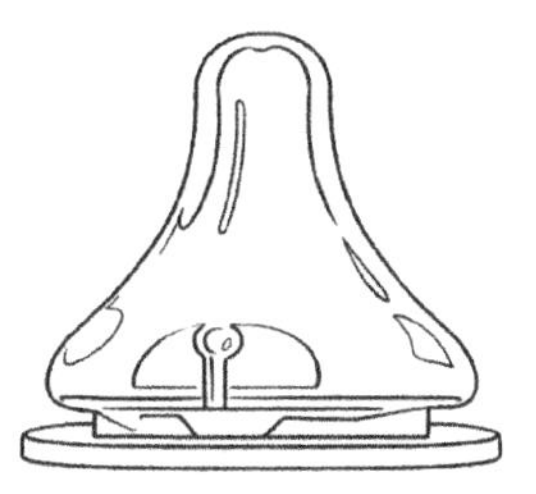

Wide-based

Wide-based nipples have a domed appearance. While the base is wide, the shaft of the nipple is short and narrow.

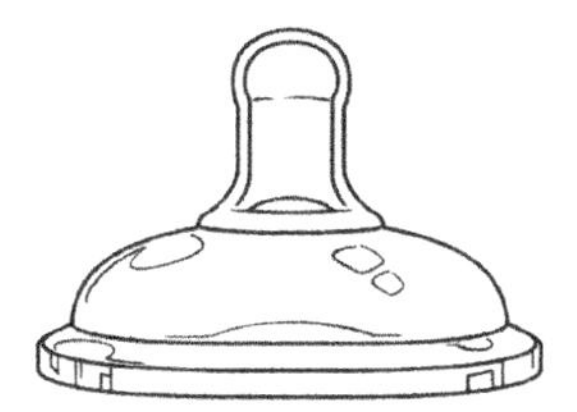

Wide-based nipples are my least favorite of all nipples because a baby can only suck from the small protruding part at the end. The shape of these nipples encourages a narrow gape, and the shaft can be too short for many babies, resulting in clicking caused by loss of suction. However, many babies feed just fine with these nipples. If you feel your baby is feeding well while using wide-based nipples, I don't recommend you change.

Orthodontic

Orthodontic nipples are wide at the tip and base and narrow in the middle. These were designed to fill the baby's mouth in a similar way as a mother's nipple does when a baby breastfeeds. However, no bottle nipple can enable a baby to feed in exactly the same way as he would while breastfeeding. Some babies—exclusively bottle-fed or otherwise—may prefer the shape of these nipples while bottle-feeding.

Bottles

Baby bottles are available in many materials, shapes, designs, colors, features, and functionality. Often, they come with a price tag to match how pretty or expensive they appear or how many features are proclaimed by the manufacturer. Let's look at the main features of bottles on the market today.

Materials

Bottles come in various materials, including

- plastic;
- glass;
- silicone; and
- stainless steel.

Plastic

Hard plastic bottles are the most popular. They are cheap to produce as well as lightweight and unbreakable. This can be an advantage over glass bottles if your baby tries to hold the bottle around six months of age or wants to feed independently from around eight months of age.

A number of years ago, concerns were raised about chemicals used in the manufacture of plastics, in particular bisphenol-A (BPA), and the effect this could have on babies. However, most infant feeding bottles sold today are "BPA-free." This will be clearly displayed on the packaging.

A 2020 study[127] reported that bottles made from a very common plastic called polypropylene sheds millions of tiny, microscopic plastic particles into the milk, which the baby can then ingest. Sterilization methods that involve heat increase microplastic release.[128] The effect of this on babies' health is not yet known.

You can significantly reduce the number of microparticles by rinsing the inside of the bottle with cooled, previously boiled water before preparing your baby's feed, not shaking the bottle while the milk is inside, and not reheating your baby's formula.[129]

Plastic bottles deteriorate over time, so throw them out if you notice the plastic turning cloudy.

Glass

Glass bottles are long-lasting, but they are heavy and breakable. Several companies make silicone or hard plastic sleeves to slip over glass bottles to lower the potential for breakage if dropped. Glass bottles are more expensive than plastic bottles. Parents who prefer eco-friendly products or who are concerned about chemicals in plastics often choose glass.

Silicone

Silicone bottles are soft and squeezable, which enables a parent to use **positive pressure** to gently squeeze milk into their baby's mouth, as opposed to negative pressure when a baby sucks milk from a bottle.

Soft silicone bottles could be helpful for babies who have a weak suck or who tire easily because of cardiac or lung conditions, or who for various medical reasons might benefit from positive pressure while bottle-feeding. Some "special feeder" bottles for babies with cleft palate are also silicone, soft-sided bottles.

However, in the case of normal healthy babies who are strong and capable of sucking from a bottle, any benefit gained from positive pressure is questionable. Positive pressure undoubtedly makes it easier for a healthy baby to suck. But "easier" may prevent him from gaining the benefit of building facial muscle strength to prepare for eating solid foods and for speech development, as occurs when using negative pressure feeding.

A silicone bottle makes it easy for a parent to squeeze milk into an unwilling baby's mouth, meaning it gives the parent greater control to decide how much milk their baby receives ... which is not a good thing in the case of healthy babies. A silicone bottle could increase the risk of overfeeding in the case of newborns who have a limited ability to self-regulate their milk intake. Squeezing milk into the mouth of an unwilling baby to control how much he eats can cause a feeding aversion.

It takes longer to warm the milk using silicone bottles compared to other bottles.

Stainless steel

Stainless steel bottles don't contain any plastic and are lighter than glass bottles. They are the least popular because it's not easy to tell how much the baby is drinking.

Given that from a biological perspective, parents are not meant to decide how much their baby drinks—as is the case for breastfed babies—not being able to see how much your baby has consumed—and instead being guided by his behavioral cues, stopping when he shows signs of satisfaction—could be a good thing if you have become obsessed with numbers and have a strong urge to control how much your baby drinks.

Size

Baby bottles are available in two sizes: 4 ounces (120 milliliters) and 8 ounces (240 milliliters). Most babies will require the larger size by three to four months of age or sooner. If your baby is large at birth, you might choose to purchase the 8-ounce bottles only. Alternatively, if your baby is tiny compared to other babies of his age, or if he is given high-energy feeds and hence volumes will be lower, you might find he will use the 4-ounce bottles for longer than four months.

Shape, design, and features

The crazy number of features of bottles on the market these days means I can't possibly describe them all. Quite frankly, most additional features are merely gimmicks that manufacturers include to try to make a point of difference to gain an advantage over their competitors. The main bottle types include

- standard;
- wide-necked;
- angled;
- shaped;
- hands-free;
- bottles with disposable liners;
- heat-sensitive;
- self-sterilizing; and
- bottle sets.

Standard bottles

Standard bottles are narrow and cylindrical. They are often the cheapest and most commonly used of all infant feeding bottles. You can buy these plain, colored, or decorated.

Wide-necked bottles

Wide-necked bottles make it easier to get powdered formula into the bottle. However, you will be restricted to using a matching wide-based nipple, which is often bell-shaped with a narrow, short shaft.

Angled bottles

Angled bottles have a bend in the bottle. You might find these helpful if your baby insists on feeding while sitting upright because the bend makes it easier to keep milk in the nipple.

Shaped bottles

Plastic can be molded into many different shapes. Some bottles are designed for the baby to hold. A disadvantage is that they can be difficult to clean with a bottle brush.

Hands-free bottles

Hands-free bottles allow a baby to feed in an upright position without your baby or you holding the bottle. These have a long, flexible, silicone straw that links the nipple, which is held in the baby's mouth by suction, to the bottle, which might be sitting in the baby's lap. Baby needs to maintain suction to keep the milk in the straw. As soon as he releases the suction, the milk will fall back into the bottle. These bottles don't support an emotional attachment, which occurs when a parent holds and engages with their baby while feeding.

Bottles with disposable liners

Bottles with disposable liners are generally designed for babies who are bottle-fed breast milk. The mother pumps the milk, which is then stored in the presterilized disposable liner. When ready to use, the liner containing pumped breast milk is then warmed and placed inside a specially designed bottle. These bottles don't have vacuum problems (described on pages 301-306) because the disposable inner liner collapses as the baby feeds.

Heat-sensitive bottles

Heat-sensitive bottles have a built-in temperature sensor that changes color if the milk is too hot.

Self-sterilizing bottles

Self-sterilizing bottles enable you to sterilize the bottle individually. You simply pour water into the base and microwave for three minutes to sterilize. You can drop your baby's pacifier into the bottle to sterilize it at the same time.

Bottle sets

Bottle sets have additional attachments such as handles and trainer spouts. The handles can be helpful when a baby starts to self-feed. Trainer cups with a spout are **not** generally recommended (see pages 395-396 for reasons).

Bottle handles

You can purchase handles that can be attached to the bottle when your baby starts to show signs of wanting to hold his bottle and self-feed.

"Special-feeder" bottle systems

Specialized feeding nipples and bottles are available for premature infants or babies with oral or facial problems, like cleft lip or palate, which affect their ability to suck. These are sometimes recommended for babies with weak suck. A speech-language pathologist (SLP) will be the best person to advise you on suitable options if your baby requires specialized feeding equipment.

Avoid switching equipment unnecessarily

Babies are creatures of habit. They are comforted by familiarity. Each nipple style will feel different in your baby's mouth, and the flow rate can vary between brands. Once you have decided on a suitable nipple, use the same style for every feed to avoid frustrating your baby by repeatedly switching between nipples of different shapes.

Of course, sometimes you genuinely need to change a baby's feeding equipment—for example, if you discover that the equipment you originally purchased is not suitable for your baby.

You might be tempted to switch equipment if your baby is experiencing a feeding problem. I encourage you to be sure the equipment is responsible before switching. If your decision to switch is based on a vague hope that different equipment might help—without evidence that the equipment is causing or contributing to feeding difficulties—you could make the situation worse by frustrating your baby with unfamiliar feeding equipment. (Chapter 23 describes the top feeding equipment problems, how to recognize these, and what to do to remedy the situation.)

Be wary of advertised benefits

Beware of advertisements claiming that bottle-feeding equipment can prevent swallowed air or solve problems such as colic or reflux, or that it's just like a mother's nipple or provides other advantages. Companies that produce feeding equipment often make promises that their product can fix all sorts of problems. Never forget that this is a multimillion-dollar industry, and rarely do such claims stack up. Let's consider the major claims now.

Vacuum-free feeding

Vented nipples and bottles prevent a vacuum from forming in the bottle and ensure constant and consistent milk flow—provided they are assembled and functioning correctly. Such equipment is not fail-proof. Vacuum problems can still occur with vented feeding equipment (see pages 301-306 for reasons).

Anti-colic valves

Advertisements claim that their "proven," "unique anti-colic valve system," "advanced technology," or "award-winning design" will protect babies from colic—inconsolable crying that is often **assumed** to be caused by swallowed air—by "redirecting air away from the baby's mouth and tummy" and thus preventing the baby from swallowing air while feeding.

Such features are more hype than help. I explain why in the following pages and chapters.

- Page 303 explains why such equipment is not necessary.
- Pages 233-234 explains why babies swallow air and what happens to swallowed air that's not burped up.
- The chapters in Part F describe common reasons for infant feeding and sleeping problems that cause healthy babies to cry for prolonged periods.

Mimics a mother's nipple

The majority of bottle-fed babies start out breastfeeding. The percentage drops considerably during the first three months and continues to drop after that time. Most women experience feelings of guilt and worry that their baby might not develop a secure emotional attachment if not breastfed. Others find it difficult to get their breastfed baby to feed from a bottle (reasons are described on pages 253-257). And so, claims that a synthetic nipple can imitate breastfeeding would understandably be very appealing.

Some companies claim the nipple they produce mimics the shape, feel, and movement of a mother's nipple. They're implying that a nipple that looks similar to mother's will be more readily accepted by the baby or will work with the baby's natural feeding instincts, which are attuned to breastfeeding. Three features that are claimed to replicate the actions used when breastfeeding include

- the shape of a mother's nipple;
- peristaltic action; and
- positive pressure.

I will explain why these don't provide the benefits claimed.

Shape of a mother's nipple

Wide-based nipples are often claimed to be "like a mother's nipple." While some might **vaguely** resemble the shape of a mother's breast and nipple, the similarity stops there. A breastfed baby does not "nipple feed," he "breastfeeds," meaning he doesn't latch on only to the nipple but also places most of the areola (the colored part around the nipple) into his mouth. Once the baby draws his mother's nipple into his mouth, the shape is completely changed and not even remotely similar to the shape of a synthetic nipple.

Peristaltic action

Companies that produce peristaltic nipples claim the subtle movement that occurs replicates the movement of a mother's nipple as a baby breastfeeds. But they don't! No matter how flexible a silicone nipple is, it will not extend two to three times its length like a mother's nipple does while her baby breastfeeds.

Positive pressure

Some companies claim their silicone bottles can mimic the positive pressure that occurs when a baby breastfeeds due to milk ejection reflex (let-down). Squeezing milk into a baby's mouth using silicone bottles doesn't imitate the pressure achieved as a baby's tongue moves in a wave-like action while breastfeeding. First, the milk ducts below the mother's nipple are compressed as the baby's tongue rises, and he receives milk through positive pressure. Then his tongue lowers and creates negative pressure. In other words, the baby controls when positive pressure is applied and not the mother.

While babies don't know much, a breastfed baby knows what his mother's breast and nipple looks, feels, and smells like and how it responds while he feeds. He will not be fooled by the nipple-like shape, the flesh-color tone, the feel of "skin-like" silicone, or peristaltic movement of a synthetic nipple. Therefore, if you were hoping that a nipple that's "like Mom's" might

- resolve a bottle-feeding problem;
- encourage an unwilling breast-feeder to accept bottle-feeds;
- prevent "nipple confusion" (where a baby tries to use a bottle sucking motion while breastfeeding but is unable to feed as a result);
- prevent "bottle preference" (where a baby starts to favor bottle-feeding and refuses breastfeeds); or enhance bonding, you will be disappointed.

How you manage your baby's feeds—breastfeeding and bottle-feeding—is what minimizes the risk of problems and enhances bonding, **not** the shape and functionality of a synthetic nipple. If you want to learn more about ways to encourage a breastfed baby to bottle-feed, see chapter 19.

By all means, buy a particular bottle or nipple if you like the look of it and can afford it and it works well for your baby. But just be aware that the benefits spouted by companies that produce, market, and sell baby feeding equipment are often not proven.

More expensive doesn't necessarily mean better.
It may simply be the company has a bigger marketing budget.

If you suspect your baby is having issues with the equipment

First, check out the top equipment problems described in chapter 23. But also confirm that you're fulfilling other responsibilities when feeding your baby, in particular the way you position him for feeds (chapter 15), and that you're providing an appropriate response to his feeding cues (chapter 16).

Next

Now that you have chosen suitable feeding equipment, the next step is to learn what constitutes good and poor positioning while feeding a baby.

15 Safe and Unsafe Feeding Positions

HELPFUL AND UNHELPFUL FEEDING POSITIONS • HOW YOU MIGHT UNKNOWINGLY MAKE IT HARDER FOR YOUR BABY TO FEED EFFECTIVELY

The way you position your baby for feeds and the angle at which you hold the bottle might seem like small and insignificant details. However, the smallest details often make the biggest difference. Good positioning will support optimal feeding. Poor positioning can be responsible for poor feeding. Some feeding positions can make feeding difficult or frustrating for babies. Many infant feeding problems can be traced back to poor feeding positioning.

Why is positioning important?

The act of feeding requires complex sequential and coordinated contractions of numerous muscles that allow sucking, swallowing, and breathing. Infant feeding reflexes, such as sucking, swallowing, and others that protect your baby's airways while swallowing, will help her physically achieve these actions. However, her sucking abilities will be affected by her head, body, and bottle positions. As a completely dependent little person, your baby is reliant on you to hold her and the bottle in ways that enable her to suck effectively and feed comfortably and safely.

By "positioning," I am not simply referring to whether your baby is held upright, in a cradle, or in side-lying positions. Positioning includes various aspects such as the alignment and angle of your baby's body, her head, and the bottle position.

An optimal feeding position—which is one that complements an **individual** baby's anatomical and physical characteristics, sucking ability, and stage of development—is the foundation to problem-free feeding. It enables a good latch, physical comfort, efficient sucking, minimal disruption of breathing, ease of milk transfer from bottle to baby, and a satisfied baby.

"Poor" positioning—includes any position—there are many—that is contrary to a baby's physical attributes and capabilities, thus hindering her ability to achieve or maintain a good latch, suction, or synchronize sucking, swallowing, and breathing.

Let's look at signs that indicate good and poor positioning.

What to look for

Optimal positioning for feeding is important for all babies. What this looks like varies. The anatomical structure and physical strength of preterm babies are different from those of full term babies, which differ again from three- and six-month-old babies. Older babies are stronger and may adjust their own body position, whereas newborns are weak and have limited ability to move independently and change position.

No single body position for feeding would match the needs of all babies. However, certain key aspects of optimal feeding don't change, and these include

- head position in relation to the baby's body;
- bottle position in relation to the baby's face and mouth;
- body position;
- elevation of the baby's body;
- your comfort.

According to the American Academy of Pediatrics, "breastfeeding and human milk are the normative standards for infant feeding and nutrition."[130]

This is all well and good, but it's simply not possible to exactly replicate the positioning of a breastfeeding baby. The movements for breast- and bottle-feeding appear similar, but differences exist between these feeding methods. However, we can still try to mimic the breastfeeding experience as closely as possible.

Head position

Your baby's head position has a significant effect on her sucking abilities. As a newborn, your baby can't support the weight of her head, and she's not capable of deliberately changing her head or body position until around two months of age. Even then, her voluntary movements are limited, so you need to be mindful of her head position.

The structures within your baby's mouth, the movement of her tongue, jaw, and facial muscles are affected by her head position.

To appreciate how it might feel for a baby to feed in different head positions, try the head tilting exercise below.

Head tilting exercise

Take a sip of water, but don't swallow yet. Turn your head toward one shoulder. Now swallow. Take another sip, tuck your chin into your chest, and swallow. Take another sip. This time, tilt your head so you are looking at the ceiling, and swallow. Last, with your head in line with your body and your head in a neutral or "sniffing" position, swallow.

You will notice how much easier it is to swallow when your head faces forward in a neutral or "sniffing" position. Your baby is not a miniature adult. Her head is large and heavy in relation to her body. Her head is rounded at the back ... or should be—if it's flat, discuss this with her doctor. Her tongue is relatively large for her mouth. Her neck is short. Her larynx (voice box or vocal cords) sits higher in her neck. As difficult as you might find drinking with your head flexed forward, extended back, or twisted to the side, your baby would find it **much** harder.

Next, I will describe what happens to the structures within your baby's mouth when her head is in a neutral, flexed, and extended head position.

Note: The illustrations provided are not anatomically exact. They're included to provide a visual example of how different head positions affect the shape and position of a baby's tongue.

Neutral head position

A neutral head position, where your baby's neck is in a natural alignment with her spine, helps her to control her jaw, cheeks, lips, and tongue movements.

A neutral head position for a baby requires support at the back of her neck and upper shoulders. Typically, this would occur as your baby's neck and upper shoulders—but **not** the back of her head—rest on your forearm while held in a cradle position. But it can also be achieved in other ways.

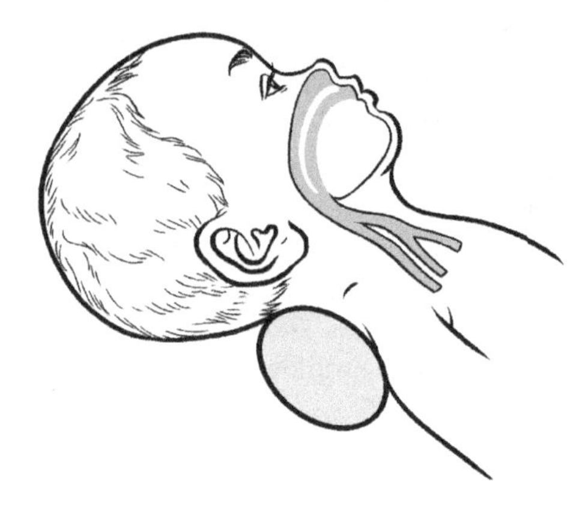

When your baby's head is in a neutral position, her tongue is forward and down, allowing her to comfortably "cup" the nipple with her tongue.

There should be no restraint on the movement of your baby's head to maintain her head in this position. If she's turning away, she might be

- signaling that she wants to stop, perhaps to burp or poop or because she has had enough;
- more comfortable with her head turned to the side, possibly from torticollis—a tightening of the muscles on one side of the neck. If she sleeps with her head turned to the same side, discuss this with her doctor;
- averting eye contact because of overstimulation or because she has developed a feeding aversion; or
- distracted.

Head flexion when feeding flat

If the back of your baby's head rests on a firm surface, this will cause her upper shoulders to move back, her neck to flex, her head to be pushed forward where her chin drops toward her chest (called **chin down position**). Her tongue then falls back, and her facial muscles tighten, restricting movement.

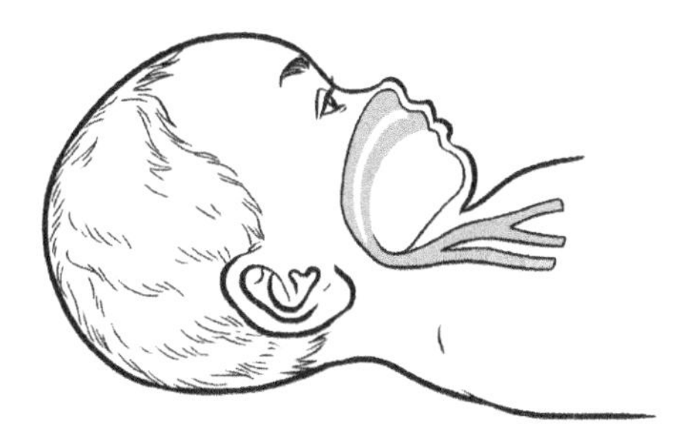

Lying a baby flat on her back is recommended for sleeping, but it's not ideal for feeding.

"Flat" does not necessarily mean horizontal. A baby's head could be in a flexed position on a flat or relatively flat surface and yet be elevated or semi-elevated. For example, this could mean feeding upright and facing out with her back and head resting against your chest or shoulder or feeding in a semi-elevated position while facing you with her back and head resting on your legs.

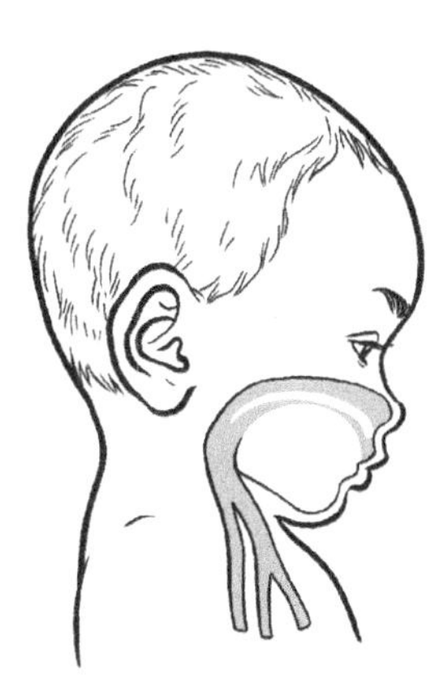

While safer than feeding flat, an upright flexed head position causes the same chin down position, but now the baby's tongue falls forward and "bunches" in her mouth, restricting the movement of her facial muscles and sucking abilities.

Head flexion in a curled feeding position

More extreme head flexion occurs if a baby's head is pushed forward as a result of a pillow **behind her head**. Or when her head and body are curled into a C shape as a result of being fed in a baby rocker or swing. Or if she's curled while being fed in arms with minimal back support and head pushed forward as a result of the back of her head resting on the parent's arm.

A head and body position in a C shape will push your baby's chin toward her chest, further bunching her tongue. This makes it even harder for shortened facial muscles to function and risks obstructing her airways while feeding.[131] (Airway obstruction is one reason a baby should not sleep with her head on a pillow.)

Very young babies, meaning those less than eight weeks of age, might not have the strength to compensate for the difficulties that a flexed head position causes while feeding. An older baby, two months or older, might try to compensate by turning her head to the side, which is also not optimal for sucking and swallowing.

Head extension

A baby's head is heavy. Even when she has the strength in her neck muscles to support her head when she's held upright—which is seldom before three months of age—she will not have the strength to support her head when lying at a 45-degree angle for as long as is required to complete a feed. As adults, we would struggle to hold our head in such a position for 10 to 40 minutes.

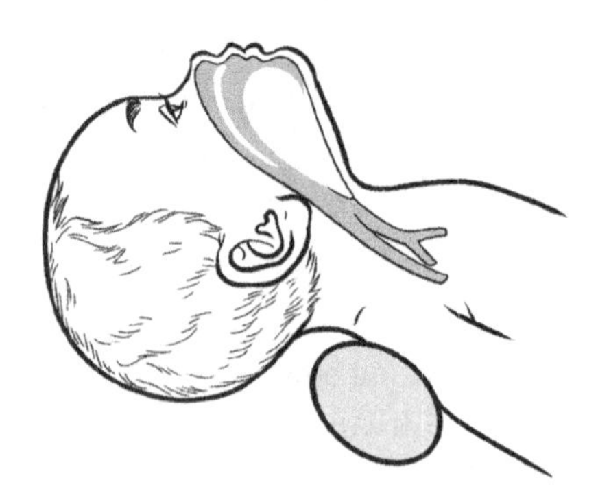

Without **appropriate** back, neck, and shoulder support, your baby's head will flop back and hyperextend her neck. This position elongates the muscles in her neck, causing tension in her shoulders, neck, jaw, and throat, changing the position of her jaw, and stretching her tongue, which is pulled back, restricting her airways. This will seriously inhibit her sucking abilities.

Head turned or falls to one side

Imagine what might be happening to the internal structures in your baby's mouth and throat if she tries to suck while her head is turned to one side. This will shorten the muscles on one side of her face and elongate the corresponding muscles on the other side, pulling her tongue off-center, making it harder for her to coordinate a synchronized suck, swallow, and breathe pattern and therefore feed effectively.

Similarly, this can also occur if your baby's head falls to one side because of a lack of appropriate support. This generally occurs when the parent's elbow is too low, resulting in the baby's back—rather than her neck and upper shoulders—resting on the parent's forearm, and usually occurs while feeding in arms, on the parent's lap, or as the parent stands.

Flexed, extended, and turned head positions make the task of feeding hard work for a baby. A poorly positioned baby can experience difficulty coordinating suck-swallow-breathe actions, is at risk of aspirating milk into her lungs, swallowing excessive air (aerophagia), consuming insufficient milk because of fatigue, and becoming frustrated or stressed while attempting to feed.

Bottle position

The angle at which you hold your baby's bottle is as important as your baby's head position because it also affects her ability to access the milk. The position of the bottle in relation to your baby's face will affect her latch and flow rate.

Latch

A baby's mouth has a wide U-shaped palate from side to side across the midline and a deeply cupped tongue when sucking. This supports the stability of her latch, facial muscles, suction, and sucking. With this in mind, let's now look at how the bottle position might support or hamper a baby from latching and sucking effectively.

For an optimal latch on the nipple, the bottle needs to be held at approximately a 90-degree angle to your baby's face.

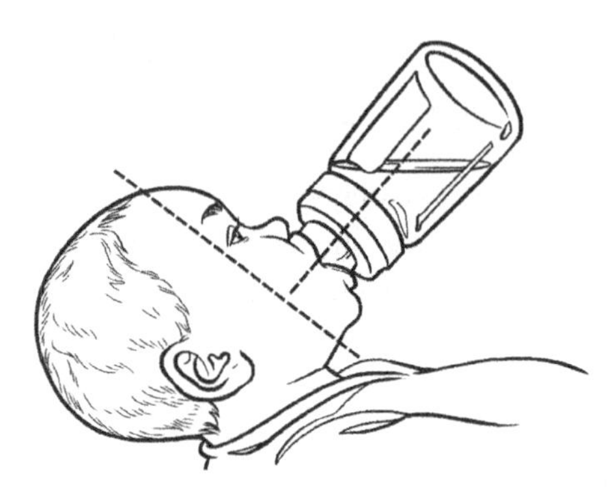

This angle means the nipple points to the back of her mouth, allowing the nipple to sit comfortably on her cupped tongue and be stabilized by the U shape of her palate.

- **If the bottle is held too low**, the nipple will press against the roof of her mouth and bottom jaw. Alternatively, your baby may be forced to drop her chin to her chest (flexed head position) in an attempt to compensate.
- **If the bottle is held too high,** the nipple will press on the back of her tongue and against her upper jaw. An older baby might push her body forward, tilting her head back (extended head position) so that she can maintain her latch.
- **If the bottle is held toward the side and not central in her mouth**—as can occur when a bottle-fed baby is fed in a side-lying position—the nipple then pushes toward one cheek.

Holding the bottle too high, too low, or to the side all make it harder for a baby to effectively latch, maintain suction, and suck effectively. These positions also increase the risk of swallowing air and gagging while feeding. Inappropriate positioning of the bottle in relation to the angle of the baby's face can also prevent a hungry baby from effectively latching and maintaining suction, causing frustration and fussy feeding behavior.

Flow rate

The elevation of the bottle will affect the flow rate. Milk flows fastest from a bottle that is held vertically (meaning pointing to the floor) and slowest when held horizontally (meaning parallel to the ground).

When the bottle is held horizontally, milk is less likely to drip into your baby's mouth, but the chance of the nipple containing air is greater.

Your choice of style and size of the hole in the nipple will have a more significant effect on flow rate compared to the angle of the bottle.

Elevation

While feeding, a baby could be held fully upright, semi-elevated, or flat. The option you choose will dictate the angle at which you hold the bottle. Table 15.1 explains.

Table 15.1: Bottle angle in relation to body elevation.

	Baby is held	**Bottle is held**
Fully upright	vertically	horizontally
Semi-elevated	at a 45 degree elevation	diagonally
Flat	horizontally	vertically

The effect of gravity on the rate of flow from the bottle has already been explained. Gravity also affects both the direction and rate of flow of milk **within your baby's body.**

Fully upright (vertical)

When your baby is held **vertically** while feeding,

- gravity aids swallowing;
- milk moves from her mouth to her stomach faster; and
- the backward flow (regurgitation or reflux) of milk from her stomach to her throat or mouth is less likely—except if she's in a slumped position.

Vertical feeding also reduces the risk of aspiration and ear infections.[132] If you hold your baby vertically, make sure you give her adequate support.

Otherwise, her head may fall into a flexed or extended position, and her torso can slump.

When the bottle is held **horizontally**,

- milk does not drip into the baby's mouth; and
- the flow rate is slowest.

If you've been advised to feed your baby upright, ensure the bottle is at a right angle to her face to enable her to latch and maintain suction and that there is milk in the nipple. There's an increased risk of air in the nipple with horizontal feeding, causing the baby to swallow air or fuss because she's not receiving milk.

An angled bottle might enable your baby to maintain an effective latch and suction while also ensuring there is milk in the nipple when feeding in an upright position.

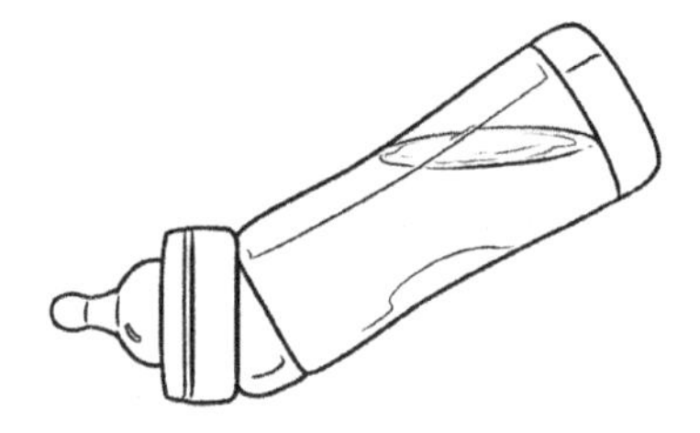

Flat (horizontal)

When your baby feeds in a **horizontal position**,

- her head will be in a flexed position;
- her swallowing is not aided by gravity;
- milk can pool in her mouth;
- movement of milk from her mouth to her stomach is slower;
- the risk of regurgitation of milk from her stomach to her throat or mouth is increased;
- it's more difficult for her to clear her airway by coughing when lying flat;
- milk can flow into her nose and Eustachian tubes and cause a middle ear infection; and

- there is an increased risk of aspiration,[133] and the risk of aspiration is even greater if she feeds unsupervised or is prop-fed (when the bottle is supported by something other than a person).[134]

When the bottle is held **vertically**,

- milk might drip into her mouth before she's ready to swallow;
- flow rate is fastest; and
- there's no risk of air in the nipple.

I advise parents to **avoid** laying their baby flat for feeding because of the risks of aspiration and ear infections.

Semi-elevated

When your baby is fed at a **semi-elevated angle**,

- her head and body can be supported in an optimal feeding position;
- gravity aids swallowing;
- milk moves from her mouth to her stomach faster;
- regurgitation of milk from her stomach to her mouth is less likely; and
- there's a reduced risk of aspiration and ear infections.[135]

When the bottle is held **at an angle**,

- milk can drip into the baby's mouth;
- flow rate is aided by gravity; and
- there's no risk of air in the nipple.

A semi-elevated angle provides the advantages associated with a fully upright position without the disadvantages related to feeding a baby upright or flat.

A semi-elevated feeding position—either while the baby lies on her back or on her side—is the most commonly recommended position, suitable for most babies.

Body position

A baby feeds with her whole body. While her mouth is the key player, the rest of her body, in particular arms, back, and hips, play a supportive role in enabling her to coordinate sucking, swallowing, and breathing while feeding. The position and movement of different body parts can have a flow-on effect on the stability of her head, ability to suck, and her comfort and hence patience while feeding.

Arms

Your baby's arms should be in a comfortable, relaxed position forward of her body with hands resting on or near the bottle. Don't try to make her hold her arms or hands in any particular position. If her shoulders or arms are **pushed forward or back** because of the way you're holding her—for example, her shoulders are pushed forward because you are holding her too tightly, or one shoulder is pushed back because one of her arms is tucked behind your back—this can cause tension in her shoulders, back, chest, neck, jaw, and throat that makes swallowing harder.

Should a baby be swaddled for feeds?

Preterm babies have an immature nervous system and are easily startled. Swaddling a preterm baby for feeding can provide an advantage by imitating a "womb-like" environment. While swaddling a preterm baby for feeds is developmentally appropriate before she reaches what should have been her expected date of birth, it may no longer be appropriate to swaddle her as she matures.

Post-term babies express themselves both vocally and through body movements. In chapter 6, I describe how babies demonstrate interest, acceptance, disinterest, rejection, and stress through their body movements while feeding. By restraining your baby's arms as she feeds, you are **severely** limiting her ability to express herself and communicate her wishes. In effect, you're silencing her, albeit unintentionally and unknowingly.

There should be **no restraint** on a post-term baby's arms when feeding.

- **No swaddling for feeds during the day.** Swaddling could make her feel restrained and frustrated. Or it could encourage her to fall asleep while feeding.
- **No tucking one of her arms behind your back.** When holding a breastfed baby in a cradle position, the baby's lower arm may be resting behind the mother's back. However, this position doesn't work for bottle-feeding. Doing so will cause the baby's body to partially turn toward yours, affecting the alignment of her body and head. This

may make it impossible to hold the bottle at the right angle without her turning her head to the side.

- **No holding her arms down.** If her arms are restrained down by her side, this may cause her body to stiffen and her hips to straighten. Not only will it frustrate her to be physically restrained, but it will also cause tension in her arms and other parts of her body, negatively affecting her sucking abilities.

I appreciate that this may be contrary to the advice you have received from health professionals previously. Many parents receive instructions on **parent-led feeding practices**. Parents are often advised to restrain their baby's movements in a bid to **control** their baby's milk intake. I promote baby-led feeding practices, which is why my advice may differ.

You may have been advised to swaddle your newly born baby for feeds to prevent her from startling. Babies are less inclined to startle while being cradled in arms or in a side-lying feeding position. An unrestrained baby will **push the bottle away** at some point. This can be **accidental or deliberate.** You need to be able to tell the difference in order to provide an appropriate response, which could be returning or removing the bottle. (See chapter 16 for recommendations on how to interpret and respond to a baby's behavioral cues while feeding.)

Not all babies object to being restrained. And some may appear to feed better. If you choose to swaddle your baby for feeds, swaddle with her arms in a central position with her hands resting on her chest and not down by her sides. Watch for subtle behavioral cues that indicate she wants to stop—such as blocking or trying to push the nipple out with her tongue or turning her head away. Also, remain mindful that just because she has not complained about being restrained so far doesn't mean she won't complain in the future. Listen to your baby, and respect her cues.

Back

Whether you have been advised to feed your baby as she lies back facing forward or on her side, it's important that the vertebrae in her neck are aligned with those of her spine—meaning her head is not turned to the side. Her torso and limbs should also be properly positioned.

Straightening your baby's back will help to decrease pressure on her stomach, which lowers the chance of her spitting up. You may need to use a pillow or cushions **behind her back** for extra support.

Hips

Your baby's hips should be in a natural flexed position as her bottom rests on your lap. If she is stiff as a board, meaning there is no flexion at her hips, this will cause stiff legs and her torso, shoulders, neck, jaw, and facial muscles to tighten.

If your baby stiffens her body while feeding, it could be a sign of frustration or stress. Be sure it's not because you are ignoring her satiety cues (pages 76-79).

Your comfort

You are going to spend **many** hours every day feeding your baby. It's important that you're comfortable, which means your body will be relaxed, and you will be more patient.

Feeding while seated

Feeding your baby on your lap and supported by your arm while you are seated is the most comfortable feeding position. Here are a few ways you can make feeding your baby more comfortable for yourself.

- Choose a comfortable chair that will provide adequate back support. Ideally, the chair will also have armrests at a comfortable height to rest the elbow of your arm, helping you support your baby's neck and upper shoulders.
- If you find it tiring to hold your arm up while supporting your baby's head in a neutral position, prop your elbow on the arm of the chair or on cushions.
- If you feel like your baby is going to roll off your lap, use a footstool to raise your legs.
- If necessary, raise the height of your baby's body by laying her on a nursing pillow or regular pillow on your lap so you're not bending forward and straining your back.

- If you have a physical disability that makes it painful to feed your baby while she's on your lap, consult with an occupational therapist (OT) for individualized advice.

Feeding while standing

It's possible to feed a small baby while held in your arms as you are standing. However, I encourage you to think about what will be sustainable over the long term. Your actions will teach your baby what to expect. Feeding a baby while standing may become burdensome as your baby grows.

Standing, bouncing, or swaying

Parents typically stand, bounce, and sway because their baby refuses to eat while the parent is seated. This scenario usually develops as a result of the parent trying to coax, encourage, or pressure their baby to continue eating until she has reached a target volume of milk. In doing so, the parent may inadvertently overlook or ignore their baby's cues that indicate she wants to stop or is stressed. In time, being fed while the parent stands, bounces, or sways may become something the baby learns to expect. I have two recommendations: first and foremost, stop applying pressure to make your baby feed (see pages 275-276 for examples of what pressure looks like), and second, gradually transition to a seated and stationary position.

Now that you understand the key aspects and importance of good positioning while bottle-feeding a baby, it will be easier for you to choose a suitable position that enables your baby to comfortably and effectively feed.

Feeding positions for healthy babies

Positions to bottle-feed healthy, post-term babies include:

- cradle feeding position;
- resting on parent's legs;
- facing-out position; and
- out-of-arms positions.

Let's now look at these positions and how you might ensure the key elements of optimal feeding—elevation of your baby's body, neutral head position, relaxed body position, angle of the bottle, and your comfort—are covered.

Cradle feeding position

The cradle position is the one most often recommended for healthy post-term babies who don't have sucking and swallowing problems. The following illustrations demonstrate the feeding position I recommend for most healthy babies.

Feeding a newborn

Feeding a larger baby

These illustrations provide examples of good body and head positioning for a newborn and an older baby. The key elements of an optimal feeding position are covered, for example.

- Baby's body is semi-elevated at around 45 degrees.
- Her head is in line with her body.
- Her neck and upper shoulders, and not the back of her head, are resting on the parent's forearm, enabling a neutral head position.
- Both of the baby's arms are to the front of her body and are free to move.

- Baby can look at and engage with her parent while feeding, which has been shown to enhance positive emotional development.
- The parent can observe their baby's head and body positioning, the angle of the bottle, and milk in the bottle and nipple.
- The parent can see their baby's face and interpret her behavioral cues.

Common mistake

A cradle position consists of resting the baby's head **over** the crook of your elbow or forearm. A mistake I often see when observing parents feeding their baby is that the parent's elbow is too low, and their arm is angled from the baby's shoulder diagonally down her back and therefore does not provide support to her neck and upper shoulders. As a result, a newborn baby's head either flops back or falls to the side; an older baby might attempt to sit upright because the weight of her head is too heavy to hold at a 45-degree angle without support.

All you need to do is to lift your elbow so that your forearm supports her neck and upper shoulders. If holding your arm up is tiresome, use the arm of the chair or cushions to rest your elbow or forearm.

Most parents recognize when their baby's head flops back or to the side and that this would be uncomfortable. However, most tend to reposition their baby **rather than reposition their arm**. Not being aware of this simple solution, parents generally change their baby's position to a fully upright feeding position so that her head is supported by the parent's chest or shoulder. This then causes subtle flexing of their baby's neck, which is better than extension or falling to the side, but not ideal.

A cradle feeding position will suit most healthy bottle-fed babies. However, it may not be the optimal feeding position for **babies with sucking or breathing problems**. Learn more about feeding babies with special needs on page 216-217.

Facing-out position

Baby is in a semi-elevated or fully upright position with her head resting against the parent's body.

Disadvantages

- Your baby won't be facing you. This makes bonding and cue-reading more difficult.
- Her head could be flexed into a chin-down position.

Recommendations

Consider returning to a cradle position with back support so that you can see your baby's face, bottle position, and behavioral cues and support her emotional development by engaging with her while feeding.

Reasons that a baby might prefer a facing-out feeding position include the following:

- A highly inquisitive baby may find it more stimulating to feed while facing out. It enables her to observe what's happening in her surroundings. You may find she is interested in feeding while facing you if you talk to her while she feeds.
- Avoiding eye contact and becoming upset when placed into a cradle position can be signs that your baby is getting stressed while feeding. Check that you have been responding appropriately to her behavioral cues (described in chapter 16).
- A feeding-averse baby may try to avoid eye contact while feeding and find feeding to be less intimidating when facing away from the parent. The solution will be to resolve her feeding aversion (see chapter 27). Then she will be happy to look at you and engage with you while feeding.

Resting on the parent's legs

This is an in-front feeding position, where the baby's body is supported in a semi-elevated position resting back against her parent's legs. It enables you to engage with your baby while closely observing her behavioral cues, thus supporting her emotional development.

Disadvantages

- Your baby's head may be flexed in this position. If so, try placing a folded baby wrap or towel behind her back and shoulders, but not her head, so that her head can tilt back into a neutral position.
- Face to face could be too stimulating for a newborn or tired baby. Watch for cues that let you know she's overstimulated—like avoiding eye contact and becoming stressed—and respond appropriately.

Out-of-arms positions

While the ideal is to feed a baby "in arms" to aid emotional development, it's not always possible. Sometimes, you need to feed your baby in other places. A baby's body can be supported in a semi-elevated position while resting on cushions or pillows, a baby rocker, bouncer, or swing.

Advantages

- Baby rockers or infant feeding chairs may be more practical when feeding multiple-birth babies at the same time.
- A parent with a physical impairment that prevents them from holding their baby while feeding may need to feed their baby out of arms.

Disadvantage

A major disadvantage to feeding in a baby rocker, bouncer, or swing is that your baby's body may mold into a C shape, meaning her chin is resting on her chest. A flexed head position will make it harder for her to suck.

To remedy this situation, place a folded (not rolled) baby wrap or towel behind your baby's back and shoulders, but not head. Remember, you're aiming for her head to be in a neutral position and not extended.

TIP: Choose a feeding position and place that will be specific for feeding so your baby will understand that when you place her in this position, your intention is to offer her a feed. If you were to feed your baby in the same place or position where you settle her to sleep or where she is placed for playtime, she might become confused and possibly upset if she misreads your intentions.

Note: These are **general recommendations** on a feeding position for typically developing babies **without** sucking or breathing problems. An "optimal" feeding position varies depending on the baby's level of maturity, physical strength, sucking abilities, and equipment used. Your baby's health professional may provide recommendations specific to your baby.

Feeding positions for babies with special-needs

Some babies require more support than others while feeding, such as babies who

- are preterm;
- are at risk or have a history of aspiration; or who have
- disorganized suck-swallow-breathe patterns;
- have swallowing problems (dysphagia);
- have chronic lung conditions;
- have congenital or metabolic disorders affecting feeding abilities.

If you are the parent of a baby requiring extra feeding support, you may have received instruction from a speech-language pathologist (SLP), occupational therapist (OT), or feeding therapist on either an elevated side-lying feeding position or a fully upright feeding position.

Bear in mind that some feeding challenges are temporary, others permanent. Be mindful that your baby is constantly developing. As time passes, her body, face, and mouth will grow. She will gain strength and skills that enable voluntary sucking.

A feeding position and feeding practices that may have been appropriate when they were recommended may no longer be appropriate as your baby matures and develops further skills. You may need to adjust your baby's feeding position and feeding strategies to keep pace with advancements in her development.

Most healthy "preemies" will be ready for a cradle feeding position within a month of being discharged from the hospital, but check with your baby's primary healthcare provider.

Next

Next, we look at how to bottle-feed a baby and how to respond to her behavioral cues.

16 How to Respond to Baby's Feeding Cues

HOW TO BOTTLE-FEED A BABY • BABY SIGNS OF ACCEPTANCE AND REJECTION • HOW TO RESPOND TO YOUR BABY'S FEEDING CUES

As your baby's parent and caregiver, the decisions you make and the actions you take or don't take will have a profound effect on how well he feeds, how enjoyable the experience will be, and also how much he eats. Your baby will communicate his wants and needs, his pleasure and frustrations, both vocally and through his body movements. Accurately interpreting and responding appropriately to his behavior cues is one of your responsibilities as a parent. In this chapter, I provide recommendations on how to respond to different behavioral cues during the act of feeding your baby.

Newborn

Feeding a newborn requires an approach different to that for an older baby for many reasons, including that he's smaller and his infantile reflexes (described in chapter 5) are still active. First, you need to meet all the responsibilities regarding equipment choice, in particular that the flow rate is a good match for your baby's sucking abilities (see chapter 14). Then consider the following.

- Feed in a quiet environment.
- Ensure you've settled your baby into a good head and body position for feeding. This is extremely important for a newborn. (Chapter 15 describes safe and unsafe feeding positions.) Also, make sure that you're comfortably seated.

- Your baby won't recognize a bottle, so you may need to stroke his lips or the side of his mouth to encourage him to open his mouth to accept the nipple.
- Make sure you support the bottle at 90 degrees relative to his face so he can effectively latch.
- Observe him while feeding. You can talk to him, but watch for signs like averting eye contact or fussing that might indicate he's getting overstimulated by too much happening at the same time.
- Allow him to continue sucking while he's willing to do so.
- Let him set the pace and pause if he needs to.
- If he fusses or shows signs of stress (described on pages 81-82), stop. Figure out the cause and respond accordingly to resolve the problem, and decide whether to return to feeding or end the feed. It may be that he needs to burp or that the flow rate is too fast or too slow, or that he's annoyed by what you're doing.
- If he's getting sleepy, talk to him, stroke him, and try to keep him awake.
- Watch for signs of satiety (described on pages 76-79) and end the feed.

Remember, your role in feeding your newborn is **support and not control.** Don't try to make him finish the bottle or consume a predetermined volume.

After the feed, your baby could feel full but not satisfied. If he's crying after drinking his usual amount, don't assume he's still hungry. He may not yet have experienced the sensation of satisfaction—maybe he ate too quickly. Or something else may be troubling him, perhaps tiredness or an unsatisfied sucking urge.

- Offer him something to suck on—for example, a pacifier or your little finger (palm-up position so that the tip of your finger touches the roof of his mouth). He is young, but he's intelligent enough to realize that he's not receiving milk and will likely start to fuss if he's still hungry. However, he may also fuss if he's tired. Use timing and context to decide on a probable cause (see chapter 7).
- If he's still fussing after 10 minutes, offer more.
- If you have been advised to hold your baby upright for 20 to 30 minutes after feeds, be aware of the potential consequences of him becoming accustomed to falling asleep in this position (see pages 297-298).

Baby 3 months+

Feeding your baby is now much easier because he is bigger, stronger, more aware, and more capable of doing things for himself, and he will give clearer signals of his desire to feed or not feed.

Of note is that your baby is learning what to expect from the steps you take when providing his care. For example, he is learning the sequence of events that lead to him being offered a bottle. If past feeding experiences have been enjoyable, he may stop fussing and get excited as soon as he realizes he is about to be fed. However, if past feeding experiences have been annoying, frustrating, stressful, or painful, he may become upset or distressed while having a bib placed around his neck or when laid in a feeding position or at the sight of the bottle.

During the feed, you still have all the responsibilities for choosing equipment and a suitable feeding position. But when it comes to the act of feeding your baby, your main responsibility is to **follow his lead**. This means you need to

- Offer. Don't just stick the nipple into his mouth without first checking if he wants it.
- Allow him to decide when he wants to stop, pause, burp, or end the feed.
- Figure out the reason for any fussing during the feed and act accordingly (see chapter 28). And make sure you're not frustrating or stressing him by your actions or inactions or by trying to control how much he eats.

After the feed, try to burp him. If he hasn't burped in two minutes, then move on to playtime, and watch for signs that indicate that he's tired (see pages 288-289). Anticipate that sleep may be the next step when he gets to the "active-alert, fussy" stage.

How to offer and respond

To provide responsive care, you will need to look for signs that indicate your baby wants to eat. Once he is in a feeding position, move the bottle into his line of sight, but **pause** about six to eight inches (15 to 20 cm) from his face. As a sign of respect, literally ask him if he wants the bottle.

Asking is more for your sake than his. It will help you to get into the habit of watching for signs of acceptance or rejection.

Your baby will let you know if he wants it or not by his behavior. As you pause, gauge his reaction when he sees the bottle. Your next step will then vary according to his response at seeing the bottle.

How to translate your baby's response

When your baby is offered a bottle, he might respond in four different ways.

1. Acceptance.
2. Rejection.
3. Neutral response with mouth shut.
4. Crying with mouth open.

When first born, a baby doesn't know what a bottle is or link it with feeding, so he can't give clear signs of acceptance or rejection. At the time he is offered a bottle, he will either be calm with his mouth shut or fussing or crying with his mouth open.

From around **eight weeks** of age, a baby who has been regularly bottle-fed is starting to recognize the bottle as a means to satisfy his hunger and will sometimes show signs of acceptance and rejection when offered a bottle. However, his response will be an unpredictable mix between the four responses listed.

From around **three months** of age, a baby who has been regularly bottle-fed will give clearer signals. He will move toward mostly showing signs of acceptance or rejection and be less inclined to cry, except when ravenous, or have a neutral response when offered a bottle.

I encourage you to watch for these signs and provide an appropriate response. This will influence how your baby reacts. If you provide the response he wants, he will be content whether he has chosen to feed or not. However, if you don't respond the way he wants, or you act contrary to what he expects, he will fuss or get upset.

Below are my recommendations on how to respond to your baby's signals when you offer him a feed.

Acceptance

If your baby is looking at the bottle, opens his mouth, or reaches for it, this generally signals acceptance.

You have his permission to place the nipple into his mouth. He will accept the nipple, latch quickly, and start to suck.

Rejection

Baby signals rejection by clamping his lips or crying, turning his head away, or arching back or to the side. He might push the bottle away or try to block the bottle from getting to his mouth.

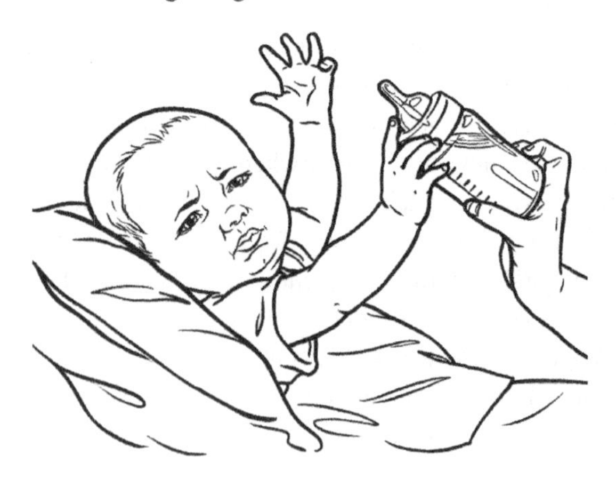

A **passive rejection** is with clamped lips and turning away with no crying. It's like the baby is politely saying, "No thanks! I'm not interested." This is more likely to occur when a baby has learned to trust that his rejection will be accepted.

An **aggressive rejection** can be described as the baby getting tense, fussing, or crying while turning and arching away—to distance himself from the bottle—or while trying to push the bottle away—another way to distance himself. It's like he's shouting, "NO! GET IT AWAY FROM ME!" This strong reaction generally occurs because a baby has learned that subtle signs of rejection **do not** receive the desired response.

Whether your baby rejects passively or aggressively or any way in between, you **do not** have his permission to place the nipple into his mouth. And you could frustrate, anger or stress him if you try.

What to do when your baby rejects

- Accept his right to decline your offer. Remove the bottle. Don't stroke his lips or linger or hover with the bottle or offer repeatedly, trying to persuade him to accept. Responding to his rejection in these ways may frustrate him. Receiving an inappropriate response to passive signs of rejection may encourage him to use aggressive behaviors to get the message across.
- As you remove the bottle, I recommend you verbally acknowledge his rejection. "Okay, Johnny, I can see you don't want it now. You can eat later," or something along these lines. Saying these words is as much for your sake as for his. You are acknowledging that you have observed signs of rejection. This will help you become more attuned to his behavioral cues in the future. He will learn to recognize that your words mean you're going to stop.
- Quickly take him out of a feeding position. While you continue to hold him in a feeding position, he may think you're going to try again, and he may become frustrated or stressed.

Neutral response

Baby is calm while being held in the feeding position, his mouth is closed, he's looking at the bottle, but he's not giving clear signs of acceptance or rejection. You're not sure whether he wants it or not.

What to do when your baby's response is neutral

- Stroke his lips from the base of his nose to chin **two or three times** using the tip of the nipple. This will usually elicit one of three responses.

    1. **He will open his mouth, indicating acceptance**. In this case, place the nipple into his mouth.
    2. **He will turn his head away, indicating rejection**. Accept his rejection, remove the bottle, and take him out of the feeding position.
    3. **He will do nothing.** Consider "no response" a lack of interest and respond as if he rejected.

- Don't continue to repeatedly stroke his lips in the hope of persuading him. He will eventually become annoyed.
- And don't try to push the nipple through his clamped lips, as this may frustrate or anger him.

A note on coaxing newborns to feed

A calm newborn baby can usually be coaxed into opening his mouth by stroking his lips or the side of his mouth with the end of the nipple, triggering his gape or rooting reflex. Hence, acceptance into his mouth is **not** proof that he wants to feed.

A newborn will suck and swallow if his sucking reflex is triggered by pressure on the top of his tongue and the roof of his mouth by the nipple. This effect can be enhanced by applying gentle upward pressure under his chin while the nipple is in his mouth. If you do these things to "encourage" a newborn to open his mouth or suck, and he sucks contently, he's happy to feed at this time. However, if he fusses, you need to reassess whether he is in fact hungry and willing to feed.

Crying

If your baby is crying **before** he sees the bottle, don't assume he is hungry. Use timing and context as described in chapter 7 to help you decide if hunger is likely. If you decide to offer your baby a bottle while he's crying, first try to soothe him with cuddles or a pacifier.

If your baby can be soothed

Once calm, he can see you're offering him a bottle. Once the bottle is in his line of sight, remove his pacifier and ask him if he wants the bottle. Look for signs of acceptance or rejection, and take appropriate action. If he turns away, consider this a rejection. Remove the bottle, return his pacifier, take him out of the feeding position, and consider other potential reasons for his crying. He might have been crying because he simply wants a cuddle or his pacifier to satisfy his sucking needs or because he is tired.

If your baby is unable to be soothed

If you are unable to calm your baby, and you strongly suspect he is crying from hunger, place the nipple into his mouth, taking care to place it over his tongue. Babies raise their tongue while crying. Milk will dribble out of his mouth if the nipple is accidentally placed under his tongue.

- If he quickly latches, **calms, and begins to suck,** he probably was crying because of hunger.
- If he latches, **calms, but does not suck,** my advice varies depending on his age.
- If he's **a newborn,** apply gentle upward pressure under his chin while the nipple is in his mouth to see if this will trigger his sucking reflex.
- If he's **over three months** of age, **don't** apply upward pressure under his chin. His sucking reflex is gone, and touching his face could annoy him. If he's not sucking, he's probably not interested.
- If all **attempts to calm him are unsuccessful**—in other words, he continues to cry—he could be crying for other reasons. If this is the case, it's doubtful he will decide to eat at that point in time. Abandon your attempts to feed him for now. Continue to try to soothe him. And consider other reasons for crying, like tiredness, overstimulation, or tummy discomfort. You will only stress him more if you persist in trying to make him feed when he's upset and unwilling to suck. Wait until he has calmed before offering again.

If your baby starts to cry after he sees the bottle

Sometimes babies cry after seeing the bottle. It may be because he's very hungry and desperately wants it. Alternatively, it could be because he is aggressively rejecting the bottle. There are subtle differences in behavior when a baby is crying in hunger and crying in rejection.

- **When crying is caused by hunger**, your baby is not turning away. If you place the nipple into his mouth, he willingly accepts, latches quickly, and starts to suck.
- **When crying in rejection,** your baby might try to distance himself from the bottle by turning and arching away or pushing the bottle away. If you try to place the nipple into his mouth, his crying will escalate. He will not latch or suck. He calms quickly once you remove the bottle and take him out of a feeding position.

When to stop

In the ideal situation, a **newly born** baby might feed smoothly in a calm and relaxed manner, drinking the prescribed volume of milk as recommended by his healthcare professional. However, this situation will change. Around **eight weeks of age**, your baby's sucking reflex has faded but not completely disappeared. He'll stop sucking when he chooses to. From that point on, he's going to stop for many different reasons.

"Stopping" doesn't necessarily mean it's time to end the feed … but it could. Stopping might include a pause, a short break, or the end of the feed. Stop if you see behaviors that indicate your baby is

- full or satisfied;
- not interested;
- fussy or distressed;
- conflicted; or
- getting drowsy or falling asleep.

Fullness or satisfaction

When a baby is full or satisfied, he stops sucking, pushes the nipple out with his tongue, or turns his head away, or he might also push the bottle away. If he's drowsy, his jaw will relax.

What to do when your baby indicates he has had enough

- If the volume consumed seems reasonable, end the feed. Don't try to make him squeeze in those last ounces or milliliters remaining in the bottle or to continue until he consumes the volume that **you or others expect** him to drink. If he doesn't want to continue eating, you will upset him and make the feeding experience unpleasant or stressful if you try to make him eat more.

- If you have doubts about him having finished feeding, take a 5- to 10-minute break and reoffer, as described previously. And provide an appropriate response to signs of acceptance or rejection. If he rejects at that time, end the feed.

Remember, deciding how much to eat is your baby's responsibility, not yours. The amount he eats each feed, each day, and each week will fluctuate.

Also remember, a "full" baby will not necessarily be a content baby. A baby could be upset for many reasons, like an unsatisfied sucking urge, tiredness, boredom, or overstimulation. If after your baby has indicated he no longer wishes to continue feeding he's fussing, look to other reasons why he might be unsettled. Don't assume it's because he's still hungry. And don't try to make him eat more if he's unwilling. You could cause him even greater distress if you try to make him eat against his will or overfeed him.

Lack of interest

You can offer your baby a bottle-feed when **you think** he might be hungry. But that doesn't mean he is hungry at the time or interested in feeding.

If your baby is not interested in eating, he might reject when offered or accept and take a little and then start to play, rolling his tongue around the nipple, chewing the nipple, playing with your hair, your clothing, or his own. Basically, he may do anything other than suck. He might appear to be more interested in engaging with you or looking at what's happening in his surroundings than he is in eating.

If your baby is not interested in feeding

End the feed. Try later. Ideally, wait until he shows signs of hunger. However, if he isn't a baby who demands a feed, offer again in an hour or two.

If your baby is not hungry when you're expecting him to be—for example, the first feed in the morning or at the times his healthcare professional recommended you offer feeds—it could be related to his feeding pattern. It could be that he's feeding more at night than he needs from a developmental perspective (see chapter 24) or the recommended feeding pattern does not match his biological needs (see chapter 4).

Frustration or stress

Your baby could stop sucking, turn away or push the bottle away for reasons other than wanting to end the feed. These include

- a fright;
- distraction;
- to burp;
- to poop;
- tiredness;
- equipment frustrations; or
- "feeder frustration," meaning what you're doing or not doing.

What to do if your baby is fussy or stressed while feeding

- Stop. Remove the nipple from his mouth, take him out of a feeding position, and figure out what's troubling him. (Chapter 28 describes reasons for concerning feeding behavior.)
- If the reason for his fussing has passed—for example, he burped or pooped, and he's now calm—you could offer again to check if he's finished feeding.
- If you can't figure out the cause of his fussing, and you haven't been able to remedy the situation, take a 5- to 10-minute break and see if the situation naturally resolves during that time. If so, return and offer once more. And respond appropriately according to his cues of acceptance or rejection. End the feed if he rejects it at this time.
- If you have no success in soothing him, end the feed and wait until you can. Consider other potential reasons for his distress. Don't persist in trying to make him eat while he's upset. You will only inflame the situation. A hungry baby doesn't fuss or show signs of stress while he's feeding if hunger is the cause. He will be too busy sucking! When stressed, a baby's digestive system shuts down and appetite is suppressed, so you will not get him to eat without force-feeding him, which will make for an extremely stressful experience for you both.

Don't let anxiety drive you to force your baby to eat or fail to consider other reasons for his fussing or refusal.

Conflicted feeding behavior

"Conflicted" feeding behavior is disjointed feeding behavior, where baby appears to be confused about whether he wants to eat or not. He takes a little, then turns away in a tense manner; he might then give a little cry and turn back to face the bottle and indicate he wants it again. He willingly accepts the nipple into his mouth, takes a few sucks, and turns away again, repeating this broken feeding pattern. The most common reasons for conflicted feeding behavior include

- tiredness;
- feeding aversion; and
- pain.

Tiredness

A baby could be both **hungry and tired** at the same time, in which case his frustration tolerance will be **very low**. He wants to sleep, but he needs to eat, and he can't decide what he wants to do. (See chapter 22 for more on sleep and tiredness cues.)

If frustration is getting the better of your baby, end the feed and try to get him to sleep. Offer a feed if he shows signs of hunger after he wakes.

Feeding aversion

A feeding aversion is a fear of feeding. However, the survival instinct is strong, and a baby must eat to survive. And hunger will eventually drive a feeding-averse baby to eat, albeit not willingly, despite his fears. When he does eat, he might be conflicted about eating because **hunger and fear** are pulling him in opposing directions.

In the case of a feeding aversion, repeatedly returning the bottle can reinforce or encourage a baby's broken feeding behavior to be repeated with greater frequency in the future. (See chapter 27 to discover if your baby has developed a feeding aversion.)

Pain

Babies can experience discomfort or pain while feeding and appear conflicted because of the clash between **hunger and pain**. Baby is hungry and wants to eat, but discomfort or pain is preventing him from doing so. So, he swings between desperate sucks and pulling away in pain. (See pages 409-411 to decide if pain is the most likely cause.)

If your baby is experiencing discomfort or pain while feeding, take a short break, try to soothe him, wait for him to calm down, and then try again.

If your baby is falling asleep

I agree with the principle of following a baby's lead. However, there are **a few exceptions**. Allowing a baby to fall asleep while feeding is one of them. Read about feeding and sleeping problems directly linked to babies falling asleep while feeding in pages 297-298. Check these out, and make an informed decision about whether you wish to allow your baby to fall asleep while feeding with the knowledge of potential consequences.

I encourage parents to avoid letting their baby feed drowsy in the day, though drowsy feeding at night is okay. I recommend that parents prevent their baby from falling asleep with the nipple in his mouth during both the day and night.

What to do if baby becomes drowsy while feeding during the day

- If you see the vacant look in your baby's eyes as he starts to become drowsy, prompt him to remain awake. Talk to him, stroke him, remove the nipple from his mouth, and try to arouse him. Once awake, reoffer.
- If you are unable to keep him awake, end the feed, and don't allow him to feed in a drowsy state.

Of course, this could mean he consumes a little less at that point in time. If so, he will likely demand a feed a little sooner next time or consume a larger volume feed later in the day to make up for it. And over the course of the day consume roughly the same total volume.

If you allow him to feed drowsy, sure he might drink a little more, but more could then last until the end of his next awake period where he once again feeds drowsy. Over time you may find that drowsy feeding becomes the only way he feeds—which would be very restrictive on family life. If he repeatedly falls asleep while feeding—which is very likely if allowed to feed drowsy—this will encourage a **feeding-sleep association**. (See chapter 22 for feeding and sleeping problems associated with a sleep association problem.)

What to do if your baby becomes drowsy during the bedtime or night feeds

The priority of feeds during the day is that your baby is awake and aware he is feeding. Sleep becomes a priority at night.

- Allow baby to continue to suck while drowsy.
- When you get to the end of the feed, stir him awake. Perhaps leave a diaper change until the end of the feed as a way to stir him awake. Then settle him to sleep without the nipple of a bottle in his mouth. This will discourage him from developing a feeding-sleep association.

Other reasons

Your baby may want to pause, take a break, or end the feed for other reasons. See chapter 28 for different types of behavior a baby might display while feeding to decide on an appropriate response.

Next

Next, I will expose myths about swallowed air, describe different ways to burp a baby, make suggestions on reasons to burp a baby and how to tell when it's time to stop.

17 What to Know About Burping a Baby

HOW AND WHEN TO BURP A BABY • DOES IT MATTER IF A BABY DOESN'T BURP? • MYTHS ABOUT BURPING • WHAT HAPPENS TO SWALLOWED AIR

You might have read or been told that it's essential to burp your baby, possibly multiple times, during a feed and after. And you may have been warned that if you don't or can't get your baby to burp up swallowed air, it could become trapped in her stomach or intestines and cause painful abdominal cramps and intense crying. **It won't!** In this chapter, I will explain what happens to swallowed air, and why some myths about swallowed air describe a physical impossibility.

Myths and misinformation

Myths about swallowed air being the tormentor of newborn babies have been around for centuries. Below are some of the many myths and misinformation that are widely spread by parents, grandparents, health professionals, authors of parenting books, and websites today.

- It's essential to burp a baby. (It isn't.)
- Swallowed air causes colic. (It doesn't.)
- Air accumulates in a baby's stomach as a result of air swallowed from multiple feeds, which then limits her stomach capacity for milk. (Impossible.)
- Air gets trapped in a baby's intestines, causing pain. (Incorrect.)
- Taking a baby out on a windy day or driving with the car window down will cause her to swallow air. (This is an old wives' tale.)
- Pulling up knees means a baby has abdominal pain. (Not usually.)

- Baby could wake in pain if you don't get her to burp after feeding. (She could wake, but not because you didn't burp her.)

You've probably heard many more myths. This list doesn't include the numerous old wives' tales related to the reasons newborns cry or are troubled by intestinal gas. I will explain why the claims above are false.

What happens to swallowed air?

Because of the shape and angle of a baby's stomach, bubbles of swallowed air will accumulate in it as she feeds. The mix of milk and air can cause a feeling of fullness or minor discomfort as she continues to feed, and she might fuss and squirm. You can help her release some air and make more space for a larger feed—if she chooses to drink more—or relieve minor discomfort related to a bloated tummy by burping her.

She won't burp up all the air she has swallowed no matter how long you try to burp her. After burping, some air will remain in her stomach, but not indefinitely. Air that is not burped up will be pushed into her small intestine along with the milk as her stomach contracts.

Air is made up of gases, mostly nitrogen and oxygen, and a tiny percentage of carbon dioxide, hydrogen, and others. Some of the oxygen and carbon dioxide from the air swallowed will be absorbed through tiny blood vessels in the walls of her small intestine along with nutrients from food.[136] Her blood already contains oxygen and carbon dioxide, so it's readily absorbed.

Gas not absorbed into her bloodstream is pushed through into her large intestine (also called colon or bowel), where it combines with gases that are **produced in her intestinal tract** as a byproduct of multiple digestive processes. Eventually, any gases not absorbed come out of her bottom as flatulence (a.k.a. flatus, farts, toots, or bottom burps).

Pediatrician Cindy Gellner, MD, says not to worry if your baby doesn't burp. The air in your baby will find a way out.[137]

This is probably more than you need to know about farts. But I wanted to drive home two points:

1. it's not possible for air to be "trapped" in your baby's stomach or intestines; and

2. whether you burp your baby or not, it will **not** have a significant impact on how much air is in her intestinal tract or how much and how often she farts.

Even if you could prevent your baby from swallowing air while feeding, which you can't, she would still fart as a result of the gases created inside her intestinal tract.

The only benefit of burping is to relieve **minor** discomfort that **might** be caused by the sensation of fullness in her stomach and make more space for milk.

If you have a screaming "gassy" baby, you will understandably be skeptical about my claims that, at worst, **swallowed air** causes only minor discomfort. Keep an open mind. There's more to the story. As mentioned, the gas that comes out of your baby's bottom is mostly gas that her body generates during the processes involved in digestion. You can read more about how and why gas is produced in your baby's intestines in pages 433-435.

How to burp a baby

There are a number of ways to burp a baby. Babies often bring up a little milk with a burp, so it may be helpful to have a burping cloth, cloth diaper, or towel handy.

On your shoulder

Hold your baby in an upright position against your chest with her head resting on your shoulder. Gently pat or rub her back, using a circular or up and down motion, with the heel of your free hand.

Over your shoulder

Lay her **over** your shoulder. This allows you to position her so your shoulder provides gentle pressure against her tummy. Hold her securely with one hand and pat or rub her back with the other.

On your knee

Sit your baby sideways, seated on your knee. Support her head by placing your thumb and index finger under her jaw just below her ears. Take care your hand is not pressing against her neck. Lean her body forward slightly, resting her tummy against the heel of your hand. Gently pat or rub her back with your free hand.

A slightly different method in this position is to maintain your hold at her front (as demonstrated) but at the same time support her back and neck with your other hand so she's safely sandwiched between your two hands. Then gently rock her back and forth or rotate her in a large circular motion, moving her entire upper body from her hips.

Over your knee

Lay your baby face down over your crossed legs. Position her so your upper leg provides gentle pressure to her tummy. Support her head with one hand and pat or rub her back with your other.

On your arm

Lay your baby face down along your forearm with her head near your elbow and her arms hanging down either side of your arm. Your hand of the arm she's lying on supports her diaper area. Her side is resting against your body. Once you feel you have a safe and secure hold of her, gently pat or rub her back with your free hand.

When to check for a burp

If your baby is feeling bloated from swallowing air, she will start to wiggle, squirm, and fuss. Check if she needs to get rid of swallowed air by using one of the burping methods described. However, if she doesn't burp within a minute or two, don't persist. She's likely fussing for other reasons (see chapter 28 for reasons for fussy feeding behavior).

If your baby is feeding contentedly and she's not feeling uncomfortable, there's no need to break the feed and risk upsetting her by removing the bottle when she wants to eat. If she's relaxed and enjoying feeding, leave her to feed in peace, and check for a burp once she's finished.

If, as a result of allowing her to feed to the end, you discover that she often has a huge belch, bringing up a little milk with it, so be it! Small spit-ups are very normal, especially when a baby burps. However, if she has a large spit-up along with the belch, include a "burp check" next time you feed her, during a natural pause in her sucking. Add another burp check at the end of the feed.

Know when to stop

- **If your baby has not burped within two minutes,** either return to feeding or take other steps that you deem appropriate. If she's fussing, consider if she wants to suck to satisfy her sucking urge. She may be bored or due for a nap.
- **If she starts to cry** while you're checking for a burp, you need to stop. See if she wants to continue eating. But if she doesn't, then try to soothe her in other ways. Offer her something to suck on. Use timing and context to assess possible reasons for crying (see chapter 7).

Why baby might not burp

If your baby doesn't burp, the most likely reason is that she doesn't need to. Sure, she has undoubtedly swallowed air, but if it's not causing her discomfort, you don't need to do anything.

Babies **three months** and older are less inclined to burp compared to **newborns** because they can better control the flow rate of milk from the bottle and are better able to pace their sucking and self-regulate their dietary intake. Once your baby is between **four and six months** of age, you will start to realize that she seldom burps after the feed. You can stop checking for a burp when this happens. If playtime follows feeding, she might burp then. But if not, no matter. She will burp if she needs to but won't if she doesn't.

A **sleepy baby** is less likely to burp because she will eat at a slower pace and won't swallow as much air while feeding. If your baby is falling asleep in your arms, then swallowed air is obviously **not** causing her any discomfort. You might try one of the described burping methods for a couple of minutes, but if nothing comes up, give up and settle her down for a sleep.

Why baby might burp excessively

If your baby has a good latch, is in a good feeding position, and she feeds calmly and smoothly at a comfortable pace, she will swallow some air. However, it is possible for a baby to ingest **excessive** amounts of air—the medical term for which is called aerophagia.

If you notice your baby noisily gulping, slurping or spluttering as she's feeding, it's possible she could be ingesting a lot of air. She might fuss during feeds and require frequent burp breaks. Or bring up swallowed air with a "man-sized" belch once she has finished.

Basically, anything that has a negative effect on a baby's latch, suction and suck-swallow-breathe coordination could result in her swallowing an excessive amount of air. The following are examples of situations where this might happen.

1. **Speed-feeding.** A nipple that is too fast for your baby's stage of development might release the milk too quickly and impact on her sucking coordination.
2. **Ravenous or tired baby.** A ravenous baby will suck vigorously, taking in big volumes at a rapid pace. A tired baby may lack coordination.
3. **Poor body or head positioning**. If your baby's head or body is poorly positioned, she may be prevented from achieving an effective latch, maintaining suction or harmoniously coordinate sucking, swallowing and breathing.
4. **Holding the bottle at the wrong angle in relation to the angle of baby's face.** This can make it harder for a baby to latch and maintain suction. Holding the bottle horizontally—which occurs when a baby is fed in a fully upright position—could also result in there being air in the nipple.
5. **Short shaft nipple.** A nipple that is too short can affect latch, suction and sucking coordination.
6. **Excessive crying**. Babies swallow air when crying. If the baby cries a lot, she's going to swallow more air.
7. **Tongue tie.** Restricted movement of a baby's tongue may mean she cannot adequately "cup" the nipple of a bottle with her tongue, achieve a good latch or maintain suction.

The more air in your baby's tummy, the more likely she is to expel it when raised into an upright position and given a few gentle pats on her back.

When burping becomes an obsession

Some parents will spend 30 minutes or longer trying to burp their baby **after** feeds. They fear that their baby will later cry in pain because of trapped air or that she will spit up in her sleep if they don't get her to burp.

An obsession with burping babies can cause parents to develop tunnel vision. Swallowed air becomes the only reason they consider for their baby's crying during and after feeding, and they can become blinded to other causes for her crying. Despite good intentions, persistence in trying to burp their baby can become the reason their baby is crying. They could be trying to burp a hungry, tired, or overstimulated baby.

Don't let this be you! Two minutes is generally sufficient time for burping. It's then time to move on, burped or not. Remember, gas will eventually make it out of your baby's body—if not out the top end, then out the bottom! If your baby is spitting up or cries for long periods of time, prolonged burping won't help. It may even make it worse.[138] If your baby is crying, look for other causes for her distress, such as an unsatisfied sucking urge, tiredness, overstimulation, or boredom.

Next

Sometimes, a breastfed baby refuses to drink from a bottle because she does not know how to suck from it. In the next chapter, I will explain how to encourage a breastfed baby to accept bottle-feeds for those times when she might be separated from her mom.

Part E:
Combining Breastfeeding and Bottle-feeding

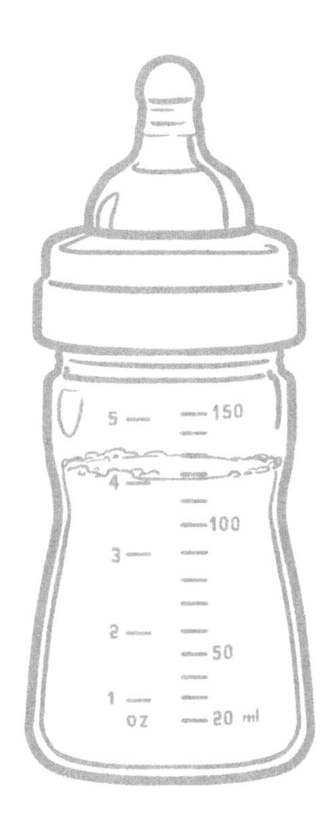

18 Bottle-Feeding a Breastfed Baby

HOW BREASTFEEDING AND BOTTLE-FEEDING DIFFER • PROS AND CONS OF GIVING OCCASSIONAL BOTTLE-FEEDS TO A BREASTFED BABY • BEST TIME TO INTRODUCE A BOTTLE • HOW TO USE PACED BOTTLE-FEEDING

You might want your breastfed baby to feed from a bottle for a lot of reasons. Maybe you're returning to work during your baby's first year. Or it might be helpful if he would drink milk from a bottle so another caregiver can feed him, allowing you to have an occasional sleep-in. Or perhaps you need for your baby to be partially fed formula. Regardless of the reason, forward planning may make for an easier transition.

Timing is everything when it comes to getting a breastfed baby to feed from a bottle. You have a narrow window of opportunity where it can be relatively easy. If you have missed the window, don't despair; it's still possible to get your baby to accept bottle-feeds, but it just won't be as easy.

How are breastfeeding and bottle-feeding different?

While both breastfeeding and bottle-feeding provide for a baby's nutritional needs, the physical actions required to successfully breastfeed are very different from those required to bottle-feed. Table 18.1 compares the two.

Table 18.1: Breastfeeding and bottle-feeding comparison

	Breastfeeding	**Bottle-feeding**
Feeding instincts	Biologically "normal" feeding method for babies. Babies instinctively know how to breastfeed **in the early weeks.**	Babies can learn to bottle-feed. An active sucking reflex helps a baby to learn to bottle-feed.
Gape (how wide baby opens her mouth)	Wide gape	Narrow gape
Time required to receive milk	Baby may need to wait for 30 to 60 seconds for the mother's milk to let down.	Baby receives milk instantly.
Flow rate	Varies	Consistent
Baby's control over the rate of flow	The roll of a baby's tongue can compress the milk ducts behind the mother's nipple to stem the flow.	Minimal control on the flow from synthetic nipple before eight weeks of age. A baby may not be in full control until closer to three months.
Tongue movement	Wave-like movements of the baby's tongue compress the milk ducts behind the nipple.	Baby's tongue cups the nipple. Minimal movement of tongue in comparison to the movement required to breastfeed.
Pressure forces	Involves alternating **positive** pressure to compress milk ducts and **negative** pressure caused by lowering of the tongue.	Sucking involves **negative** pressure caused by suction.

Why parents want their baby to accept a bottle

A mother may want her baby to accept breast milk or infant formula from a bottle for any number of reasons. Some of these include

- anxiety caused by not knowing how much milk her baby receives;
- concern about low milk supply;
- painful, cracked nipples or repeated bouts of mastitis;
- returning to work;

- breastfeeding strike;
- to share feeding responsibilities with others;
- worry that baby is reacting to foods eaten by mom; or
- medical reasons—baby or mother.

The top four reasons I have observed for mothers who start out with the goal to breastfeed but later reluctantly switch to bottle-feeding include:

1. **Breastfeeding-sleep association.** Nursing mothers often mistakenly blame hunger or lack of milk supply as the reason for their baby's broken sleep and desire to breastfeed more often than expected. In reality, the reason may be that their baby has learned to associate the act of falling asleep with suckling at their mother's breast. (See chapter 22 to learn how a feeding-sleep association affects a baby's behavior.)
2. **Maternal exhaustion.** Many desperate, sleep-deprived mothers mistakenly believe that bottle-feeding or providing formula for their distressed little babies may increase their baby's contentment and improve sleep and therefore provide much-needed relief. Unfortunately, most are disappointed to discover that their baby experiences similar problems when bottle-feeding. This is because hunger is seldom the cause of babies' distress or broken sleep.
3. **Misdiagnosis of milk allergy or intolerance.** This is usually caused by mistaking gastrointestinal (GI) symptoms related to functional lactose overload (see pages 439-448) as a maternal diet issue. Maternal dietary restrictions will make no difference to a baby's GI symptoms caused by functional lactose overload.
4. **Breastfeeding strike or breastfeeding aversion.** The baby refuses to breastfeed while awake, though may be willing to feed in a drowsy state or asleep, and the mother may feel she has no option other than to offer bottle-feeds. A breastfeeding aversion is typically caused by a forceful letdown or repeatedly pushing a crying, resistant baby to the breast. (See chapter 27 for other reasons for breast- and bottle-feeding aversion.)

You may have other reasons to give your breastfed baby milk from a bottle. When making a decision it's helpful to know the pros and cons.

Pros and cons of offering bottle-feeds

If you are planning to be a stay-at-home mom to care for your baby for the first 12 months or longer, you may not foresee a reason for other caregivers to feed him. Unfortunately, unexpected events pop up at the worst of times.

You've probably been warned of the potential risks associated with providing bottle-feeds to your breastfed baby. But have you ever been warned of potential drawbacks linked to not familiarizing a baby with bottle-feeds in the early weeks?

Risks associated with giving bottles

Giving bottles to a breastfed baby is linked to an increased risk of problems such as

- **nipple confusion,** because bottle-feeding requires a very different sucking action compared to breastfeeding. Avoid giving your baby bottles during the first four weeks following birth to reduce the risk of this;
- **bottle-feeding preference,** which develops when babies prefer the instant and consistent flow rate of bottle-feeding. Minimize the risk of this problem by controlling the flow rate using "paced bottle-feeding" (explained later in this chapter); and
- **loss of confidence,** which is when baby is given **infant formula** "top-ups" when a mother has concerns about low milk supply, or in the hope of increasing the baby's rate of growth, but this places mom on a slippery slope that leads to further decline in milk production and an early end to breastfeeding.

The more formula you give to your baby, the less milk your breasts produce. The less you produce, the more formula your baby will drink.

If bottle "top ups" have been recommended, provide breast milk from a bottle that you have pumped or hand-expressed. And consult with a lactation consultant to check your baby's latch, and provide appropriate recommendations to increase your milk supply.

Risks associated with avoiding bottles

As odd as it might sound, avoiding giving bottles is also associated with a risk to breastfeeding. Imagine if your baby needed to bottle-feed on a regular basis—say you got sick or needed to get back to work—and he didn't know how. Some of the associated risks are

- **reverse nipple confusion,** which means the baby accepts the nipple of a bottle into his mouth and attempts to suck using a breastfeeding technique, which does not work on a bottle. So, he receives no milk and becomes frustrated.
- **breastfeeding preference,** which is great for a breastfed baby except when it might be necessary for him to bottle-feed, but he refuses because he wants to breastfeed.
- **bottle refusal** is a common problem if a breastfed baby doesn't gain bottle-feeding experience before the age of eight weeks and for babies who prefer breastfeeding. Bottle refusal can cause a great deal of stress for all involved if a hungry baby is separated from his mother. In desperation, a hungry baby may be forced to feed from a bottle. While force is not required, and breastfeeding does not need to end, trying to encourage a baby who rejects bottle-feeds to feed from a bottle may not be smooth sailing if you have missed the window of opportunity.

When to introduce a bottle

If your baby accepts bottle-feeds in the early weeks, you might then think that he'll accept a bottle whenever it's offered, even weeks or months down the road. This will not necessarily be the case.

An active sucking reflex will enable your baby to feed from both breast and bottle in the early weeks following birth. However, only with repetition does he learn to feed either way, or both. Once his sucking reflex has disappeared, whether he "knows how" to breastfeed or bottle-feed depends on prior learning. While a baby can learn to bottle-feed after his sucking reflex has disappeared, it's not as easy.

If you want to encourage a breastfed baby to not only accept a bottle but easily learn to feed from a bottle with minimum risk to successful breastfeeding, it's all about the timing. Introducing a breastfed baby to bottle-feeding too soon can make it harder for him to learn to breastfeed. Too late can result in bottle refusal.

Birth to 4 weeks

Sucking is an automatic, involuntary action that occurs in response to a baby's sucking reflex being triggered. Trigger baby's sucking reflex, and he will suck from a bottle. This is why babies can feed from a bottle in the first few days of life.

Unless there are no other options, it's not a good idea to give a breastfed baby bottle-feeds during the first month. This is the time when he's learning to latch and breastfeed. Providing bottles, which require a different latch and sucking action compared to breastfeeding, at this young age is associated with an increased risk of **nipple confusion.**

Four to 8 weeks

If breastfeeding is going well, between 4 and 8 weeks is an ideal age to familiarize your baby with bottle-feeding so he will be comfortable with both feeding methods. He has had weeks to become accustomed to breastfeeding. His sucking reflex is still strong enough to support his learning to suck from a bottle.

It's not enough to offer him a few bottle-feeds and then not offer again. Babies learn through repetition. Offer him a bottle-feed once a day or every second day. It doesn't need to be a full feed. Even one ounce (30 mL) of pumped breast milk will be sufficient to help him learn how to bottle-feed with minimal risk to breastfeeding.

Limiting the number of bottle-feeds and paced bottle-feeding will also help to minimize the risk of his developing a preference for bottle-feeds.

Eight to 12 weeks

If you are only now starting to provide a bottle for the first time, it's going to be more challenging. By this age, your baby has learned to psychologically link **breastfeeding** with satisfying his hunger. If you place the nipple of a bottle into his mouth, he's likely to object or consider it a plaything.

His sucking reflex, though present, is not as strong as it was. You might find you can trigger his sucking reflex by applying gentle upward pressure under his chin while the nipple is in his mouth. It's very important that you don't continue if he becomes upset or wants to stop. Some of the gentle persuasion methods described in pages 254-256 might help at this age.

Three months+

If your baby has not been offered regular bottle-feeds before three months of age, unfortunately, he will be less likely to accept a bottle and may refuse outright. By this age, his sucking reflex has either disappeared or is close to disappearing. Upward pressure under his chin will no longer be effective.

With no, or limited, prior bottle-feeding experience, it's going to be much harder for him to learn to feed from a bottle. A synthetic nipple will feel nothing like his mother's nipple. He will have no idea why you're placing "that thing" into his mouth or what he's supposed to do with it. If he's not hungry, he's likely to chew and play with it or push it out. If he is hungry at the time, he will be expecting to receive a breastfeed and will become frustrated, cry, or spit it out.

Breastfeeding is not just his preferred method of feeding; it's all he knows. If he tries to use a breastfeeding technique while bottle-feeding, he's not going to get anything other than what drips into his mouth.

But don't lose hope. A healthy baby can learn how to bottle-feed—after his sucking reflex has disappeared—but it's not going to be easy. Expect resistance to bottle-feeding. With no sucking reflex, learning how to suck from a bottle will involve trial and error.

Is your baby refusing the bottle completely? (See chapter 19 for options.)

Combining breast and bottle-feeding

It's possible for babies to both breastfeed and bottle-feed. Assuming your baby is willing to accept and feed from a bottle, consider paced bottle-feeding.

Paced bottle-feeding

When breastfeeding, your baby may need to suck for around 30 to 60 seconds before his mother's milk lets down. Multiple letdowns during a breastfeed are separated by a brief pause when your baby might not receive milk or receives very little. The flow rate while breastfeeding varies as well. Two of the reasons babies develop a preference for bottle-feeding is because they receive milk as soon as they start to suck from a bottle and the flow rate is consistent. Paced bottle-feeding can help minimize the risk of bottle-feeding preference.

Paced bottle-feeding aims to mimic the periodic letdowns a baby experiences while breastfeeding. Paced bottle-feeding means you control the flow rate in a way that responds to your baby's cues. This feeding method slows down the flow of milk from the nipple, allowing the baby to eat more slowly and take breaks.

How to begin paced bottle-feeding

- Test the temperature of the feed by shaking a little milk from the nipple onto the inside of your wrist. If it is body temperature, it will feel neither warm nor cool.
- Seat your baby in an upright position. Support his head and neck with your hand rather than with your arm.

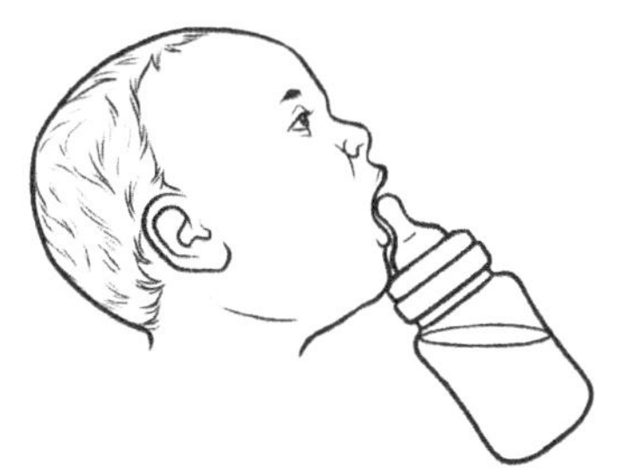

- Gently brush down the middle of his lips with the tip of the nipple to stimulate a gape reflex response. When he opens his mouth, place the nipple into his mouth.
- Your natural inclination is to hold the bottle upright. However, with paced bottle-feeding, the bottle should be held horizontally, which slows the flow.

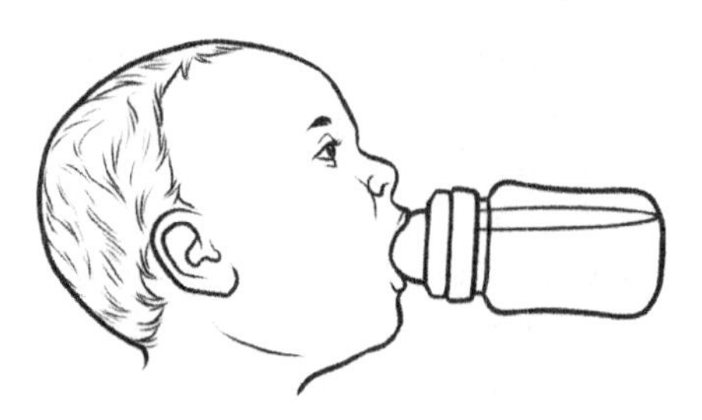

- Give your baby a break every 30 seconds or so to make the experience more like a breastfeed. Instead of pulling the bottle away from his mouth, lower the base of the bottle so that milk no longer fills the nipple while keeping the nipple in his mouth. As he begins to suck again, raise the level of the bottle back to the horizontal so that milk is again available in the nipple.

- Burp midfeed or sooner if he pulls away or seems fussy, and then offer the bottle again.
- Switch sides halfway through the feed or with every other feed to mimic the experience of breastfeeding from both sides.
- Allow him to decide when he's satisfied. He might stop sucking or push the nipple out with his tongue. Don't try to make him empty the bottle. If he becomes drowsy and releases the nipple before the bottle is empty, this signals he's finished feeding. Stir him awake at the end of the feed to discourage him from developing a bottle-feeding-sleep association.

Is paced bottle-feeding necessary?

Paced bottle-feeding is not essential. If you plan to do a **combination of breastfeeding and bottle-feeding** for a newborn, paced bottle-feeding might be helpful to minimize the risk of bottle preference. It may also help newborns regulate their milk intake when bottle-feeding.

I don't recommend it for babies **over the age of three months**—whether they are also breastfed or not—because I don't believe it provides benefits to a baby of this age. At this age, healthy, typically developing babies are capable of pacing themselves, sucking when they choose to, pausing if they need to take a break, and ending the feed when they have had enough. If you try to control when your baby will receive milk and when he won't by "pacing" his bottle-feeds beyond the age of three months, this could frustrate or anger him.

Pumping

If you are planning to combine breastfeeding and bottle-feeding, ideally, you will pump or hand-express to remove milk at regular intervals when you are separated from your baby so you can maintain your milk supply. Remember, breast milk is produced on a supply-and-demand basis. If the demand drops because you're giving your baby formula, your breast milk production will also drop.

Next

Next, we look at ways to cease breastfeeding, both sudden methods and slow ones, plus the issue of bottle refusal.

19 Switching from Breastfeeding to Bottle-Feeding

HOW TO SWITCH A BABY FROM BREASTFEEDING TO BOTTLE-FEEDING • COMBINING BREASTFEEDING AND BOTTLE-FEEDING • ALTERNATIVES TO BOTTLE-FEEDING • STEPS TO TAKE IF YOUR BABY REFUSES TO BOTTLE-FEED

A baby is considered "weaned" when she stops nursing and gets all her nutrition from sources other than the breast.

If your baby is under the age of six months, the only viable option will be to wean to bottle-feeds. If she is nine months or older, you could wean her onto solid foods and a cup if she refuses to drink milk from a bottle. The two options for weaning from breastfeeding to bottle-feeding are gradual and sudden (or rapid) weaning. I will describe both methods in this chapter. I will also explain steps to take if your baby refuses to feed from a bottle.

Before ceasing breastfeeding

Holding lactation consultant qualifications, among others, I know the benefits of breastfeeding and I promote and support breastfeeding mothers. However, I appreciate that parents choose the best option for their baby in the context of their baby's and family's unique circumstances. Every parent, regardless of their choice of infant feeding method, should be supported.

I respect the parent's right to decide how to feed their baby. However, I know from experience that many nursing mothers have regrets about giving up breastfeeding. I would like you to feel confident that it is **your decision** to switch from breastfeeding to bottle-feeding, and that you have not been misled into believing your baby would be more content or better off being bottle-fed or switched to infant formula—because rarely is this the case.

If there is a need for your baby to feed from a bottle—there are numerous reasons why this might be the case—have you considered combining breastfeeding and bottle-feeding? This is possible, even in situations where a breastfed baby currently refuses bottle-feeds or when it is suspected that the baby is suffering from gastrointestinal or other symptoms caused by a food allergy or intolerance linked to foods eaten by the mother.

If you have doubts or regret your decision to give up on your goal to breastfeed your baby, consider consulting with an International Board Certified Lactation Consultant (IBCLC). An IBCLC can advise how to resolve common breastfeeding problems that may be affecting your baby's feeding or causing you pain, confusion, or anxiety.

If you have decided it is necessary for your baby to accept milk feeds from a bottle, the next step is to determine if she is willing to accept milk from a bottle. If she outright refuses to suck from a bottle at this point in time, your options may be limited.

Bottle refusal

It is common for breastfed babies over the age of three months who have limited bottle-feeding experience to reject bottle-feeds. Bottle refusal can be caused by one or more of the following

- breastfed baby not knowing how to bottle-feed;
- breastfeeding preference; or
- bottle-feeding aversion.

Important: Be sure you understand the reason for your baby's bottle refusal, as **different causes require different solutions.** You might notice that some of the strategies I recommend you try to support a baby to learn to feed from a bottle or encourage a baby with a breastfeeding preference to feed from a bottle—described in this section—might be listed in other chapters as something to avoid. Some of the "gentle persuasion" strategies described in this section are counterproductive in the case of a bottle-feeding aversion.

If you start introducing your baby to bottle-feeding **late**—after the age of three months—or if she has developed a breastfeeding preference, she may reject the bottle. Either because she doesn't know how to bottle-feed or she wants to breastfeed instead. However, you can use strategies to encourage and support her to learn to feed from a bottle or to bypass bottle-feeding completely. These can be grouped under the following categories:

- gentle persuasion;
- alternatives to bottle-feeding; and
- desperate measures.

Gentle persuasion

If your baby rejects a bottle-feed, firstly try gentle persuasion. The following tactics will be more effective if your baby is under the age of 12 weeks, but they are worth trying for older babies.

Basically, gentle persuasion methods involve trying a multitude of different scenarios to see if your baby may be more receptive to sucking from a bottle under certain circumstances.

- **Level of hunger.** Try when hungry, when not hungry, before a breastfeed, after a breastfeed, between breastfeeds.
- **Level of consciousness.** Try offering a bottle as your baby drifts off to sleep, is stirring from sleep, or while already asleep. **Note:** Only do this until she gets used to sucking from a bottle, which may be your goal at this time. If you repeatedly feed her while drowsy, you will encourage a feeding-sleep association, which can cause feeding and sleeping problems down the road.
- **Nipple shapes.** Try different shaped nipples. I recommend you try a latex, orthodontic-shaped nipple, which is brown and softer than a silicone nipple and has a shape more similar to the mother's nipple when in the baby's mouth compared to others.
- **Flow rates.** Experiment with nipples with different flow rates.
- **Feeding positions.** Try feeding positions different from the one used when breastfeeding.
- **Locations.** Try bottle-feeding your baby in places she does not normally associate with feeding, such as a baby rocker or stroller.

- **Distractions.** For instance, offer your baby the bottle as you walk around with her in your arms, rocking her and singing to her, or when dangling a toy within her arm's reach. **Note:** This is a temporary measure. Don't do it over the long term because it's exhausting and not necessary. Also, avoid this if your baby has developed a bottle-feeding aversion.
- **Other caregivers.** Your baby may associate you with breastfeeding. Let others try bottle-feeding. Ask your partner, mother, or mother-in-law to try to feed your baby using a bottle.
- **Fresh breast milk.** Offer freshly pumped milk rather than milk that has been refrigerated or frozen.
- **Drip feed.** Drip some milk into your baby's mouth before placing the nipple into her mouth. **Note:** Not recommended if a baby has a bottle-feeding aversion.
- **Silicone bottle.** Use a soft-sided silicone bottle which enables you to gently squeeze a little milk into your baby's mouth, which may help her to connect the bottle with satisfying her hunger. **Note:** Stop doing this once she is willing to actively suck from a bottle. This too is not recommended for babies with a bottle-feeding aversion.
- **Encourage sucking.** Encourage your baby to latch and suck on your nipple, finger, or pacifier and then quickly replace this with the nipple of a bottle. **Note***:* Not recommended if a baby is averse to bottle-feeding.
- **Stop if your baby becomes tense or upset.** Try again once she is calm or at another time.
- **Don't pressure or force.** If your baby isn't drinking from the bottle, it's because she does not know how or because she has developed an aversion to bottle-feeding owing to being pressured to bottle-feed in the past. Trying to pressure or force her will only upset everyone involved.
- **Discourage a breastfeeding-sleep association.** Your baby may reject bottles if she has developed a breastfeeding-sleep association—learned to depend on suckling at the breast as a way to fall asleep (see pages 297-298). Before you can leave her in the care of others, you may need to be sure that she can easily be settled to sleep in your absence.
- **Remain patient.** Your baby is not being deliberately difficult.

It could take weeks of repeated exposure before your baby accepts the nipple into her mouth and sucks from a bottle using gentle, persuasive strategies. Unfortunately, these measures won't work for every baby. Some babies will continue to resist, fuss, or cry until they finally receive a breastfeed.

Alternatives to bottle-feeding

If you are concerned about nipple confusion, or if your baby refuses to feed from a bottle, she can receive milk **during your absence** in other ways, including from a spoon, syringe, or feeding cup, or through milky solids.

Birth to 6 months

If your baby is only days or weeks old, you can use a syringe, spoon, or baby cup feeder. Although these are time-consuming options, they can be a helpful temporary alternative to bottle-feeding in the following circumstances:

1. **nipple confusion**. They minimize the risk of nipple confusion while a newly born baby is learning to breastfeed;
2. **substitute for a breastfeed**. They can stand in during a brief separation from mom when baby refuses to bottle-feed.

A **supply line** is also an alternative if you're concerned about how much milk your baby receives **while breastfeeding**. This tiny tube is taped to mom's nipple, delivering formula or pumped breast milk, so your baby still has the sensation of latching to the breast while feeding. A lactation consultant can advise on this option.

Six to 9 months

When a baby is between six and nine months, milk from an open cup or milk added to cereal can be an effective alternative to bottle-feeding during **brief periods** of separation from mom—up to six hours or so.

While a baby can begin to feed from an open cup or straw cup at this stage, few babies of this age have developed sufficient skills for a cup to be a substitute for a breast or bottle-feed during **regular or long periods** of separation, for example, if mom returns to full-time work.

Nine months+

If your baby is over the age of nine months, you may find her hunger can be satisfied by solids. You would breastfeed when with your baby. When separated, you could leave breast milk to be offered in an open cup or straw cup or mixed with cereal or vegetables. You could add a food thickener to breast milk to make a milky pudding to be spoon-fed. Provided your baby is not allergic to dairy, you can give yogurt and cheese too.

Desperate measures

Desperate times call for desperate measures. If it's essential for your baby to feed from a bottle—for example, if she is younger than six months of age and you are returning to full-time work—it's not going to be practical for a caregiver to provide milk using alternative means in the long term.

If your baby currently rejects milk from a bottle, you may then need to decide how important it is that she bottle-feeds. If this is not practical for your baby to feed from a syringe, spoon or cu, it may be necessary for you to do a sudden wean described on pages 258-263 or partial wean described on page 262.

Gradual weaning

With gradual weaning, you will take away one breastfeeding session at a time until your child is no longer nursing. Gradual weaning can take weeks, months, or years to fully complete. Wait until you and your child have adjusted to the change and are comfortable with the new routine before eliminating the next feeding.

Advantages and disadvantages

Gradual weaning allows you and your child time to adjust physically and emotionally to the eventual end of breastfeeding. Also, your body has time to adjust, which enables your production of breast milk to decline slowly. That way, you may be able to avoid painful breast engorgement, plugged milk ducts, and mastitis, which can occur with weaning suddenly.

A gradual wean may not work for a baby who refuses to bottle-feed. Even when motivated by hunger, a baby who has no prior experience with bottle-feeding or who has a breastfeeding preference or who has developed a bottle-feeding aversion may repeatedly reject bottle-feeds and wait, albeit unhappily, until she is finally offered a breastfeed. She might start to demand breastfeeding more often during the night to compensate for skipped feeds in the day and develop a reverse-cycle feeding pattern where her nutritional needs are met in the night rather than in the day.

Sudden weaning

Sudden weaning, also called abrupt weaning, involves swapping all breastfeeds for bottle-feeds.

Sometimes, unexpected situations or medical emergencies can arise that make it necessary for a breastfed baby to be suddenly switched to bottle-feeds. A sudden wean may be the only viable option if a gradual wean is not working because of bottle refusal.

Advantages and disadvantages

It's a quick method of ceasing breastfeeding.

Stopping breastfeeding abruptly can be unsettling for a breastfed baby who willingly bottle-feeds. It can be distressing for a baby over the age of three months who refuses bottle-feeds because she doesn't know how to bottle-feed.

For mom, a sudden wean is associated with an increased risk of breast engorgement, plugged ducts, and mastitis. However, you can prevent or manage these problems by pumping or hand expressing to relieve pressure and any lumps and gradually reduce the frequency of pumping and hand expressing over time to allow milk production to slowly decline.

When your baby accepts bottle-feeds

If your baby willingly accepts bottle-feeds, a sudden wean will be a simple matter of offering bottle-feeds when she signals hunger. It may be a little unsettling for your baby for a few days, but she will adjust quickly.

When your baby rejects bottle-feeds

If your baby doesn't willingly accept bottle-feeds, a sudden wean will not necessarily be "sudden". A baby over the age of three months who does not have prior bottle-feeding experience will require time to learn how to suck from a bottle.

A neurologically healthy baby can learn to bottle-feed, even after her sucking reflex has disappeared. Renee thought it might help her four-month-old to learn how to suck from a bottle if she demonstrated the skill. But bottle-feeding is not something a baby learns by example. Without an active sucking reflex, she's going to need to learn through trial and error.

Plan in advance

- **Choose a nipple.** Don't be swayed by claims that a particular nipple is "like mom's." A synthetic nipple will not feel anything like a nursing mother's nipple. Decide on what you feel is the most appropriate nipple for your baby, and stick with it. Repeatedly switching nipples will only confuse her even more.
- **Choose the type of milk.** If possible, provide pumped breast milk during the weaning process. If you need to switch her onto infant formula once she is weaned, do so gradually. (See pages 138-139 for how to switch from breast milk in a bottle to formula in a bottle.)
- **Choose a time to start.** Suddenly weaning a baby who does not know how to bottle-feed from the breast to bottle is going to be upsetting for your baby, and you, at the start. Plan for a time when you do not have other commitments. And plan on being home for at least three days. If your baby willingly accepts bottle-feeds sooner, that will be a bonus.

Kayla didn't realize that lack of planning would make separation more stressful for her baby, Maisy.

> **Kayla's email**
> *"I am in my first week back to work and have had no success getting my three-month-old to bottle-feed yet. We started trying when she was four weeks old. My husband got her to take almost an ounce once at that time but barely anything since. We've tried several different bottles and positions and working with a lactation consultant. She gags and also seems to get upset anytime I try the bottle.*
>
> *I work 11 hours, four days a week. Daycare has been trying to get her to take the bottle. She gets upset pretty quickly but has let them keep the bottle in her mouth longer than she lets me. She's not sleeping because she's not eating, and she is distraught. This week, I've had to go to the daycare center to breastfeed her two to three times a day, but I can't keep that up long term. I don't know what to do to make her*

drink from a bottle. I'm so stressed. It's breaking my heart to see her so upset. I feel so guilty. If she doesn't start to take a bottle, I might have to quit my job." Kayla

Not only did Maisy not know how to suck from a bottle, but she had also learned to rely on breastfeeding as a way to fall asleep. She was distraught by the situation of abruptly needing to learn to feed and fall asleep in ways that were foreign to her, especially at a time when she was also separated from her mother for extended periods while cared for by strangers. This was a **huge** number of changes for a little baby to make at the same time.

Following a consultation with me to discuss ways to encourage Maisy's acceptance of bottle-feeds and to support her to learn how to fall asleep without being breastfed to sleep, Kayla decided to take a week off work to fix these problems before sending Maisy back to daycare. Resolving these problems enabled Maisy to receive nutrition from the bottle and get the sleep she needed. Having her nutritional and sleep needs met meant Maisy was significantly more content at daycare than she was previously, and Kayla was able to work without the burden of her precious little baby being distraught in her absence.

Important: If your baby currently falls asleep while breastfeeding, remedy this situation before attempting to switch to bottle-feeds. If you don't, getting her to accept bottle-feeds will be doubly stressful because she's going to have to learn to fall asleep in a new way at the same time that she's likely to be hungry. Teaching her to fall asleep without breastfeeding to sleep **before** switching her to the bottle will help reduce the stress she may experience when learning to bottle-feed.

What to expect

It could take a number of days for your baby to learn to feed from a bottle. Below is an example of what to expect during this time.

- **Refusals.** A baby who doesn't know how to suck from a bottle is not going to suddenly start to do so simply because she's hungry. Expect a number of complete rejections in the early days.
- **Small volumes.** When she does accept and suck from a bottle, she may take only a small amount before rejecting. Expect low volumes in the early days. The volume will gradually increase over a number of days.

- **Crying and irritability.** She will likely become upset from hunger and confused and frustrated because of the sudden denial of breastfeeds and being offered a bottle instead. This too will resolve as she learns how to bottle-feed.
- **Clinginess.** She's going to require a **lot** of attention. Plan to be home in the early days so you can provide the attention she needs.
- **Sleep disturbance.** She may find it difficult to fall asleep and stay asleep until her milk intake improves. You might need to give her extra support to fall asleep and stay asleep.
- **Weight loss.** She could lose a little weight over the first few days but experience "catch-up" growth once she's feeding well from a bottle.
- **Be patient.** Expect gradual improvement over a period of three to five days.

How to offer

- **Offer.** Get into the habit of offering your baby the bottle as described on pages 220-221. However, because she doesn't yet associate a bottle with satisfying her hunger, she won't give signals of acceptance at the start. But don't give up. She will once she learns to associate bottle-feeding with satisfying her hunger.
- **Don't pressure her to accept.** Respect her right to reject by removing the bottle.
- **Offer twice only per feed.** Avoid harassing her with repeated offers over a short period of time.

How to respond to crying

Expect crying episodes when suddenly weaning a baby who refuses bottles. This is how I recommend you respond:

- **If your baby is crying in rejection,** stop. Go for a break and help her to calm, and try a second offer when she's calm.
- **If your baby is crying from hunger,** you may need to place the nipple into her mouth. If she pulls her head away or rejects in other ways, accept her rejection. If she's not rejecting but also not latching, give her five minutes to see if she starts to suck. But stop sooner if she becomes upset. If she's not sucking after five minutes, remove the bottle, and take a break or end the feed.

- **If your baby is distraught because of hunger**, try offering her an ounce of pumped breast milk or infant formula from a spoon, syringe, or cup to take the edge off her hunger pangs, and once she's calmer, offer the bottle.

Remain patient. As distressing as it is for you to observe your precious baby crying in hunger and refusing to suck from a bottle, don't try to pressure or force her to accept the nipple into her mouth or suck. Pressure will make the experience of bottle-feeding even more upsetting. Repeated pressure risks causing her to become fearful of bottle-feeding. This will significantly delay the process of weaning to bottle-feeds or cause a bottle-feeding aversion. Bottle-feeding might then become a battle that continues over the long term.

Prevent dehydration

Dehydration is not a common problem during a sudden wean of a physically well baby, but you need to be mindful of it.

Before attempting a sudden wean, consult with your baby's healthcare professional to discuss a plan to prevent dehydration. They can provide advice specific to your baby's age and situation. You may not need to use the plan if your baby quickly figures out how to bottle-feed, but having a plan you don't need is better than panicking because you are unsure what to expect or how to handle the situation.

Here are options to discuss with your baby's healthcare professional.

1. **Consider doing a partial wean**, where you might only offer bottles during the day (meaning an 11- to 12-hour period), but breastfeed at bedtime and on-demand during the night. Once your baby is feeding from a bottle during the day, decide if you wish to switch her from breastfeeding to bottle-feeding at night. Be aware that a baby over the age of six months could develop a reverse-cycle feeding pattern, meaning she receives all or most of her milk needs at night. If that's the case, she may continue to reject bottle-feeds during the day until you reduce the number of breastfeeds you offer at night.
2. **Offer a small amount of breast milk or infant formula from a spoon, syringe, or cup** during the day. Bear in mind that the more milk your baby receives in these ways, the less incentive she will have

to feed from a bottle, and the longer it will take for her to successfully wean to bottle-feeds. At some point, she may receive enough milk in these ways to enable her to continue to reject bottles. But this also needs to be balanced against the risk of dehydration and soothing a distressed baby.

3. **Offer a little water** from a syringe, spoon, or cup. If your baby is younger than three months, you may need to limit the amount. If she is over the age of three months, she can decide how much she wants. If you have concerns about giving your baby water, discuss this with her doctor.
4. **Offer cereal mixed with breast milk or formula from a spoon before bed** if your baby is over the age of four months.
5. **Try sleep-feeding,** which is feeding your baby while sleeping during the overnight period.

If you see no improvement by the end of day three, stop and return to breastfeeding, and seek advice from your baby's healthcare professional. Sooner if you are concerned.

Next

Next we go to Part F, where I will describe behavioral (nonmedical) causes for fussy, distressed, and avoidant feeding behavior that is often mistakenly attributed to physical problems and medical conditions.

PART F:
Behavioral Problems

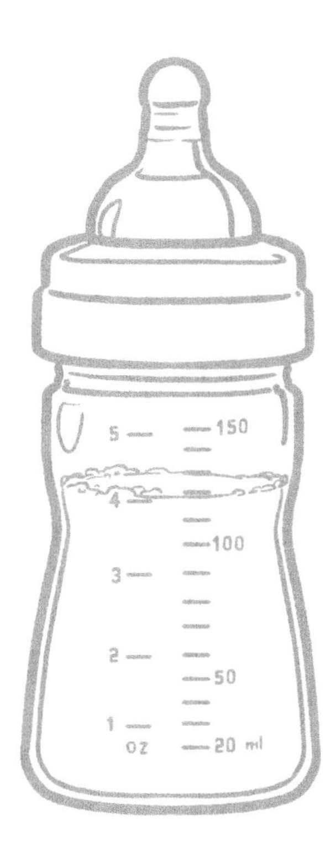

20 Types of Behavioral Feeding Problems

BEHAVIORAL (NONMEDICAL) FEEDING PROBLEMS • MINOR AND MAJOR FEEDING PROBLEMS • INFANT FEEDING PRACTICES SELF-EVALUATION CHECKLIST

"Behavioral" means the baby's behavior occurs in response to the circumstances—in particular the parent's choice of feeding equipment and infant feeding practices. The baby's behavior is **not** caused by a physical problem or related to a medical condition and therefore requires a nonmedical solution.

Behavioral causes are, without exception, **the most common** of all reasons for infant feeding problems. And yet, they are often overlooked, misdiagnosed and mismanaged by health professionals and others who are unfamiliar with behavioral reasons for healthy, typically developing babies to display problematic feeding behavior.

Some behavioral feeding problems are more prevalent at different stages of babies' development. In this chapter I describe **the types** of behavioral feeding problems. You will find details about each in the respective chapters of Part F. Physical and medical causes for infant feeding problems are described in Part G.

How common are infant feeding problems?

Between 25 and 45 percent of normal healthy babies develop feeding problems.[139] But this doesn't mean you should be worried. Most feeding difficulties are **behavioral** or nonmedical, meaning there is **no underlying physical problem or condition** responsible.[140] This is good news! It means you can do something about most feeding issues, usually without medical intervention.

Some problems naturally fade away as a baby matures. Some are corrected as a result of changes to the way feeds are managed and some from effective medical treatments. Others, such as refusal to eat—affecting three to 10 percent of children—can persist over the long term.[141]

Infant behavioral feeding problems can present in different ways. I group these as minor or major according to the complexity of the problem, how distressing it is for the baby and parents, and how easy it is to resolve.

Minor feeding problems

Minor feeding problems include the following and more:

- snacking (taking frequent small feeds);
- excessive feeding at night (feeding more often at night than would be expected for the baby's stage of development);
- repeatedly falling asleep while feeding;
- swallowing a lot of air while feeding; and
- feeding too slowly or too quickly.

Chapter 28 includes more examples of concerning behaviors before, during, and after feeding.

Minor feeding problems generally have **no ill effect on the baby's health or growth**. However these issues, plus countless other small oversights on the parent's part, can be a source of frustration for the baby and parents.

During your baby's health checkup, you may have expressed concerns about your baby's troubling behavior only to be told "it's normal," "some babies don't like to eat," "some babies prefer feeding during sleep," or "he'll outgrow it." While minor feeding problems are common, they're not "normal," and you can take action to improve the situation. Minor feeding problems are usually quick to resolve. You just need to make a few **appropriate adjustments** to your baby's feeding equipment or your infant feeding practices, or both. Once you have identified the cause, the solution will be obvious.

In some cases, minor feeding problems will pass in time without you doing anything different. But for others, inappropriate steps taken may mean the problem continues or evolves into a major feeding problem.

Major feeding problems

Major feeding problems include dietary regulation problems and feeding aversions.

Dietary-regulation problems

Dietary regulation problems primarily relate to the volume of milk or the number of calories a baby consumes or both and may include

- underfeeding;
- overfeeding;
- oversupply of breast milk; and
- reverse-cycle feeding pattern, meaning the baby receives more milk or calories during the night than he does during the day.

These problems are also linked with concerning behaviors. **Underfeeding, overfeeding and an oversupply or breast milk** can cause babies a great deal of distress and are more likely to be experienced by newborn babies. A **reverse-cycle feeding pattern,** which is usually apparent after the age of five months, is more likely to cause the parents distress.

Dietary regulation problems are usually quick and relatively easy to resolve once the causes have been identified and corrected.

Feeding aversion

A feeding aversion—where the baby displays avoidant feeding behavior despite obvious signs of hunger or only accepts feeds while dropping off to sleep or already asleep—is a common problem. It typically develops when a baby has been repeatedly pressured or forced to feed. A feeding aversion is a common reason for underfeeding and poor growth. However, not all feeding-averse babies are underfed or display poor growth.

Effect on babies and parents

I classify dietary regulation problems and feeding aversions as **major feeding problems** because they can have significant repercussions for the baby and parents, including the following:

- **Baby:** infant distress, gastrointestinal symptoms, poor or excessive weight gain, sleeping problems, delayed development, impaired infant-to-parent bonding, and feeding tubes; and
- **Parent:** extreme anxiety, depression, social isolation, fear of being judged as inadequate, loss of confidence, impaired parent-to-infant attachment, financial strain, and a strained relationship with a partner from unrelenting stress.

Only families that have had babies with major feeding problems can truly appreciate just how stressful the situation can become.

Misdiagnosis is common

When a baby has a major feeding problem, it's obvious that something is seriously wrong. If a baby wellness checkup is not due, you'd probably make an appointment with your baby's primary healthcare professional to discuss your concerns.

More often than not, in such cases, pain is blamed for the baby's distressed or avoidant feeding behavior. But this is often a mistake! For most healthy babies, physical causes or medical conditions affecting a baby's mouth, throat, or digestive tract are **not** to blame.

Top causes

Behavioral feeding problems are directly linked to the parents infant feeding practices and are more common when parents employ parent-led feeding practices compared to baby-led feeding.

The top four **causes** for behavioral feeding problems include:

1. overlooking or misinterpreting behavioral cues;
2. non-responsive or inappropriate responses to infant behavioral cues;
3. infant sleeping problems; and
4. access problems.

These might present in various ways.

Overlooking or misinterpreting behavioral cues

We are all inexperienced when we first become parents. Without an understanding of infant development and behavior, there's a good chance that we will at times

- mistake infant reflexes and other behavioral cues as hunger;
- overlook or mistakenly interpret our baby's satiety cues;
- assume signs of stress indicate pain; and
- erroneously misinterpret concerning behaviors (described in chapter 28).

Baby care problems develop because of the choices we make and the actions we take, or don't take, in response to our baby's behavioral cues, all of which have the potential to cause frustration, anger, or stress for all involved.

Non-responsiveness or an inappropriate response

Sometimes, our responses don't match the baby's cues, wants, or needs. He will let us know, perhaps with mild irritation initially. However, the longer he waits, the more intense his behavior will grow. The intensity of his reaction depends on his age, temperament and his past experiences.

If we recognize errors and change course, there is usually no harm done.

If we persist in trying to make baby bend to our will—for example, by pressuring him to feed—we risk causing him to develop a major behavioral feeding problem, either overfeeding or feeding aversion. Repeatedly providing an inappropriate response can accidentally teach the baby to react with greater intensity.

Sleeping problem

Most, but not all, babies who experience a feeding problem also have a sleeping problem. We often assume that the baby is sleeping poorly because he's not eating well. This can be true. However, the opposite also applies. If a baby is not sleeping well, he may not feed well.

The two most common reasons for infant sleeping problems include **sleep association problem** and **circadian rhythm misalignment.**

In many instances, I find a sleep association problem develops first, often very early, sometimes when the baby is as young as one to two weeks of age. This causes broken sleep and sleep deprivation, which then becomes the trigger for events that lead to dietary regulation problems such as under- or overfeeding or circadian rhythm feeding problems, such as snacking or reverse-cycle feeding pattern.

Access problems

A baby cannot feed well if he is prevented from accessing the milk. When I watch parents feeding their babies, I often observe one or more of the following problems:

- poor positioning of the baby's body, head, or the bottle;
- nipple is too long, too short, too fast, or too slow; and
- vacuum issue, which affects the flow rate.

Consequently, the baby might cough and splutter and become frightened if the flow rate is too fast. Alternatively, he may become frustrated or fall asleep when his access is hampered because of poor positioning, slow nipple flow, or a vacuum problem.

Compounding factors

Just one of the points mentioned has the potential to cause minor feeding problems. Add more, and there is a greater potential for major behavioral feeding problems to occur. Usually, more than one cause is involved—for example, if you're not sure how to interpret your baby's hunger or satiety cues, you might also miss tiredness cues. If you feel like you're constantly being challenged by one baby care problem after another, you may need to work your way through the behavioral causes mentioned above to rule them out.

How to resolve behavioral feeding problems

Most behavioral feeding problems can be prevented and solved using the same strategies.

The solution to minor or major feeding problems lies in **your** hands; you just have to identify the correct cause. The causes tend to be the same for all behavioral feeding problems, which makes life a bit easier. A combination of causes—which can vary for individual babies—can create specific feeding problems.

Let's look at how to systematically assess and identify possible causes for your baby's feeding issues.

Stage One

If your baby is physically well, check behavioral causes first. Look at the Infant Feeding Practices Self-Evaluation Checklist below to make sure you've covered all behavioral reasons for infant feeding problems.

Infant Feeding Practices Self-Evaluation Checklist

- ☐ You are aware of the caloric concentration of your baby's milk (breast milk or formula), and how this will impact his total daily milk intake. (See chapter 11 if you provide high-calorie or thickened feeds for your baby.)
- ☐ You are following a semi-demand feeding pattern (described in pages 31-37) to decide when to offer feeds.
- ☐ Your baby's head, body, and bottle are in optimal feeding position for feeds. (See chapter 15 if unsure.)
- ☐ Your baby feeds at a comfortable speed. (See page 184 for the ideal feeding duration for age.)
- ☐ The shaft of the nipple is not too short. (See pages 307-809 if unsure.)
- ☐ The bottle or nipple is venting correctly. (See pages 301-306 if unsure.)
- ☐ You are offering the bottle to your baby, watching for signs of acceptance or rejection and responding accordingly. (See chapter 16 for how to respond.)
- ☐ You allow your baby to decide how much to eat and are not using "annoying" or pressure-feeding tactics (described in 275-279) to make him continue eating after he signals that he wants to stop.
- ☐ You provide for his sucking needs between feeds. (See pages 69-71.)
- ☐ You discourage drowsy feeding during the day.
- ☐ You discourage a feeding-sleep association (described in pages 297-298) both day and night.
- ☐ You know when to anticipate and can recognize signs of tiredness (described in pages 288-289).
- ☐ You have resolved any sleeping problem your baby may have. (See chapter 22.)

If you can check all the boxes above, you will significantly reduce the chances of your baby developing feeding and sleeping problems. Alternatively, if your baby has developed a feeding problem, you can correct most, but not all, infant feeding problems by taking the steps recommended in the checklist. Some of the major feeding problems, like overfeeding, underfeeding, reverse-cycle feeding pattern, and bottle-feeding aversion, may require additional strategies, which I describe in the related chapters.

If you are unsure about your responsiveness to your baby's behavioral cues while feeding, video yourself feeding your baby and play it back. This will enable you to watch the feed from an observer's viewpoint, and you can be more objective about your baby's feeding behavior and your responses. Alternatively, ask your partner, parent, or friend to provide feedback.

If, after checking all of the boxes in the checklist above and having read more about behavioral feeding problems in the remaining chapters of Part F, your baby still has feeding troubles, move to Stage Two.

Stage Two

A small percentage of babies can experience feeding troubles because of physical problems or medical conditions that cause pain or which negatively affect their sucking and swallowing abilities. These are described in the chapters of Part G.

A confirmed—as opposed to assumed—physical problem or medical condition does **not** exclude your baby from developing behavioral problems. So don't skip Stage One just because your baby has a diagnosed condition.

Next

In the remaining chapters of Part F, I describe how and why different behavioral feeding problems develop, and how they can be resolved.

As you read through the chapters, you may recognize that you have made errors in judgment. As painful as it may be, it's important to identify these errors for the sake of your baby's health and your mental health. Recognizing the cause of your baby's troubles is the key to finding an effective solution.

In the next chapter, I will describe the most common of all reasons for babies to display problematic feeding behaviors and physical problems related to feeding—parents' infant feeding practices.

21 Unhelpful and Unsafe Feeding Practices

WAYS WE MIGHT ANNOY, FRUSTRATE OR STRESS A BABY WHILE FEEDING • SUBTLE AND OBVIOUS FORMS OF PRESSURE • POTENTIALLY HARMFUL FEEDING PRACTICES

During my career, I have observed hundreds of parents—mostly mothers, but fathers, too—feeding their babies. I find this to be an invaluable part of a feeding assessment when the reason for a baby's feeding or growth problem is unclear.

I sometimes find baby's feeding position or faulty or unsuitable equipment is making it difficult for the baby to effectively latch, suck or swallow. However the most prevalent of all reasons for healthy babies to display fussy, distressed or avoidant feeding behavior is because parents, in general, are not taught how to interpret and respond to their baby's cues of hunger and satiety, a.k.a. **baby-led feeding**, and instead, use **parent-led feeding** practices, which encourage parents to decide—possibly based on the advice of a health professional—when their baby "should" eat and how much is "enough".

If you're not following your baby's lead, it's possible that some feeding strategies that you are using could annoy, frustrate, anger or stress her, or which may be potentially harmful to a baby. While this realization would undoubtedly be a bitter pill for any loving parent to swallow, it's better that you know than to risk unknowingly cause her troubles.

Unhelpful and unsafe feeding practices

The fact that parents and caregivers might at times employ unhelpful or unsafe feeding practices is not surprising. In general, the parents of babies born at term would receive more instruction on how to drive a car than on how to care for the newest and most vulnerable member of their family.

The parents of preterm babies or babies with special-needs might have been instructed on how to use parent-led feeding practices. If their baby was **incapable** of self-regulating her dietary intake at the time, such advice would have been appropriate. However, once their baby matures and gains skills that enable her to feed effectively and display behaviors that demonstrate her ability to decide for herself when and how much to eat, the continued use of parent-led feeding practices can become the reason for their baby's troubled feeding behavior.

Feeding practices that are potentially unhelpful or unsafe include the following

- pressuring a baby to feed;
- force feeding;
- annoying feeding practices;
- bouncing, swinging or rocking while feeding;
- sleep feeding;
- unsupervised self-feeding;
- prop feeding.

Of course, some parents will tell you they do some or all of these practices, and their baby has not experienced any problems. While that might be the case, this doesn't mean such practices are without risk.

Pressuring a baby to feed

Examples of ways a baby could be pressured to feed include

- pushing the nipple into her mouth through clamped lips;
- preventing her from pushing the nipple out of her mouth with her tongue;
- following her head with the bottle when she turns or arches back in a tense manner;
- restraining her head to prevent her from turning away;

- restraining her arms to prevent her from pushing the bottle away;
- repeatedly offering when she's rejecting;
- hovering with the bottle in her line of sight after she has rejected—in the hope of persuading her to change her mind;
- using a "bait and switch" method by switching out her pacifier for the nipple;
- trying to make her suck when she's fussing or crying;
- upward pressure under her chin in a bid to trigger her sucking reflex when she pauses or stops sucking;
- gently compressing a crying baby's cheeks to apply pressure on her buccal (sucking) pads to make her seal her lips around the nipple;
- jiggling or twisting the bottle to try to make her continue sucking when she pauses; or
- squeezing milk into her mouth.

We have all used some or most of these strategies at one time, or many times, while feeding a baby. We may think we're "encouraging" baby to accept the feed because **we** have decided it's time for her to eat, or "supporting" her to take a little more because **we** don't think she's had enough. But in reality, we're using gentle or not-so-gentle forms of pressure to make her take the nipple into her mouth and continue sucking against her will. In other words, we are employing parent-led rather than baby-led feeding practices.

Why parents pressure their baby to feed

In around 75 percent of feeding-aversion cases I have been involved with, the parent first started to pressure their baby to feed because they were told by a health professional that either their baby needed to consume X ounces or milliliters of milk each feed or each day, or she was not gaining sufficient weight.

These two reasons exceed all other reasons for parents to pressure their baby to feed. But these are not the only reasons, and it's not necessarily health professionals pressuring parents to ensure their baby consumes a specified volume of milk. In many instances parents ask health professionals for targets to confirm their baby is eating enough. Other reasons why parents might overlook or ignore their baby's satiety cues and pressure their baby to consume more than she is willing to eat include:

- they don't want to "waste" expensive baby formula or precious breast milk—which took ages to pump or which might be in short supply;

- they want to help a small baby to achieve catch-up growth;
- they want their baby to grow healthy and strong;
- they hope that making their baby drink more will encourage her to sleep longer;
- they worry that their baby's crying is from hunger;
- they fear something bad will happen if their baby doesn't eat an expected volume of milk.

Most parents are unaware of the potential harm that can be caused by pressuring a baby to eat more than she is willing to eat. For example, they might cause a newborn baby to **overfeed** (see chapter 25) or make the feeding experience unpleasant or stressful for their baby which when repeated could cause her to develop a **bottle-feeding aversion**—which is one of the most common reasons for babies to underfeed (see chapter 27).

Parent-led feeding practices don't automatically cause infant feeding problems, they just increase the risk. Whether parent-led feeding practices cause overfeeding or a feeding aversion depends on

- the volume the parent expects their baby to consume—whether realistic or overestimated;
- the baby's stage of development—younger or older than eight weeks of age; and
- whether the parent responds in harmony with their baby's wishes or overlooks their baby's behavioral cues indicating satiety or rejection and persist in trying to make her eat more.

Consider how you might feel if pressured to feed. Would you be happy to allow someone else to decide when and how much you ate? If the timing and amount matched your energy requirements, maybe you would. But what if the timing was wrong or the amount provided was more or less than you wanted, would you be compliant and willing to accept if others used the feeding strategies listed? Or would you become upset or angry?

If you are feeling frustrated by your baby's feeding behavior, this may be an indication that your feeding practices are out of sync with her needs. It may be that you are trying to make her comply with your wishes rather than the other way around.

Your baby will communicate her wishes vocally and through her behavior. The question to ask yourself is "Are my feeding practices showing my baby that I'm listening"? (See chapter 16 for recommendations on how to read and respond to a baby's feeding cues.)

Force feeding

If your baby refuses to eat despite obvious signs of hunger—which is typical behavior when a baby has developed a feeding aversion—you might try to force her to feed out of **loving concern**—worried that something bad will happen to her if she doesn't eat enough. Or it may be the way you have **been taught** to feed a "resistant" baby. It was the way I was taught to feed "fussy feeders" when I was a student nurse. It's the way many health professionals are taught to respond when a baby refuses to eat "enough", and it's what many teach parents.

While a parent, caregiver or health professional may have the best intentions—to ensure the baby eats enough for healthy growth—**forcing a baby to feed is wrong** on many levels. It can cause physical and emotional harm to a baby. For example

- **aspiration.** Milk will pool in the baby's mouth if she's unwilling to feed. If she is crying at the time—which is highly likely if she is being forced to feed against her will—she may not be able to effectively coordinate sucking, swallowing and breathing.
- **vomiting.** When stressed, the digestive system shuts down increasing the risk of vomiting.
- **fear of feeding.** While force-feeding can make a baby consume more milk or food at that point in time, it can create long-term feeding battles that lead to poor growth.
- **loss of trust.** Trust can be lost when a baby is repeatedly force fed. The baby may start to avoid eye contact with the parent while feeding. Some feeding-averse babies will cry if the parent who forces them to feed holds them.

I appreciate that forcing a baby to eat is not something any loving parent wants to do. Parents usually only resort to such drastic measures when they have serious concerns about their baby's health and physical wellbeing and don't know how to resolve the problem of their baby's feeding refusal.

Forcing your baby to eat is not an effective solution. It will only make the situation worse.

If you believe your baby will choose to starve if you don't use force, it's very likely she has developed a feeding aversion (see chapter 27).

Annoying feeding practices

Being pressured or forced to feed is not the only reason for babies to display troubled feeding behavior linked to their parent's infant feeding practices. There are other ways that parents' actions or inactions while feeding their baby might unknowingly annoy, frustrate, anger or stress her. Examples of annoying feeding practices I have observed parents doing while feeding their baby include

- continuously jiggling and twisting the bottle while the nipple is in their baby's mouth, causing her to lose suction;
- constantly moving, repeatedly changing their position or their baby's position, or the angle of the bottle, which breaks the feed or causes her to lose suction;
- repeatedly breaking the feed to wipe their baby's face, adjust her clothing or to burp her;
- persisting with burping for too long, not realizing that their baby is crying in frustration because she wants to continue eating;
- keeping the nipple in their baby's mouth while she is bearing down in response to the gastrocolic reflex (described on pages 67-68);
- paying no attention to their baby while she feeds—instead playing with their cell phones or watching television;
- continuing to hold their baby in a feeding position once the feed has ended, causing her to be unsure whether the parent has ended the feed or they will try to continue to feed her;
- feeding their baby in the same position they use to settle her to sleep. She may then be confused about the parent's intentions.

Being attentive to your baby and responsive to her behavioral cues while feeding her is how you can support her to develop a healthy relationship with food and promote a strong emotional bond with you. Allow her to continue feeding while she's content to do so without interrupting the feed.

If she behaves in a concerning or confusing manner while feeding see chapter 28 for possible causes to help you decide how to respond.

Bouncing, swinging or rocking while feeding

Some parents get into the habit of using movement while feeding their baby. They might feed their baby while holding her in their arms as they stand and make bouncing movements or while they sit bouncing on a yoga ball, or they feed their baby in a baby bouncer, swing or rocking chair.

Movement while feeding can negatively impact a baby's latch, suction, and sucking and swallowing coordination and the flow rate from the bottle. It can increase the risk of

- swallowed air;
- gagging;
- aspiration; and
- gastroesophageal reflux (GER).

Usually, the parent starts to do this as a means to coax their baby to continue eating a little longer. When repeated, it becomes what their baby learns to expect. And she may then refuse to feed or eat very little while stationary. This situation may develop simply from habit—the parent's or baby's—or it may be an **early sign** of a feeding aversion.

I often find that parents **initially** use motion to help their baby to remain calm while feeding as they use gentle forms of pressure to make her "finish the feed". Pressure, subtle or obvious, can cause a baby to become averse to bottle-feeding when repeated. As their baby's aversion to feeding progresses, they then find they need to use motion to get her to accept the nipple and start to suck.

If your baby is highly likely to refuse to eat if not bounced, rocked or swinging, and this is a situation you would like to change, follow the feeding strategies I recommend for resolving a bottle-feeding aversion, described in my book, *Your Baby's Bottle Feeding Aversion*. The feeding strategies described can be used to change a habit of only willingly feeding while there is movement even if a baby does not have an aversion to bottle-feeding.

Sleep feeding

Sleep feeding or "dream feeding" describes the process of feeding a baby while she's sleeping. It's different from a feeding-sleep association (described in pages 292-298) because the baby is not reliant on feeding **as a way to go to sleep,** and hence, dream feeding does not cause sleeping problems. But it can cause feeding issues for some babies.

The parent, and not the baby, initiates the feed. In other words, the baby does not demand this feed—she's asleep. A parent might choose to feed their sleeping baby for one of the following reasons.

- **Reduce the chance of their baby waking from hunger at night.** In general, babies under the age of six months require one or more feedings during the night. Providing a baby with a feed while asleep, before she wakes to demand one, **might** help her to continue sleeping. The benefit is that the parent does not need to settle her back to sleep.
- **Change their baby's nighttime feeding pattern.** From three months of age, some babies will have their longest block of continued sleep in the first half of the night and wake in the early hours of the morning to feed. A parent might find it more convenient to provide a late evening "dream feed" before they go to bed, hoping their baby might then sleep until she wakes for the day. If the timing of the "dream feed" does not match the baby's circadian rhythms, it won't work.
- **Increase their baby's total daily milk intake.** A parent might choose to provide one or more sleep-feeds at night to increase their baby's total daily milk intake. In general, it's ineffective because it encourages a reverse-cycle feeding pattern resulting in the baby eating less the following day. So it merely changes the timing of her feeds.
- **It is the only way their baby feeds.** Some feeding-averse babies will get to the point where they will completely reject feeding while awake, but feed without resistance during their sleep. Rather than battle with their baby to get her to eat while awake, the parent might resort to feeding her at each nap and multiple times during the night.

I am not a fan of sleep feeding a baby because it's not led by the baby. It's yet another example of parent-led feeding practices that may or may not match the baby's natural biological rhythms. If you're giving feeds that are not demanded by your baby, there is potential for unintended consequences such as

- **circadian misalignment.** One thing you need to be aware of is that the gastrointestinal (GI) tract functions very differently during the day when food is consumed compared to the night. When sleep occurs, the digestive system slows down. When and for how long depends on the baby's stage of development. Providing feeds at night that are not demanded by a baby risks derailing her natural body rhythms;
- **increased risk of tooth decay.** The frequency of swallowing decreases during sleep compared to awake. Milk can pool in a baby's mouth, providing food for bacteria. The bacteria change the sugar in the milk to acid, and this will increase the risk of tooth decay;
- **aspiration.** When a baby is fed while sleeping, she may not be fully coordinated for safe feeding. Sleep feeding is associated with an increased risk of a baby aspirating milk into her lungs.[142]

Of course, many babies feed during sleep without experiencing any observable complications. However, the incidence of babies experiencing one or more of these problems is greater when fed while falling asleep or when already asleep compared to feeding while awake—when the baby is aware she is feeding and has greater control over the feed.

There are exceptions to just about everything surrounding baby care issues. In the case of a severely sleep-deprived baby who is too physically exhausted to wake and demand feeds during the night, sleep feeding might be necessary. However, a more effective solution is to resolve the baby's sleeping problem.

If you feel compelled to feed your baby while she sleeps because she refuses to feed while awake or because she appears to favor feeding in a sleepy state, check if she has developed a feeding aversion (chapter 27). If you sleep-feed her at night because you feel she is not eating enough during the day, consider if you might be encouraging a reverse-cycle feeding pattern (pages 316-318).

Unsupervised self-feeding

From around eight months of age, some babies can hold the bottle and feed independently. Self-feeding does not necessarily pose a greater risk compared to being fed by an adult. It's the fact that the baby might be left to feed unsupervised that increases the risk.

Choking is silent.

While it's okay to let your baby hold and control the bottle and feed independently, she needs to be fully supervised while feeding in case she needs your help to clear her airways.

Allowing a baby to fall asleep unsupervised while sucking on a bottle and lying flat in her bed involves three risky practices in one. (See pages 206-207 for problems associated with a baby feeding while lying flat.)

Prop feeding

Prop feeding is where the baby's bottle is supported by an object, such as a cushion or rolled towel or commercially produced bib that holds the bottle. This, too, is associated with an increased risk of aspiration. Prop feeding also denies the baby the emotional satisfaction of feeding in a parent's loving embrace and engaging with her parent while feeding.

Prop feeding is not self-feeding. Props are used because the baby is **not** capable of holding and controlling the bottle and self-feeding. Some parents choose to prop feed their baby so they can do other things while their baby feeds. This may result in the baby being unsupervised or only partially supervised.

The risk of aspiration is higher in the case of newborns who, because they lack maturity, can't control the rate of flow from a bottle, or push the bottle away if in trouble.

How to clear a baby's airways

- Don't panic.
- Hold your baby so she is lying face down along your forearm.
- Use the heel of your hand to give up to five blows in the middle of the back between her shoulder blades.

Next

In the next chapter, I will describe the relationship between feeding and sleeping, why babies have trouble sleeping, how lack of sleep negatively affects babies' feeding behaviors and feeding patterns, and where to find solutions to baby sleeping problems.

22 Sleep and Feeding Connections

SLEEP AND FEEDING RELATIONSHIP • FEEDING PROBLEMS CAUSED BY SLEEPING PROBLEMS • WHY HEALTHY BABIES HAVE TROUBLE SLEEPING

Supporting your baby's sleep may have a positive effect on his mood, appetite, feeding behavior, and the volume of milk he consumes, as well as his general contentment. It will also increase your confidence in providing for his needs. Once he's happy, feeding, sleeping, and growing well, you'll get to enjoy your role as his parent so much more than you do already.

What is the connection between sleep and feeding?

Sleep is a basic human need. It's as important to your baby's health as nutrition. Your baby's sleeping patterns are the cornerstone to stabilizing his circadian rhythms (pages 23-25) and thus his feeding patterns and willingness to feed.

Lack of sleep can wreak havoc on your baby's circadian rhythms, distorting the timing of the secretion of the many hormones that affect his bodily functions, including **appetite, digestion,** and immune function.[143] I find infant sleep deprivation is **often** the underlying cause of numerous baby care issues, including incessant crying and feeding problems.

It's difficult to resolve a baby's feeding problem without taking steps to fix a sleeping problem, and vice versa. When a sleeping problem prevails, the baby's feeding behavior, milk consumption, and growth may not be ideal. Typically, a sleeping problem develops first, which then becomes the catalyst for feeding problems. Feeding problems can then negatively affect sleep.

Your baby needs to sleep well before he can feed as well as possible.

Feeding problems linked to lack of sleep

A number of infant feeding problems can develop in **direct** response to an unresolved sleeping problem, including

- **overfeeding.** Can happen especially when tiredness cues are mistaken as hunger;
- **underfeeding.** Stress impacts appetite. A sleep-deprived baby might also fall asleep before feeding to satisfaction;
- **fussy feeding behavior**. An overtired baby may lack the coordination to synchronize sucking and swallowing, or he might appear conflicted between eating and sleeping;
- **grazing.** If your baby's naps are brief, he could develop a "snack" feeding pattern, taking small but very frequent feeds during the day; and
- **reverse-cycle feeding pattern**. If an overtired baby does not feed well during the day, he may want to make up for this by feeding more at night. Over time, he might develop a pattern where he eats more at night than he does during the day.

Misguided attempts to resolve sleep issues

A number of other feeding problems can be **indirectly** linked to an underlying sleeping problem. If you suspect your baby's short naps or frequent awakenings in the night are from hunger, you might try to make him eat more than he wants by adding extra calories to his milk feeds or using pressure tactics. But if hunger is not the reason for his sleeping problem, then employing such strategies risks:

- overfeeding;
- feeding aversion; and
- early end to breastfeeding.

What babies need to sleep well

Table 22.1 describes ways parents can support their baby to develop healthy sleep habits and what might happen if a baby does not get the type of support he needs.

Table 22.1: What a baby needs to sleep well

What baby needs to sleep well	When baby doesn't get what he needs
Someone to recognize when he's tired and provide him with an opportunity to sleep.	If his signs of tiredness are overlooked or misinterpreted, the risk of overtiredness increases. Once stressed because of physical fatigue, he will find it difficult to fall asleep.
A low-stimulation sleeping environment.	If the environment is too stimulating, he may remain awake despite his readiness to sleep, thus increasing the risk that he becomes overtired.
Familiar sleep associations—the conditions he has learned to associate with the act of falling asleep.	Without his familiar sleep associations when he's ready to sleep, he may remain awake and risks becoming overtired.
Help **calming**—if he becomes upset while settling to sleep; how much help he will need depends on his age, physical capabilities, and self-soothing skills. He does not **need** help to fall asleep—though he might want help if this is what he has learned to expect.	If you go beyond calming your baby and actively assist him in falling asleep, you could teach him to depend on your help to fall asleep. Expect that he will wake every time he notices your help is missing. If you encourage him to rely on props or aids to sleep that either fall out, switch off, or change after he has fallen asleep, he's likely to notice this during light sleep and wake prematurely.
Support to stabilize his circadian rhythms	He may develop an abnormal day-night sleeping or feeding pattern, which can stress both him and you.

How much sleep do babies need?

Knowing how much sleep is average for babies at different ages may help you determine if lack of sleep is the reason, or partial reason, for your baby's unsettled or distressed behavior.

Table 22.2: Average number of sleep hours for each age

Age	Average total sleep time (hours)	Average night sleep (hours)	Average day sleep (hours)
1 week	16.5	8.5	8
1 month	15.5	8.75	6.75
3 months	15	10	5
6 months	14.25	11	3.25
9 months	14	11.25	2.75
12 months	13.75	11.75	2

Please consider the table above as a guide only. If your baby is happy, healthy, and thriving, it does not matter how much sleep he's getting—it's enough. However, if he's not getting close to average sleep and is often fussing or distressed, don't overlook sleep deprivation as a potential cause.

How babies display tiredness

Your ability to **accurately** identify your baby's signs of tiredness is a crucial first step in supporting him to receive the sleep he needs.

Birth to three months

Behaviors that may indicate tiredness, starting from early, more subtle behavior to later, not-so-subtle behavior, include

- whining → crying → screaming;
- glazed stare → looking away → turning head away (babies cannot turn their head away until about two months of age) → back arching (usually not until around three months of age);
- frowning → facial grimacing (a pained expression, which involves tightly shut eyes and an open mouth);
- clenching fists tightly;
- pulling up knees;
- waving arms and legs → jerking, quick arm and leg movements; and
- seeking comfort through sucking or feeding.

In general, newborn babies don't display universally recognized signs of tiredness like yawning and rubbing eyes. Instead, they show signs of increasing distress. Plus, they display similar behavioral cues to demonstrate their uneasiness irrespective of whatever is troubling them—such as tiredness or hunger or a desire to suck. Hence, you may need to use **timing** and **context**—for example, how long it's been since your baby last fed or slept—to determine the most likely reason for his unsettled behavior (see chapter 7).

Three months+

By three months of age, many of your baby's infant reflexes have disappeared, and he has gained greater voluntary control over his arm and leg movements. Behavioral cues that indicate tiredness are easier to recognize in this age group. These include

- whining → crying → screaming;
- loss of interest in toys or playing;
- glazed stare;
- sucking on fingers or hands;
- pulling ears or hair;
- rubbing nose or eyes;
- yawning;
- clinginess;
- low frustration tolerance; and
- easily upset.

Babies in this age group won't necessarily yawn when they're tired. So, if you're waiting to observe a yawn before settling your baby to sleep, you could be leaving it too late.

When to expect to see tiredness cues

In addition to learning what behavioral cues to watch for, it can help to know when to anticipate your baby may be tired and ready to sleep. Below you'll find the average time awake for babies between naps during the day. During the night, you don't want to encourage any time awake other than that required for feeding.

Table 22.3: Average wake time for age

Age	Estimated wake time during the day, including feeding time
2 to 6 weeks	1 to 1.25 hours
6 weeks to 3 months	1 to 2 hours
3 to 6 months	2 to 2.5 hours
6 to 9 months	2.5 to 3 hours
9 to 12 months	3 to 4 hours

Consider the timeframe relevant for your baby's age, but watch for early signs of tiredness before trying to settle him to sleep. If the timing is right, and you notice signs that he is becoming unsettled, you could feel reasonably confident that tiredness is the cause. But also bear in mind that when naps are broken for behavioral, developmental, or physical reasons, a baby will probably show signs of tiredness much sooner, possibly within minutes of waking up, because of insufficient sleep.

Overtired baby

Overtiredness goes beyond the normal level of tiredness that indicates a baby is ready to sleep. Overtiredness means the baby is lacking sleep (sleep deprived) to the point where it stresses his body. When overtired his body releases stress hormones—cortisol and adrenaline—which trigger a "fight or flight" response. An overtired baby will find it difficult to fall asleep and will cry often and easily.

Crying is one way the body releases stress. As the parent of a young baby, you have likely suffered sleep deprivation at times to the point where you felt like you could cry. The distress displayed by severely sleep-deprived babies is **often** mistakenly blamed on pain caused by a medical condition—such as colic, reflux, or milk allergy or intolerance.

Signs of overtiredness

Unlike adults who become lethargic when overtired, babies and young children become hyperactive. A sleep-deprived baby

- receives well below the average amount of sleep for his age;
- appears to fight going to sleep;
- finds it increasingly more difficult to fall asleep as the day progresses;
- sleeps very little during the day most days;
- is easily woken by even the slightest noise, such as doors opening or people talking;
- wakes excessively or sleeps unusually long periods during the night without waking for feeds;
- appears to have an insatiable appetite;
- appears uncomfortable during feeds;
- may at times be too upset to feed;
- may feed briefly or fall asleep before the feed is completed;
- is difficult to get to smile or engage in eye contact;
- often has a worried expression;
- is generally more content in the mornings than in the afternoons;
- has a short attention span;
- requires constant attention from you when he's awake;
- wants to be held continuously, fusses in your arms, but cries whenever you put him down;
- resists going into his pram, highchair, crib or car seat;
- likes to be jiggled or rocked endlessly;
- startles often;
- experiences extreme separation anxiety;
- displays frequent crying outbursts;
- cries often, ranging from whining to vigorous inconsolable crying.

Of course, all babies behave in these ways from time to time. It is the degree and frequency to which a baby displays these behaviors—particularly if he's getting much less than average sleep for his age—that points to sleep deprivation.

Why babies become overtired

There are several reasons for a baby to be lacking sleep. In the case of physically well babies, broken sleep and lack of sleep mostly occurs because parents do not fully appreciate what their baby requires from them to sleep well (described in table 22.1). Consequently, the parent does not provide the type of support their baby needs or at the right time.

Most new parents, and some experienced parents, are unaware of the profound effect sleep associations will have on their baby's ability to fall asleep and stay asleep; hence on the amount of sleep he receives. Next I will explain what sleep associations are.

Sleep associations

Sleep associations are the conditions, props, and activities we learn to link with the act of falling asleep. When a baby repeatedly falls asleep in a particular way—for example, while feeding, being cuddled, rocked, or patted—he learns to link these activities with the act of falling asleep. Over time, he starts to rely on familiar conditions to be present when he needs to sleep.

Babies as young as two weeks of age may have already linked certain sleep associations with the act of falling asleep. Others may be more flexible about how they go to sleep or take longer to learn to rely on particular sleep associations.

Your baby's sleep associations **strongly** influence his sleeping patterns as well as his ability to fall asleep and stay asleep. Therefore, identifying his sleep associations and understanding how they affect his sleep will greatly benefit you and your baby.

Sleep associations can be divided into two groups: **positive** and **negative.**

Positive sleep associations

A positive sleep association remains **consistent and unchanged** from the time the baby falls asleep throughout the time he needs to sleep. If it's always there, the baby can smoothly move from one sleep cycle to the next, and the risk of him waking prematurely between sleep cycles is minimized. Examples of positive sleep associations include

- baby's bed (crib, cot, or bassinet), but only if he falls asleep while in his bed;
- swaddling (babies under the age of three months);
- infant sleep sack (babies over the age of three months);
- thumb or finger sucking; and
- security blanket or soft toy (after the age of six months).

Your baby will still wake if he has a physical need that requires attention, but he's not going to repeatedly wake as a result of noticing his sleep associations are missing because positive sleep associations are always present. The chance of him sleeping longer is greatly enhanced.

Babies generally learn to rely on more than one sleep association. These could involve a combination of positive and negative ones. Reliance on even one negative sleep association could override the benefits of multiple positive sleep associations.

Negative sleep associations

A negative sleep association is **present when the baby falls asleep but absent once he has fallen asleep**. This may be because it has been removed, falls out, switches off, or changes in some other way. Examples include parent-assisted sleep associations and unreliable props that a baby learns to depend on **as a way to fall asleep**, such as when being:

- fed (breast or bottle);
- cuddled in a parent's arms, on a parent's chest, or while bed sharing;
- carried in a sling;
- patted to sleep;
- stroked;
- shushed;
- rocked to sleep in a bouncer, rocker, crib or stroller, baby swing, or hammock;
- jiggled, bounced, swayed;
- driven around in a car until asleep; or
- given a pacifier to suck.

Occasionally settling a baby to sleep in one of these ways does not mean he has learned to connect it with sleeping. It would require repetition for the baby to link these things with the act of falling asleep and learn to depend on them as a way to go to fall asleep. When a baby has learned to depend on something to fall asleep, it becomes a sleep association.

Whether negative sleep associations disrupt your baby's sleep—and by extension, your sleep—depends on his level of awareness, his temperament type, and your ability and willingness to provide your baby's sleep associations **as often and for as long** as he needs. Key times when negative sleep associations are first likely to be observed as problematic are around the age of two weeks, and if not at that young age, they may start to disrupt sleep around four months of age.

Whether you consider wakefulness problematic or not depends on individual circumstances. What is problematic to one parent might not be an issue to another.

"Negative" does not imply these sleep associations are wrong or bad. It means they have the potential to have a negative impact on a baby's sleep if they do not remain with him throughout the time he needs to sleep. If you are able to maintain parent-assisted sleep associations—like being cuddled to sleep—and can do this day and night, the effect on his sleep can be positive. However, few parents find they can sustain this level of support 24/7 for an indefinite period. The toll this takes on their own sleep and their physical and mental health is too great.

Why babies appear to fight against going to sleep

During the **first two weeks after birth**, most babies are "good sleepers." Most have not learned to rely on specific sleep associations yet.

Once your baby has learned sleep associations, which for some can be as early as two weeks after birth, he now may no longer fall asleep easily. Instead, he will want his sleep associations to be present when he is tired and ready to sleep.

When your baby first displays early and subtle signs of tiredness, you have a small window of opportunity to provide his sleep associations, possibly five to 15 minutes for a newborn and up to 30 minutes for babies over three months. If you provide his sleep associations within this window, he will settle to sleep with relative ease. However, if you **withhold his sleep associations** because you overlooked his tiredness cues—for example, misinterpreted his cues as hunger—or were unaware that he needs his sleep associations to fall asleep, he will remain awake. The longer he's denied his sleep associations, the more desperate he becomes to sleep. His tiredness cues escalate from minor fussing to whining to crying and eventually to screaming.

Once he's overtired and distressed, his body releases stress hormones that hype him up. At this point, unwinding and falling asleep is really difficult, even if you have provided his sleep associations by then. It then appears like something is preventing him from falling asleep or that he is fighting going to sleep.

> The distress displayed by overtired babies is often mistakenly attributed to pain, typically colic or reflux. Believing colic is caused by gas, the parent might try burping, bathing, or tummy massage. However, by doing so, they may be overstimulating an overtired newborn and inadvertently adding to his distress. He then screams inconsolably for what can be hours until finally falling asleep out of sheer exhaustion.

This scenario is played out in countless households every night, mainly because parents don't know how to recognize babies' tiredness cues or the effect of sleep associations on their baby's sleep.

Why babies experience broken sleep

During light sleep, your baby is semi-aware of what happens to him. He can sense if he's being moved—for example, if he has learned to fall asleep while being held upright in your arms, he may then notice if you try to lay him down in his bed to continue sleeping. If he has learned to fall asleep in his crib while you pat or rock him, he may wake if you stop while he's in light sleep or wake when you try to creep out of the room and the floorboard creaks.

During deep sleep, it's like he is in a semi-comatose state; you could change his clothes or place him into his crib, and he wouldn't notice. But he won't stay in a deep sleep stage for long. He will return to light sleep before arousing or awakening.

The length of a **sleep cycle** varies with age. In general, the younger the baby, the shorter the sleep cycle. Sleep cycles also vary depending on the time of day and level of tiredness. The average length of time for one daytime sleep cycle is approximately

- 20–40 minutes for babies up to three months;
- 30–60 minutes for ages three to 12 months; and
- 60–90 minutes for over 12 months.

A **daytime nap** can consist of one sleep cycle or two or more sleep cycles linked together. Babies usually require at least one or two of their daytime naps to consist of two or more sleep cycles to receive the necessary amount of sleep.

During the first half of the night, when the need for sleep is greatest, babies tend to spend more time in deep sleep; therefore, their sleep cycles are longer. In the latter part of the night—the very early hours of the morning—sleep cycles are shorter.

When moving from one sleep cycle to the next, a baby experiences a brief period of **arousal,** where his levels of consciousness and awareness are increased. He's not fully awake but not asleep either.

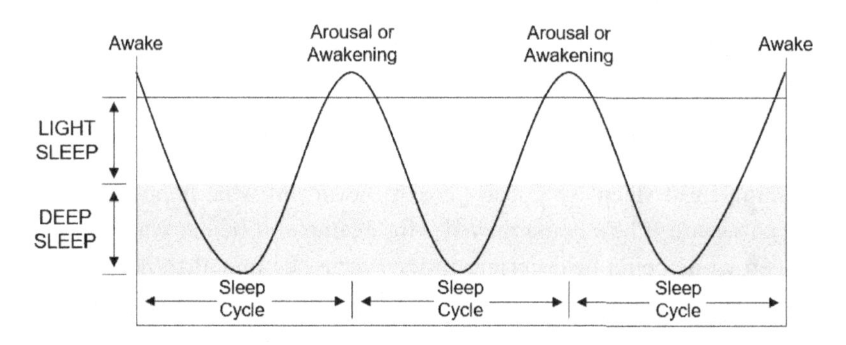

These arousals enable him to subconsciously check his comfort and safety. You might hear or see him stirring during an arousal; he might stretch or give a brief cry and then go quiet as he moves into a new sleep cycle. This repeats until his sleep needs are met, and he wakes refreshed. Three different scenarios can occur that lead to broken sleep.

1) You misinterpret his arousal as him waking, and you might get him up prematurely.

2) He might sense the absence of his sleep associations when he arouses—for example, he is now in his crib instead of being held upright in your arms where he first fell asleep.
3) He may have a physical need that requires attention—for example, he is hungry, feels hot or cold, has a soiled diaper, or feels other discomfort.

When a healthy baby consistently wakes after a brief nap—the length of one sleep cycle—or wakes excessively in the night, it's usually because he notices the absence of his sleep associations. That's when parents who are unaware of infant tiredness cues or the effect of negative sleep associations might take misguided steps to try to make their baby consume more food.

Feeding-sleep association

Parents are often actively encouraged to allow their baby to fall asleep while feeding by people who claim that it's "natural." While it is common for babies, especially newborns, to fall asleep while feeding it is linked with a number of problems. While I promote baby-led feeding, feeding a baby to sleep is not something I recommend. I will explain why.

All babies will at times fall asleep while feeding. When this happens only occasionally, it doesn't usually cause problems. However if a baby repeatedly falls asleep while feeding this can encourage feeding to become a sleep association.

A feeding-sleep association means the baby learns to depend on feeding—breastfeeding or bottle-feeding—as a means to fall asleep. Of all possible sleep associations, none is more problematic than this one because the **potential to create both feeding and sleeping problems** is greater compared to other negative sleep associations.

A feeding-sleep association will cause the baby to appear hungry and display a desire to feed—regardless of whether he is actually hungry or not—whenever he is tired and ready to sleep. This means he will at times be feeding for the wrong reason. It also makes it very difficult for his parents to tell the difference between hunger and tiredness.

His sleep can be broken if he notices his sleep association (breast or bottle) absent during arousals that naturally occur between sleep cycles, resulting in brief naps and frequent night awakenings—similar to what can happen with any negative sleep association. But with a feeding-sleep association, the baby wants another feed simply because he is reliant on feeding as a way to go to sleep or return to sleep. If not given another feed, he may remain awake and risks becoming overtired.

The combination of broken sleep and feeding for the wrong reason can cause circadian rhythm misalignment (pages 23-25), resulting in an erratic and unpredictable feeding and sleeping patterns and increase risk of the feeding problems listed on page 286… **and more**.

Circadian rhythm sleeping problems

A circadian rhythm sleeping problem means the baby's sleeping pattern is out of sync with a normal 24-hour pattern. Examples include:

- Baby's feeding and sleeping patterns are erratic and unpredictable.
- Baby sleeps long periods in the day but is awake for hours in the middle of the night when parents need to be sleeping.
- Baby may stay awake into the late evening, well beyond when his parents would like to be sleeping, but then sleeps in late the following morning.
- Baby falls asleep for the night in the afternoon (before 5:00 pm) but is then awake in the **very** early hours of the morning, energetic and ready to start his day long before the family is ready to get up.

A circadian rhythm sleep problem tends to cause the parents more distress than baby. However, if parents take inappropriate steps to resolve the problem, such as leaving their baby—who is not tired at the time because of his misaligned circadian rhythms—to cry for hours in the evening, night, or morning, this will obviously cause distress.

Typically, a circadian rhythm sleeping problem develops on the back of a sleep association problem.

Based on my experience, broken sleep and sleep deprivation caused by a sleep association problem is the most frequent cause of **circadian misalignment**, which in turn creates circadian rhythm sleeping problems (mentioned above) and circadian rhythm feeding problems (described in chapter 24), also dietary regulation problems such as under- and overfeeding.

Solve your baby's sleeping problem (if he has one) and you could prevent a multitude of baby care problems.

How to improve your baby's sleep

For more information about infant sleep and how to change a baby's sleep associations or resolve a circadian rhythm sleeping problem and improve the quality of his sleep, refer to my book *Your Sleepless Baby: The Rescue Guide*, available in print and various ebook formats from leading online booksellers.

Next

Now that you understand the importance of sleep, the next step is to confirm that your baby's feeding equipment is not making it hard for him to access milk from the bottle.

23 Top Equipment Problems

VACUUM PROBLEMS • NIPPLE FLOW RATE ISSUES • FAULTY, DAMAGE OR INAPPROPRIATE EQUIPMENT • HOW TO RECOGNIZE AND REMEDY EQUIPMENT PROBLEMS

If your baby is not eating as much as you expect, fusses or cries, appears uncomfortable when feeding, or has been diagnosed with colic or reflux, you might question if the feeding equipment is causing these problems. You may be tempted to change the type of nipples or bottles that you provide in the hope that this will help.

Babies are comforted by familiarity. Switching nipples or bottles without evidence that these are causing problems risks creating new problems if your baby objects to the change. Certain telltale signs point to equipment problems. Knowing these might help you decide if you need to change equipment or look elsewhere for reasons for your baby's feeding troubles.

How to tell if the equipment is at fault

In most cases where a baby is a fussy feeder and is refusing feeds or not eating enough, the feeding equipment is usually not the reason. However, in a small percentage of cases, the equipment **is** making it difficult for the baby to feed effectively. So how can you tell if the equipment is the problem?

Consider this question. How well does your baby feed in a relaxed, drowsy state or while sleep feeding? If your baby feeds comfortably at a good pace at these times, her equipment is fine. In this case, look elsewhere for the cause of her troubled feeding behavior or poor milk intake. If she doesn't feed well in this state, read on.

I will start with the most common equipment problem, which is when a vacuum forms in the bottle.

Vacuum problem

Neutral pressure within the bottle is maintained by air entering to replace the space left by the consumed milk. If air is prevented from entering, a negative pressure forms within the bottle and creates a vacuum, which affects the flow rate. As the vacuum builds, it begins to hold the milk back. Initially, a healthy baby can suck against the vacuum. However, as more milk is removed from the bottle without being replaced by air, the greater the strength of the vacuum within the bottle and the harder it will become for your baby to suck and receive milk.

Newborns may not have the stamina to continue sucking as the intensity of the vacuum builds. They can tire from the effort required and fall asleep without having eaten to satisfaction, only to wake hungry an hour or two later. Older babies can become frustrated by the effort involved.

You might knowingly or unknowingly partially counteract the effect of this problem by regularly removing the nipple from your baby's mouth to burp her. An older baby might also partially resolve this problem if she learns that releasing suction—by letting go of the nipple or turning her head periodically—makes it easier to suck. But periodically releasing suction is not the most effective solution to this problem.

How to recognize a vacuum problem

1. Your baby releases suction, and you see and hear air bubbles flooding into the bottle.
2. You remove the bottle from her mouth, and you see and hear air flooding into the bottle.
3. The nipple collapses in her mouth, she loses suction, you see and hear the air bubble flooding into the bottle, and the nipple pops out.

In all three scenarios, **the release of your baby's latch** enables air to enter into the bottle through **the hole in the end of the nipple**. The air flows through the milk in the form of tiny bubbles. (Note: Your baby cannot swallow these bubbles because she's not latched and not sucking at this time and may not even have the nipple in her mouth.)

Depending on the shape and stiffness of the nipple, some collapse and some don't. Silicone nipples are less likely to collapse compared to latex (rubber) nipples.

Let's look at what happens when baby feeds using nonvented nipples and bottles first. This may help you better recognize when vented nipples and bottles are not working.

Nonvented feeding equipment

When sucking from a nonvented nipple and bottle, air can enter the bottle only in two places: the hole at the end of the nipple and the tiny spaces between the nipple base and the bottle rim, which are hidden by the nipple ring.

While the baby is sucking, her tongue seals the hole at the end of the nipple. She can draw milk out, but air is prevented from entering through the hole while she maintains suction.

If the nipple ring is NOT screwed down too tightly

As a baby sucks, a negative pressure forms; this causes air to be drawn into the bottle past the nipple ring and through the tiny spaces where the nipple base and bottle rim meet. While the baby is latched and sucking, the entry point of air is nowhere near her mouth, and therefore, this air cannot be swallowed.

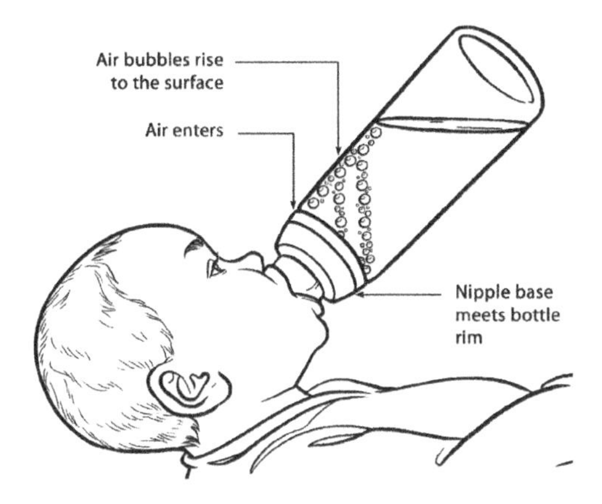

As the air enters the milk, it forms tiny bubbles. Air being lighter than milk means the bubbles quickly rise to the surface, where they disperse.

As the baby continues to suck, more milk is removed from the bottle, which in turn draws in more air. What you see is a constant and steady flow of bubbles moving through the milk and replacing the space of the milk that is removed by the baby's sucking. This constant flow of bubbles maintains a neutral pressure inside the bottle, prevents a vacuum from forming, and ensures an even flow rate. The baby can suck easily and access the milk at a consistent rate. This means she can continue feeding without being annoyed by vacuum issues negatively affecting flow rate.

Make sure you don't twist the nipple ring on tightly.

If the nipple ring IS screwed too tightly

To avoid leakage, the nipple needs to be secured to the bottle by the nipple ring. But if it's screwed down too firmly, it creates a seal between the nipple base and bottle rim and prevents air entry. If air can't enter the bottle while the baby is actively sucking, vacuum problems can result.

You might have been firmly tightening the nipple ring because you were told or read that your baby could swallow these bubbles and, in turn, suffer colic from swallowed air. **It's not physically possible for a baby to swallow these bubbles.** Or you might have been advised to tightly fasten the nipple ring to slow down how fast your baby feeds. (If your baby is feeding too fast, see page 184.)

The solution is simple. Loosening the nipple ring will allow air to enter the bottle between the base of the nipple and the bottle rim. This tiny detail will maintain a neutral pressure and a constant rate of flow throughout the entire feed and make feeding more comfortable for your baby.

Try fastening the nipple ring to the bottle until it just catches. It can take practice to find the right spot where the nipple is loose enough to allow air to enter but not so loose as to cause major leakage. When you can see a steady flow of bubbles into the bottle while your baby is sucking, you've got it right. You won't see a rush of bubbles after, when your baby has released suction or when you remove the nipple from her mouth. However, a little leakage when you tip the bottle upright can occur even when you have it right, so have a bib or burp cloth across your baby's chest while feeding to catch any drips.

Alternatively, you could choose a vented nipple or bottle system, which can prevent a vacuum from forming in the bottle, provided the venting system is working correctly. It doesn't always work, so check occasionally.

Vented nipples and bottles

Vacuum problems are now less common because of the wide range of vented nipples and bottles available today. However, equipment can become damaged and malfunction or be assembled incorrectly, preventing the venting system from working correctly.

There are various types of vented nipples and bottles. These fall into different groups based on how they function.

- vented nipples;
- "anti-colic" valves;
- base-ventilated systems; and
- reservoir tube systems.

Let's look at vented feeding equipment available and reasons why they might not work.

Reasons vented nipples might fail

Some nipples have a vent, a small indentation or dimple near the base of the nipple in which there is a tiny narrow cut through which air can be drawn into the bottle as the baby sucks. Hence, air can still enter the bottle even if the nipple ring is screwed down tightly. When it's working, you will see bubbles continuously flowing through the milk as your baby is sucking.

Sometimes, the edges of the cut get stuck together and prevent the nipple from venting correctly, in which case, you will only see bubbles after your baby releases suction. Squeeze the dimple to ensure the cut opens before attaching the nipple to the bottle to make sure it will work as intended.

Reasons "anti-colic" valves might fail

You will find a large variation in design between brands. Some have a valve integrated into the side of the nipple ring, and others are attached to the underside of the nipple before the nipple is attached to the bottle to allow air entry and prevent vacuum buildup.

Most work by enabling air to either pass through the milk—in which case, you will see bubbles flowing through the bottle while your baby feeds—or via a tube through which air travels toward the base of the bottle—in which case, you will not see bubbles.

A venting system might fail to vent correctly if the pieces are not assembled according to the manufacturer's instructions.

Reasons base-vented systems might fail

Base-vented systems either have an extra plate attached to the base of the bottle or a valve situated in the base of the bottle. This provides a third entry point for air into the bottle; hence, even if the nipple ring is tightly fastened and the baby maintains suction sealing the hole at the end of the nipple, the bottle can still vent. Because air is drawn through the base of the bottle, you won't see bubbles as your baby is drinking.

If you see bubbles while your baby feeds or as she releases suction, this could mean the venting system is not working correctly. The base of the bottle may be screwed on too tightly, or the small vents may have become blocked with clogged partially mixed baby formula.

Reasons a tube and reservoir system might fail

A tube and reservoir venting system channels air from the nipple or nipple ring toward the base of the bottle. You will not see bubbles as your baby feeds. These venting systems might not work effectively if you've

- **overtightened the nipple ring,** preventing air from entering the reservoir;
- **heated the bottle with the vent in place,** causing fluid to be pushed into the vent as the milk expands;
- **overheated the bottle**, causing steam to rise and condense in the vent;
- **shaken the bottle with the vent inserted,** causing milk to get into the venting system and leak out around the nipple ring;
- **overfilled the bottle,** causing milk to leak out around the nipple ring;
- **submerged the end of the tube** under the milk as your baby feeds, causing milk to flow back into the tube; or
- **offered a nipple that is too fast,** causing your baby to block the flow and the resultant pressure to force milk into the vent.

With these problems, all you need to do is stop the feed, turn the bottle upright, and loosen the nipple ring to release the built-up pressure. The milk will fall back into place at the bottom of the bottle, and you can then retighten the nipple ring and reoffer the bottle so your baby can resume feeding.

While there are a lot of reasons why this bottle system might not work, I find the tube and reservoir system to be one of the most reliable venting systems.

Are vented nipples and bottles necessary?

No, you don't need to use vented nipples and bottles. Previous generations of parents successfully bottle-fed their babies long before vented bottle systems were developed. While vented nipples and bottles can prevent a vacuum buildup—if assembled correctly—they achieve nothing more than can be achieved by slightly loosening the nipple ring on a nonvented bottle.

Nipple flow is too fast

If the speed of the nipple is too fast for your baby, she might display the following troubled behaviors.

- She may appear stressed as she tries to keep up with the flow.
- She might cough if milk threatens her airways.
- She could swallow a lot of air.

- She might stop because her stomach is full but fuss because she's not yet feeling satisfied. Feeling full and feeling satisfied don't necessarily occur at the same time (see pages 76-79 for explanation).
- She could overfeed, causing discomfort from the overstretching of her stomach, or she may spit up during the feed or soon after the feed has ended.

What to do

- Check the ideal feeding duration for each age on page 184.
- If your baby is feeding too quickly, move back a flow-rate level.

Nipple flow is too slow

If the nipple flow rate is too slow, this too could be problematic for your baby, and she may display some of the following behaviors.

- She might fuss and cry in frustration and swallow air as a result of her crying.
- She might give up before eating to satisfaction.
- She could fall asleep before completing the feed.

What to do

- Check the table on ideal feeding duration for age on page 184.
- First, confirm that the slow flow is not caused by a vacuum problem.
- If there is no vacuum problem, purchase the next level of nipples.

Nipple shaft is too short

Remember, the shaft is the part of the nipple that sits inside the baby's mouth. A nipple with a short shaft will sit forward in your baby's mouth and change her sucking action. To understand how the shaft length can affect a baby's sucking, try this exercise.

> Place your index finger in your mouth to the first joint and suck on it. Now insert your finger to the second joint and suck. Compare the difference. You will notice that it's easier to suck on something slightly longer.

A short shaft will require more effort on your baby's part to maintain suction. It will also increase the risk of her swallowing air. You might hear her making repeated clicking sounds while she's sucking. (See page 389 for other reasons for clicking.)

Bear in mind that your baby is growing at a rapid rate. The nipple shaft may have been a good length when you first purchased the nipples, but as her face and mouth grow, the nipple shaft could become too short for her.

What to do

- First, check the ideal feeding duration for your baby's age (see page 184).
- If the duration of the feed is slow, try moving up to the next level flow rate of the current brand of nipples, which will be larger but also faster.
- If, however, the timing is already within a normal range for her age, then switching to the next level of the same brand might cause complications if it's too fast. In this case, try a different brand of nipple, one with a slightly longer shaft like a narrow-based bell-shaped nipple (see page 186).

Nipple shaft is too long or too large

The length of the nipple increases along with the flow rate to accommodate the fact that a baby's face and mouth are getting bigger as she matures. If the shaft of the nipple is too long or too large, this could cause your baby to gag (see pages 381-382 for other reasons for gagging). It will affect her ability to maintain suction, increase the risk of swallowing air while sucking, and can cause her to tire from the effort. If she gags often, the unpleasantness of this experience could cause her to develop an aversion to bottle-feeding.

While companies provide recommendations on the nipple size for age, they won't suit all babies. A nipple that might be perfect for a large baby could be too big for a petite baby of the same age.

If you're providing **nipples meant for older babies**—because you want your baby to feed faster or because you are thickening her feeds—these could be too big for her.

What to do

- If a nipple recommended for age is causing your baby to gag, try a medium-wide-based nipple (page 187).

- If thickening your baby's feeds means you're providing nipples recommended for older babies, I advise you to reconsider this practice. (See pages 154-158 to determine whether you need to provide thickened feeds and read about more effective strategies to prevent milk regurgitation (reflux) on pages 432-433.)

Wear and tear

The length of time nipples last before requiring replacement depends on how often they're used. Sterilization methods that involve heat will cause the nipple to perish sooner compared to chemical sterilization methods. Replace **silicone nipples** every three months or earlier, if they show signs of wear and **latex (brown rubber) nipples** every three months or sooner if they feel sticky.

If you have any doubt about the condition of the nipples, replace them.

Mismatched equipment

Feeding equipment, in particular vented bottle systems, are designed to work with matching bottles and nipples. Attaching the nipple from one brand to a different brand of bottle can have a negative effect on the venting system and flow rate. I always recommend that you use matching equipment.

Incorrect assembly

Vented bottle systems need to be thoroughly cleaned and assembled correctly. A common mistake might be not pulling the nipple into the correct position in the nipple ring. Another is not using all parts of the venting system, for example, leaving out the tube of a tube and reservoir system, or disc of a vented nipple system. Be sure to follow manufacturer's instructions carefully when assembling your baby's feeding equipment.

Altering the equipment

Parents sometimes try to make the hole at the end of the nipple larger by cutting or using a red-hot needle if they believe their baby's current feeding nipples are too slow or become blocked from thickened feeds, but then also find the next level nipples are too fast.

What to do

- First, check the ideal feeding duration for your baby's age (see page 184).
- If the duration of the feed using current nipples is too slow, but the next level is too fast, consider switching brands.
- If the next-level nipples are not too fast, it may be a matter of allowing your baby time to adjust to the faster flow.
- If thickening your baby's feeds, confirm if there may be more effective strategies to prevent milk regurgitation, starting with prevention of overfeeding (chapter 25).

What to do if your baby has feeding problems

If your baby appears to experience problems feeding, confirm that she is well.

If your baby is well

1. Check for venting issues and whether the nipple size and flow rate are suitable. If she feeds well in a relaxed or drowsy state, her equipment is fine. Look elsewhere for the cause of her troubled feeding behavior or poor milk intake.
2. See my Infant Feeding Practices Self-Evaluation Checklist on page 272 to check if you are fulfilling your responsibilities related to feeding your baby.
3. Read remaining chapters in Part F, which describe behavioral reasons for feeding problems, some of which can cause distressed and avoidant feeding behavior; gastrointestinal symptoms such as vomiting and diarrhea; insufficient milk intake; and poor growth.

If your baby is unwell

Consult with her doctor, but don't overlook the possibility of behavioral reasons for her feeding problems.

Next

Next, I describe problematic feeding patterns, why they occur, and what you can do to support your baby to feed in a way that matches her circadian rhythms.

24 Feeding Pattern Problems

SNACK FEEDING • EXCESSIVE NIGHT FEEDING • REVERSE-CYCLE FEEDING • WHY BABIES' FEEDING PATTERNS GO ASTRAY • HOW TO FIX A FEEDING PATTERN PROBLEM

Consider the following questions.

- Is your baby consuming only small feeds in the day and then wanting to feed often?
- Does he wake more often at night to feed than you would expect for a baby of his age?
- Does he eat more at night than he does during the day?

If you answered yes to any of these questions, your baby may have developed a **circadian rhythm feeding problem.** This means a baby is feeding in a pattern that is out of sync with his natural body rhythms or a typical day-night pattern.

When a baby's feeding patterns go astray, it usually means he requires **more or less** guidance from his parents. An effective solution lies in identifying and correcting the cause and not in employing further methods to control when and how much he eats.

In this chapter, I describe how babies' feeding patterns can become misaligned with their circadian rhythms (see chapter 2), how this influences their appetite, and why some strategies that parents use to correct a feeding pattern problem cause their baby distress.

Circadian rhythm feeding problems

Circadian rhythm feeding problems can present in the following ways

- **snack feeding.** Baby has small, frequent feeds, and the number of feeds is significantly more than what is generally expected for babies of his age.
- **feeding excessively during the night.** Baby feeds more often at night than expected for his stage of development.
- **reverse-cycle feeding pattern.** Baby consumes more calories at night than he does during the day.

The degree to which a baby's feeding pattern could be misaligned with his circadian rhythms can vary. Let's look at these feeding patterns and what you can do to support your baby to feed in harmony with his natural body rhythms.

Snack feeding

Snack feeding (also referred to as "grazing") means baby consumes small but frequent feeds. His total daily volume is sufficient to support healthy growth, but he feeds more often than expected for a baby of his age. For some babies, this can be as frequent as every hour or two during the day. The following table depicts the average number of feeds per day for age.

Table 24.1: Average number of daily bottle-feeds for age

Age	24-hour period	Average range
Birth–1 month	7	6–8
1–3 months	6	5–7
3–6 months	5	4–6
6–9 months	4	3–5
9–12 months	3	2–4

One or two feeds more than the average for age is still within a normal range; however, more than this might indicate snack feeding. The following signs might mean a healthy baby is snacking:

- baby's weight is within a healthy range in relation to his length;
- he shows signs of being well fed (page 42);
- he consumes only a small volume at each feed during the day;

- he appears to be satisfied at the end of the feed; and
- he demands—or appears to demand—feeds more often than expected for his age.

If you suspect your baby is snacking, the next step is to identify the reasons—there is generally more than one. Your perspective of this situation will make a big difference in how successful you will be in solving this common baby care problem.

Broaden your perspective

Snack feeding can be viewed from a number of perspectives.

- Baby is incapable of consuming larger volumes; therefore, he needs to feed often.
- Baby eats very little; therefore, he needs to eat more often.
- Baby feeds often; therefore, he only needs to eat a little at each feed.

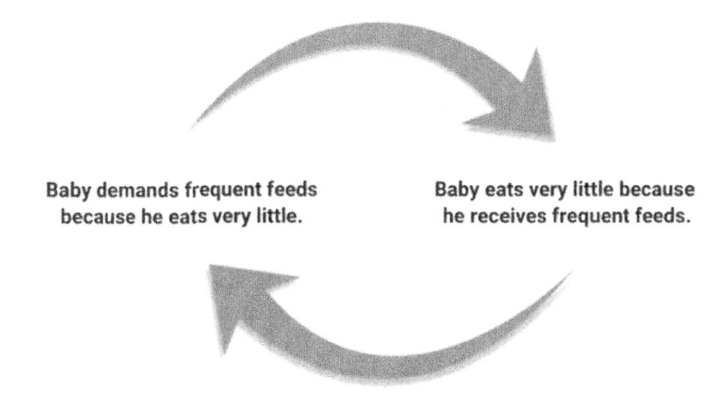

A narrow perspective limits the number of possible solutions. If you consider snack feeding from all perspectives, this will reveal more options on possible causes. For example, if he's a healthy baby with normal development or if he's consumed larger volumes in the past or currently does so at some feeds, you can establish that he's physically capable of consuming larger volumes. You can then look for other reasons that might be causing him to eat very little at each feed (described in pages 349–352).

If you believe your baby is physically **incapable** of taking bigger volumes, then discuss your concerns with his primary healthcare professional, who might recommend calorie-enhanced feeds so that he receives more calories in a smaller volume. This may help him to go for a longer period between feeds.

Excessive night feeding

Excessive night feeding refers to a situation where baby feeds at night more often than required at his stage of development. By night, I am referring to a 12-hour period, for example, 7:00 pm to 7:00 am or whichever 12-hour period represents an individual baby's "night." **Feeding during the night** refers to the number of times the baby wakes to be fed or is offered a sleep-feed after being settled for the night and **does not count the feed prior to bedtime**.

As a baby's circadian rhythms mature, the number of times he needs to feed during the night decreases. Whether or not a baby feeds "excessively" during the night depends on his age, how often he wakes to feed, or whether he is fed while sleeping. The following table depicts the average number of nighttime feeds for healthy, thriving, full-term babies according to age.

Table 24.2: Average nighttime feeds for bottle-fed babies

Age	Average number of feeds overnight	Average number of hours without feeding during the night
Birth–3 months	2 or 3	3–5
3–6 months	1 or 2	5–8
6–9 months	0 or 1	8–12
Over 9 months	nil	10–12

There are exceptions, of course. Babies who are not gaining sufficient weight, who are sick or disabled, or those who have certain medical conditions that affect their feeding abilities may need to feed more often than average during the night.

Babies who struggle to gain sufficient weight might benefit from continued feeds overnight for longer than the table indicates. However, in most instances, additional feedings during the night will do little to increase a healthy baby's total daily intake. It can cause him to take less the following day.

> *"Evan will be five months old next week, and he's still not sleeping thru the night. For a brief time, he was only waking up once in the night to feed, but now he has reverted to feeding two to three times a night. At first, I put it down to a growth spurt, but he's been doing this for over a month. He was feeding less at night when he was a newborn." Nadia*

Evan was born at term, and he's a healthy weight. Most five-month-old babies are still feeding at night. However, from a **developmental perspective**, there's no reason why a healthy, thriving five-month-old **needs** to feed two to three times during the night, like a newly born baby does. Yet Evan is genuinely hungry when he wakes during the night. This is a pattern Evan has developed over time. Nadia can change this situation.

Nadia has made many attempts to cease night feeds, such as refusing to provide feeds at night and offering less milk than usual, but these steps have failed to solve the problem. Nadia first needs to understand what is causing this pattern so she can develop an **effective** plan. To identify the cause, Nadia needs to broaden her perspective of the situation.

Broaden your perspective

Excessive night feeding can be viewed from these two perspectives:

1. Baby is not eating enough during the day, and therefore, he needs to eat more at night.
2. Baby does not need to eat much in the day because he eats more often than he needs to at night.

I make this distinction because the way in which you view this situation will influence your actions. Nadia believed if she reduced the number of times Evan fed at night, it would encourage him to eat more in the day, which is true. But it's not the complete story. What Nadia was not conscious of is that Evan had learned to depend on bottle-feeding as a way to fall asleep. Without a bottle to suck on, Evan found it difficult to fall asleep; hence, he would continue to cry until he received a bottle. Nadia needed to teach Evan how to fall asleep without sucking on a bottle before he would stop demanding frequent feeds at night.

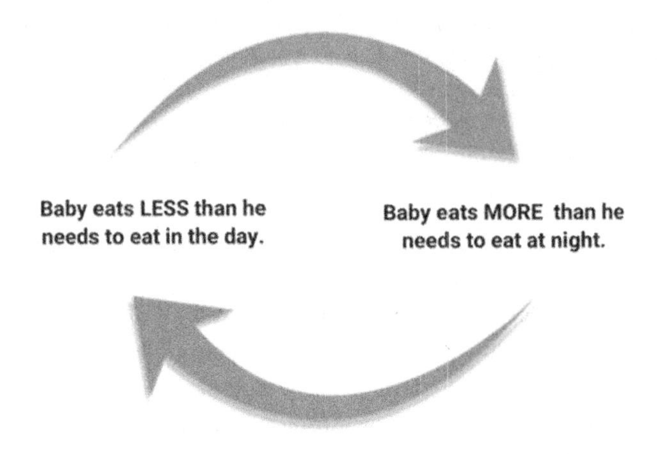

Reverse-cycle feeding

A reverse-cycle feeding pattern typically occurs when frequent night feedings continue beyond the age of six months. This phenomenon, in which a baby appears to get his day and night turned around for feeding, is relatively common.

This is the most confusing and frustrating of the circadian rhythm feeding problems from the parent's perspective. It can result in sleep deprivation for parents, milk wastage, and stress for the baby if parents take inappropriate steps to try to force him to eat more during the day or cut out night feeds without resolving the underlying cause (see page 319 for potential causes).

A reverse-cycle feeding pattern involves the following criteria:

- Baby is over the age of six months.
- He displays signs of being well fed (see page 42).
- During the day, he doesn't appear to be interested in feeding. He does not show signs of hunger for long periods. When offered a feed, he either rejects or takes very little.

- During the night, he demands feeding more often than is considered "average" for his stage of development.
- He appears to be hungry when he wakes at night and feeds well, consuming larger volumes than during the day.

What happens to appetite hormones?

A reverse-cycle feeding pattern is an indication of a circadian rhythm misalignment. (See pages 25-27 for examples of typical feeding and sleeping patterns for age.)

In the situation of a reverse-cycle feeding pattern, the 24-hour release of hunger and satiety hormones is reversed. Baby continues to release **ghrelin** at regular intervals during the night, stimulating appetite and creating pangs of hunger that cause him to wake and motivate him to eat regularly.

The long period of **leptin** release, which suppresses appetite, shifts into the day. Now he may go six to 12 hours during the day with no signs of hunger or little interest in eating. If offered a feed, he either rejects or nibbles a little here and there. The period of decreased appetite is often, but not always, in the mornings.

By the middle of his day or later, his appetite appears to return. He feeds well before bed and during the night. He might wake to demand night feeds, or the parent might wake him to feed because of concern that he is not eating enough during the day. He's genuinely hungry during the night, taking larger feeds than he does in the day, and consuming more calories from multiple night feeds.

Once a reverse-cycle pattern has been established, the baby's lack of appetite during the day causes the parents to believe there's something wrong with their baby that causes him to not feel hunger. **There's nothing wrong with the baby!** He is simply following the feeding pattern that his parents have unwittingly encouraged and reinforced.

A reverse-cycle feeding pattern does not **directly** cause a baby distress. However, parents often take well-intentioned but inappropriate steps to resolve the problem, which then causes their baby distress. This was the case for Bayden.

Baby Bayden

"I am desperate. I think I will end up in a mental hospital over my son's feeding. Bayden is eight months. He has never been a good eater. It's been getting worse over the last few months. He used to drink five to six ounces (150 to 180 mL) every four hours. Now, he only drinks like two ounces (60 mL) each feed during the day, and it can take over an hour to get him to drink that much. I will stop if he gets upset but offer every five minutes until he has taken at least two ounces. I have tried syringing milk into his mouth, but he spits it out. He acts like he's not hungry, but he should be. Two ounces is not enough. Even if we leave him for five hours between feeds, it makes little difference. He's happy in the day. He only gets upset at feeding times. He will drink a six-ounce (180 mL) bottle at bedtime. Because he has not had enough to eat in the day, I dream-feed him at least twice, sometimes three times at night. I know he is hungry because he scarfs down five to six ounces in about 10 minutes with no fussing each time. In total, he drinks around six ounces (180mL) during the day and 18 ounces (540mL) at night. He has been diagnosed with acid reflux. His pediatrician said babies with acid reflux feed better while asleep because they are not aware of the pain. I am so stressed and so tired. Is there nothing I can do to get him to want to drink more during the day?" Chelsea

Bayden's feeding patterns and behavior is not caused by acid reflux. He has developed a reverse-cycle feeding pattern. The misdiagnosis of acid reflux, and false claim that babies don't feel pain when feeding during sleep, has caused Chelsea to feel powerless to change the situation.

Chelsea is not aware that feeding Bayden while sleeping is contributing to this problem. This pattern first started to develop because she would provide extra feeds at night to ensure he received the amount recommended by his doctor for his total daily milk intake.

Chelsea believes the answer lies in trying to make Bayden eat more during the day. Her attempts to do so risk making the situation worse. At present, Bayden eats very little during the day because his appetite is low. Bayden is getting upset by Chelsea's insistence on trying to make him eat when he doesn't want to. If Chelsea continues to pressure Bayden to eat, this could cause him to develop a feeding aversion, in which case he would start to display distressed behavior when offered feeds during the day and is likely to eat even less.

Causes of circadian rhythm feeding problems

As with all baby care problems, it's important that you don't jump to conclusions about the reasons your baby snacks in the day or eats often during the night. A narrow perspective of the situation will limit your possibilities for solutions. Ask yourself the following questions:

- Is something preventing my baby from eating larger volumes per feed? Or from consuming sufficient calories during the day?
- What could cause my baby to demand frequent feeds during the day and, therefore, only need to eat small volumes?
- Could there be reasons for his appetite to be suppressed during the day?
- Could I be encouraging him to eat more often at night than he needs—for example, by offering feeds that are not demanded?

There is usually more than one cause of circadian feeding problems. Check off any that you think may apply. It's okay to select more than one.

- ☐ access problems
- ☐ sleep association problem
- ☐ misinterpreting behavioral cues
- ☐ distractibility during the day
- ☐ sleep-feeding at night
- ☐ feeding aversion

If it's not a problem, it's not a problem.

If your baby is happy, healthy, and thriving, and his current feeding pattern is not bothering you, you don't need to do anything different. If, however, he has no desire to eat solid foods as a result of receiving extra milk feeds at night, you might reconsider.

How to resolve a feeding pattern problem

Follow the steps of my Infant Feeding Self-Evaluation Checklist on page 272. Once you have been able to correct any problems identified, you may find any circadian rhythm feeding problem naturally resolves. If your baby continues to wake and demand additional night feeds—in other words, more than typical for his stage of development—and displays a lack of or reduced appetite during the day, the final step will be to **gradually** reduce the volume you offer at night and eventually, eliminate **extra** nighttime feedings.

Why gradually? Because it's possible that his appetite-regulating hormones have been altered, in that he is genuinely hungry when he wakes at night, and it will take time to adjust to a typical 24-hour day-night pattern, where he eats more in the day than at night. Gradually reducing the volume offered will enable his internal body clock to adjust to lower volumes at that time and avoid prolonged periods of upset during the night, which can occur if you were to suddenly withhold a feed that he is accustomed to receiving.

How to gradually reduce night feeds

1. Allow your baby to wake and demand feeds.
2. Target **one of his extra night feeds** for elimination, but not all. I suggest the one he is least interested in. If unsure, then the feed closest to his morning wake-up time.
3. Gradually reduce the volume of milk you offer at this one feed only. For example, if he would typically take 4 ounces (120 mL), then offer 3.5 ounces (105 mL), then 3 ounces (90 mL), 2.5 ounces (75 mL), and so on, until he no longer wakes to demand a feed at that time. You might choose to drop the volume in this way each night, every second night, or every few days. The speed depends on how readily you can settle your baby back to sleep after the reduced-volume feed.
4. Repeat this process with other excessive feeds, eliminating one feed at a time.

Caution: Don't try to eliminate night feeds considered to be appropriate for your baby's stage of development (see page 314). Trying to make a baby go through the night without eating before his body can physically achieve this will not only fail, but it's likely to stress him. If your baby is underweight or not gaining as expected, see chapter 26 for reasons for underfeeding and remedy this problem before considering reducing night feeds.

Note: Ceasing night feeds doesn't mean your baby won't wake during the night, but it does mean he will not want to feed when he wakes. If you want to minimize the risk of him waking during the night, cease all **negative** sleep associations (described in pages 293-294).

Be wary of unhelpful solutions

If you don't recognize what's happening or understand the reasons for your baby's feeding patterns going astray, you might be tempted to employ some not-so-helpful strategies to solve the problem. The following are examples of strategies often recommended to encourage age-appropriate feeding—**but not encouraged by this book**:

- extend the time between feeds during the day;
- withhold night feeds;
- water down the baby's milk or offer water only in his bottle at night;
- pressure or force the baby to consume larger volume feeds or eat more solids during the day;
- add cereal to baby's daytime bottle or bedtime bottle; and
- begin to give baby solid foods before the age of four months.

I don't recommend any of these strategies, mainly because they don't address the cause(s) that are preventing your baby from following his natural body rhythms. **These methods are simply other ways of trying to control when and how much a baby eats**. As such, they have the potential to create new problems, such as

- infant stress;
- poor growth; and
- feeding aversion.

If the reason for snack feeding or frequent night feedings—for example, a feeding-sleep association problem—is not resolved, then stretching out the time between offers to feed is likely to stress your baby.

Before your baby can feed in a way that matches his circadian rhythms, you need to address the causes of his circadian rhythm feeding problems. When you identify the cause, the solution is clear.

Next

Next, I describe overfeeding, including why it occurs, signs and symptoms, which babies are vulnerable, and why this problem is often overlooked or misdiagnosed.

25 Is Baby Overfeeding?

WHY BABIES OVERFEED • WHAT HAPPENS WHEN A BABY OVERFEEDS • WHY OVERFEEDING IS OVERLOOKED OR MISDIAGNOSED • PROBLEMS ASSOCIATED WITH OVERFEEDING

You might have been told, "You can't overfeed a baby" or "Your baby will stop when she's had enough." It's not true! Helpless little babies, in particular newborns, are vulnerable to overfeeding, especially when others decide how much they "should" eat.

Overfed babies seldom gain excessive weight, which may be why overfeeding is so often overlooked. Instead, they spit up, poop more, or both. The mistaken belief that babies can't be overfed means gastrointestinal (GI) symptoms connected to overfeeding are either dismissed as "normal" or, more often than not, misdiagnosed as colic, reflux, milk protein allergy, or lactose intolerance.

For your baby's contentment, it's important that **you** develop an awareness of the reality of overfeeding. In this chapter, you'll learn why overfeeding occurs and how to recognize the signs and minimize risks to resolve this common but poorly recognized problem.

What is overfeeding?

Overfeeding is not solely about volume. Also called overnutrition, overfeeding is when a baby receives an excess of nutrients—more than she needs for healthy growth, development, and energy to fuel daily activities.

A baby could be overfed on small volume feeds **if the total nutrients and calories exceed what her body requires.**

Overfeeding misdiagnosed as medical issues

Overfeeding is incredibly common; hence, it is so disappointing to see it misdiagnosed as various medical issues. When parents share concerns about their **distressed, constantly crying, and sleepless newborns,** I often discover cases of overfeeding. The combination of overfeeding and overtiredness—caused by a sleep association problem—is the most common reason for newborn babies distress. I also often identify cases of overfeeding retrospectively, after the age of three months, which is when babies are better able to stop eating when they have had enough. That's also when parents discover they are no longer able to "encourage" their babies to consume a certain volume of milk or "as much as she should."

Most parents—and many health professionals—are unaware of overfeeding. Consequently, around 80 percent of the babies that I see in my practice have already been diagnosed with medical conditions. They've been given medications or have had changes in diet to treat GI symptoms, which in reality are related to overfeeding.

Let's look at why babies overfeed.

Causes

As painful as the realization may be for you as a loving parent, you may be overfeeding your baby, and consequently, she may suffer from abdominal discomfort because of your caregiving decisions—in particular, choices related to feeding equipment, ability to differentiate signs of hunger and satiety cues and related responses. The most common reasons for babies to overfeed include

- overestimation of milk needs plus parent-led feeding practices;
- societal belief that chubby babies are healthy babies;
- underlying sleep problems;
- mistaking fussing as hunger; and
- an active sucking reflex plus speed feeding (feeding too quickly for the baby's stage of development).

There is usually more than one reason for an individual baby to overfeed. If you suspect that your baby is overfeeding, explore all possibilities.

Which babies are at risk?

Some babies are more susceptible to **overfeeding** because of their stage of development or temperament. Others are vulnerable to being **overfed.** If you have been misled into believing you know better than your baby how much she needs to eat, then she is at risk of being overfed.

Don't feel bad! **A lot** of babies are at risk, as most parents are encouraged to overfeed rather than risk underfeeding. In addition, babies' milk needs are often overestimated (see chapter 4 for reasons).

Babies most likely to overfeed or be overfed include

- **babies with a spirited temperament** because their behavioral cues are not as easy to read and interpret compared to others;
- **constantly crying babies** because hunger is typically the first thing suspected when a baby cries;
- **intrauterine growth restricted (IUGR) babies** because of the misperception that the more a baby eats, the faster she will grow;
- **genetically small babies** because they don't gain "average" weight;
- **genetically lean babies** because it's assumed that skinny babies are underfed babies;
- **babies that need to gain weight** in preparation for cardiac surgery or other types of surgery;
- **chubby or overweight babies** if their milk needs are estimated based on their chubby weight;
- **babies going through catch-down growth** because they gain weight at a slower-than-average rate—which is often mistaken as poor growth from not eating enough;
- **bottle-fed newborn babies** because they cannot control the rate of milk flow through a stiff silicone nipple like they could if they were breastfed. A parent may also try to "encourage" continued feeding to "empty the bottle;" and
- **tube-fed babies** because others decide how much they receive, and the baby is prevented from self-regulating her caloric intake.

Newborns are especially vulnerable

Above all others, newborn babies are especially vulnerable to overfeeding because

- their behavioral cues are difficult to read;
- once their sucking reflex is triggered, they will suck whether they are hungry or not;
- they can be easily "encouraged" to continue eating using parent-led feeding practices;
- they often fall asleep while feeding, which can cause some to develop a feeding-sleep association—and consequently learn to rely on feeding as a way to fall asleep; and
- the newborn period is a time of adjustment in many ways, including alignment to genetically programmed body shape—some will go through catch-up and others catch-down growth.

It is not coincidental that healthy newborns are often gassy, spit up or vomit, tend to have more frequent bowel movements compared to babies over the age of three months, and are especially vulnerable to overfeeding. These issues are directly linked! Of course, there can be other reasons for these physical signs and behaviors. But the best place to start looking for answers is with an assessment of your infant feeding practices.

Signs of overfeeding

The symptoms associated with overfeeding are **directly** linked to a baby's homeostatic mechanisms **doing exactly what they are designed to do**. When a baby overfeeds or is overfed, this creates an imbalance between what she receives and what she needs. Her body will respond to overfeeding in various ways in an attempt to restore or maintain an internal state of balance, and she may exhibit

- gastric (stomach) signs;
- intestinal signs;
- energy, or fat, storage; and
- behavioral symptoms.

Some overfed babies display mostly gastric symptoms, some only intestinal symptoms, but many show both. The amount of energy stored as body fat owing to overfeeding might surprise you.

The type and intensity of symptoms and how much these affect a baby's behavior vary depending on the degree of overfeeding. If overfeeding is minor, so too will be the baby's bodily response, and behavior may be unaffected. If overfeeding is considerable, then the GI symptoms will be greater, and the baby could be distressed because of abdominal discomfort.

1. Gastric signs

If the volume of milk your baby takes in exceeds her stomach's storage capacity, she will regurgitate her stomach's contents (known as "reflux").

Normally, your baby's stomach will stretch to accommodate a feed and then shrink as milk or food empties from her stomach, but her stomach can only hold so much. If her stomach hyperextends from large volume feeds or small, frequent feeds provided before the previous feed has emptied, she might regurgitate milk. This could range from a small spit-up that dribbles from her mouth to a large projectile vomit that shoots out with such force that it lands many feet away.

Occasional small spit-ups are inconsequential. However, when a physically well baby spits up a lot or projectile vomits, overfeeding and speed feeding should be the first things you consider.

> *"Mia is eating me out of house and home. She puts down about 6 oz (180 mL) of formula every two hours or so. I tried to make her wait a little longer, but she acts like she's starving all the time and screams if I keep her waiting. She has trouble keeping her milk down. She vomits a lot, sometimes straight after her bottle and sometimes hours later. Everyone tells me she has reflux and that she wants to eat all the time to soothe her throat, but her pediatrician says that even though she's throwing up, she's gaining weight, so he doesn't think she has reflux. How can a baby be vomiting and not have reflux? Should I take her to another doctor?"*
> *Jocelyn*

When the doctor stated Mia does not have reflux, what he meant is that Mia is not experiencing physical complications—like acid reflux, respiratory or growth problems—as a result of milk regurgitation and, therefore, does not require medical treatment.

Spitting up and projectile vomiting caused by overfeeding does not cause pain and does not require medications. However, it could cause a fright for the baby and parents when she unexpectedly spits up, especially if it's a large volume.

While overfeeding is a likely cause for Mia's vomiting and fussy behavior, it's probably not the only reason. If an overfed baby cries a lot or sleeps poorly, it's mostly for reasons such as sleep deprivation caused by a sleep association problem or related to abdominal discomfort caused by intestinal symptoms connected to overfeeding.

2. Intestinal symptoms

Intestinal symptoms linked to overfeeding are more likely to cause pain or discomfort compared to spitting up. Intestinal symptoms include

- frequent or massive, sloppy, or watery bowel movements;
- bloating;
- extreme flatulence; and
- diaper rash.

When a baby is **overfeeding**, her intestinal tract is overloaded with more lactose than she can digest. In other words, she experiences **functional lactose overload**—not to be confused with lactose intolerance. (See pages 439-448 for more on lactose overload.)

In the case of overfeeding, the baby will display **the same GI symptoms as with a milk protein allergy or intolerance.** Her body is correcting the imbalance between the nutrients she receives and what she needs. Growth is generally good—in most but not all cases. Her body simply can't cope with the excess nutrients.

On the other hand, if she were to have a **milk protein allergy**, her body would be trying to inhibit antigens (the protein triggering an allergic reaction) from entering her bloodstream. In the case of milk protein allergy, she cannot digest **normal volumes** of milk, and **growth is typically poor.**

When you see your baby's frequent, gassy, watery, or explosive bowel movements, no doubt you'll be concerned that she's not tolerating her milk, and you'll be tempted to switch her formula. Depending on the amount of lactose in the new formula, this may or may not make a difference to intestinal symptoms. Low-lactose or lactose-free formulas will reduce the symptoms because they lower the lactose load.

If her stools also contain mucous or blood specks, you will understandably be worried about a cow's milk protein allergy if she's formula-fed or that it's related to her mother's diet if she receives breast milk. Either way, you'll be eager to discuss your observations and concerns with her primary healthcare professional. And she is very likely to receive a medical diagnosis to explain her GI symptoms.

I urge you to **not** overlook the possibility of GI symptoms due to overfeeding, as misdiagnosis is common.

3. Energy storage

Gaining excessive amounts of weight is what most people expect when a baby is overfed. However, because her body's homeostatic mechanisms trigger vomiting and pooping of the undigested nutrients just to bring itself back to balance, an overfed baby's body does not necessarily **retain** excess nutrients. Some nutrients and calories will be lost as a result of spitting up and more as a result of undigested nutrients passing through her digestive tract. Most overfed babies display healthy growth. Only a small percentage of overfed babies gain excessive weight. And as strange as this might sound, a tiny percentage of overfed babies gain poorly. I will explain.

Normal weight gain

A baby could overfeed, and yet her weight gains could consistently remain within a normal range. If **excess** nutrients are not retained—due to spitting up—or not digested, they cannot be absorbed into the baby's bloodstream and cannot be used by her body as energy or stored as body fat. If homeostatic mechanisms are functioning as they should, an overfed baby will gain weight at a healthy rate.

Slow and poor weight gain

Overfeeding is probably the last thing you would suspect if your baby is growing poorly. However, a small percentage of overfed babies can display slow or poor growth as a result of extreme vomiting.

Lily's case provides an example of how **an absence of a thorough feeding assessment** can cause overfeeding to be overlooked when growth is slow.

Baby Lily

Lily was born at 28 weeks of gestation. She was tube fed following her extremely premature birth because she lacked feeding skills. Oral feeding had been attempted in the neonatal intensive care unit (NICU) from around 32 to 38 weeks gestational age. However, she didn't consume the recommended volume and continued to be tube fed after discharge from hospital.

She is now six months actual age (three months adjusted age). Poor growth has been attributed to the fact that Lily vomits multiple times each day. She has been diagnosed as "failure to thrive."

All means of medical treatments have been employed in an attempt to reduce or eliminate her vomiting. She is continuously tube fed for 22 hours per day, having only one hour of "tube-free time" in the morning and another in the afternoon. She is given an amino acid-based formula, plus oral nutritional supplements to reduce the volume required without sacrificing calories. She also receives acid-suppressing and prokinetic medications (given to speed up the time for milk to empty from her stomach). A gastric feeding tube has been inserted through her abdomen and into her stomach in a bid to minimize regurgitation of stomach contents associated with a nasogastric tube. Despite these treatments, her mother, Megan, estimates that she loses approximately 100mL (3.5 ounces) of the total of 560mL (19 ounces) she receives via the tube over a 24-hour period. She has been advised that if Lily's weight percentile continues to drop, the next step will be surgery, called a Nissen fundoplication, which will physically prevent her from throwing up.

Megan wants to avoid surgery and so books a consultation to see if I can provide any insight into the situation.

During a consultation, Megan tells me that Lily spends most of the day and night seated in a semi-upright position in a feeding chair. She claims she's afraid to move her for fear she will vomit and lose even more milk. She informs me that Lily is miserable most of the day. She spends her entire day trying to soothe and entertain her as best she can without her vomiting. They have not left the house in the past three months, when she was discharged home.

A feeding assessment reveals that Lily is receiving **40 percent** more calories than the upper normal range for age and weight. I suspect this is to try to compensate for the milk that is lost. However, I also suspect her vomiting occurs as a result of overnutrition. Giving her more via the tube has resulted in her losing more. Megan is understandably skeptical of my assessment of overfeeding. It doesn't seem logical that overfeeding would cause poor growth—that is until you understand how a baby's homeostatic mechanisms function to correct overfeeding and overnutrition. I suggest she test my theory. Because Lily is losing an estimated 100mL (3.5 ounces) per day from vomiting, I suggest Megan reduce the amount provided via the tube by 100mL for just one day—which would still provide a little more than the upper normal number of calories for age and weight—and see if this reduces her vomiting. It does! Not completely, but vomiting is considerably less. Lily appears to be more comfortable, and Megan can now lift her from the rocker for "play time" without causing her to vomit.

I recommend she continues with the lower total daily volume on the proviso that vomiting is reduced and weigh her in a week's time to check how the reduced volume—both consumed and vomited up—impacts her growth. She reports back that her doctor is pleased with Lily's weight gain. She confesses to not telling the doctor that she was providing less milk via the tube. One week is not long enough to confirm whether Lily is retaining enough for healthy growth, and I encourage her to have her weighed each week and to disclose to her doctor that she is giving her less. Lily continues to gain in a normal range.

Now somewhat confident about the total daily volume Lily needs to support healthy growth, I provide further recommendations to enable intermittent tube feedings rather than continuous tube feeding so there are more opportunities for the family to leave the house for short periods and lead a somewhat-normal life with a tube-fed baby. The duration of each feed is gradually reduced over a period of a week to monitor for increased vomiting.

Lily continues to gain weight well, and her weight moves to a higher percentile. She is able to avoid further surgery. Once she has added a little more body fat and her body mass index (BMI) is in a healthy range for age and length, a tube wean is successfully attempted. All medical treatments are ceased. Lily then gets the chance to show that she is capable of orally consuming the volume of a regular, normal-strength baby formula that **she needs** to support healthy growth. But she never eats the amount her doctor claims she needs because the doctor has overestimated her milk needs.

When an overfed baby throws up, the amount brought up is not limited to just the excess her body doesn't need. Once reflux or vomiting mechanisms were triggered, all Mia could do was empty her stomach.

If a baby gains poorly because of vomiting, this can be viewed from two different perspectives:

1. Baby is throwing up, growth is poor, and therefore, she requires more milk or calories to compensate for what she's losing. Consequently, the baby may be given thickened feeds, additional nutrients by way of calorie-energy feeds, or medications and in some cases, surgery to prevent vomiting, and thus, try to minimize the loss of calories.
2. Baby's caloric intake exceeds what is expected. Overfeeding—which is not all about volumes but also includes overnutrition—may be causing her to throw up and gain poorly. In such cases, less can be more.

Less milk or nutrients → less vomiting and/or pooping → more nutrients retained and absorbed by her body → better growth.

Overfeeding is the last thing most of us would think of when a baby is growing poorly. However, if the baby is losing nutrients and calories from vomiting and pooping, the possibilities of overfeeding and overnutrition need to be considered.

It's actually a very simple process to determine the difference between the baby needing more calories because of vomiting **and** a baby vomiting because she's receiving too many calories. Stop pressuring her to reach a specific target. Allow her to consume the amount she chooses. If vomiting is reduced, discuss your findings with your baby's healthcare professional and see if they are agreeable to a longer trial of trusting your baby to decide how much to eat while observing for signs of a well-fed baby (page 42) and monitoring her growth.

Rapid or excessive weight gain

Rapid or excessive weight gain refers to the **rate at which weight is gained** and not the size or shape of the baby. Even underweight babies can be overfed and gain an excessive amount of weight or gain rapidly. This is not desirable if body fat accumulation occurs too quickly because **rapid weight gain** is associated with a two- to three-fold increased risk of obesity later in childhood and adulthood.[144]

A small percentage of overfed babies gain excessive weight. Some are naturally inclined to accumulate more body fat than others. The risk of an excessive accumulation of body fat generally occurs when the baby's **natural homeostatic mechanisms are hampered** by strategies to treat "reflux"—for example, thickened feeds and calorie-enhanced feeds—which aim to prevent or minimize spitting up or vomiting.

Lactose-free formulas—which include soy and most hypoallergenic formulas—will reduce intestinal symptoms and loss of nutrients caused by lactose overload. Baby formula such as amino acid formulas—given to babies with suspected milk allergy—eliminate the need for digestion, enable absorption of nutrients directly into the baby's bloodstream. Consequently, these formulas can increase the rate at which a baby gains weight.

Basically, these treatments mask the symptoms of overfeeding by hindering the baby's homeostatic mechanisms, but they don't resolve the problem of overfeeding. If the excess nutrients are not thrown up or pooped out, then more nutrients will be absorbed into the baby's bloodstream. As her blood sugar level rises, her body releases insulin, which moves glucose into cells to be used for cell function or stored as body fat. **If she continues to overfeed, she will gain weight** at a rapid rate. She may not be overweight or obese at that point, but she risks becoming so if overfeeding continues.

While an overfed baby might gain unusually large amounts of weight in the early weeks or months, most don't become overweight or obese. This is because most babies will start to self-regulate their dietary intake around the age of two to three months.

Note: Not all overweight babies are overfed. A baby might have gained large stores of fat in the womb or as a result of previous overfeeding which is now corrected. So, it can't be assumed that the baby is **currently** overfed simply because she's overweight.

If your baby is gaining too quickly, or if she's already overweight or obese, you'll need a thorough assessment of feeding practices and medical treatments.

4. Behavioral symptoms

Homeostatic mechanisms, hard at work correcting the imbalances caused by overfeeding, can cause intense intestinal contractions, bloating, abdominal cramping, acidic stools that burn baby's bottom, and varying degrees of physical discomfort. As uncomfortable or painful as these symptoms may be, the baby's homeostatic mechanisms are protecting her from greater harm that would occur from an excessive accumulation of body fat.

Behavioral symptoms linked to overfeeding can include

- irritability;
- sleep disturbance;
- grunting; and
- bearing down movements caused by activation of the gastrocolic reflex (pages 67-68) but which are more extreme in the case of overfeeding.

It's important not to assume that these **behaviors** are caused by overfeeding or any other problem. **In the absence of the gastrointestinal symptoms described,** each of these behaviors can be **perfectly normal** for healthy babies or for reasons unrelated to feeding.

Overfeeding cycle

Overfeeding can create a vicious cycle.

Diagram 25.1: Newborn overfeeding cycle

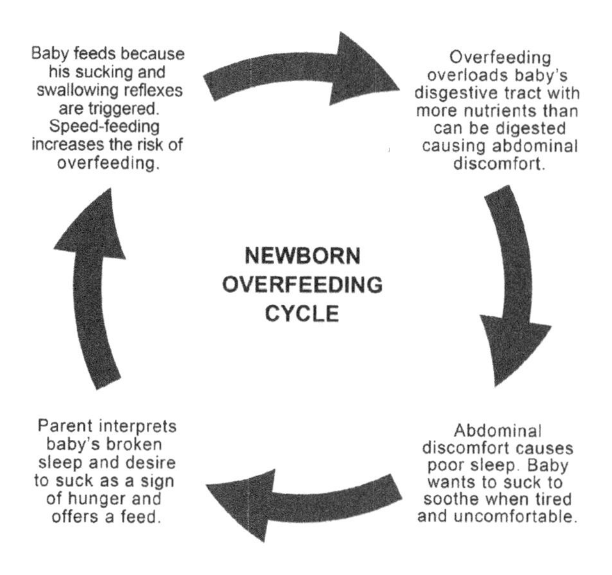

If you add a sleeping problem into the mix, the overfeeding cycle is even more likely to develop. Abdominal discomfort can cause lack of sleep that leads to overtiredness, but equally, lack of sleep caused by learned dependence on negative sleep associations is often the reason for fussiness that is mistakenly attributed to hunger.

When overfeeding is accompanied by overtiredness, the baby might be described as "high-needs." She's seldom content except for when she's feeding or sleeping. She's eating a lot and sleeping very little. When awake and not feeding, she requires constant attention. She cries if not held and entertained.

> *"I think my baby is addicted to formula! I know that sounds weird, but she is up to 5 ounces (150 mL) at each feeding, and sometimes, she can chug down more! I just fed her an hour ago, and she is already crying and sucking the life out of her binky (pacifier). She isn't even a full three weeks yet. I have been told to just give her whatever she wants. But I am worried she is eating too much."* Clare

Clare's baby appears to be caught up in the overfeeding cycle. Hence, I suspect that Clare is unknowingly perpetuating this cycle. After asking her more questions, I discovered that she had been told to feed her baby on demand. Like many new parents, her interpretation of demand feeding is "feed baby every time she fusses, cries, or appears to want to suck." Only Clare can break this cycle.

If your newborn appears to be insatiably hungry, often spitting up and pooping a lot, she could be caught up in this cycle. You can be the "circuit breaker" by checking off the boxes in my Infant Feeding Self-Evaluation Checklist on pages 272.

Medical assessment

If you are puzzled or seriously concerned about what you see, you will likely consult with your baby's doctor, whose assessment and advice will influence what you do to remedy the situation. Your baby's doctor might

- **recognize overfeeding** and provide feeding recommendations, which improve the situation to varying degrees. Resolving the cause includes an assessment and advice on the reasons for overfeeding, which are unlikely to be covered during a brief consultation. **Warning!** Feeding recommendations may be limited to restricting your baby's milk intake, which is **not** an effective solution.

- **provide reassurance that spitting up is normal; however, overfeeding is overlooked, so it continues.** If your baby is a "happy spitter," you may feel reassured. However, if your baby is an "unhappy spitter" who often cries or appears to have trouble sleeping, you will not feel reassured, and you will be tempted to go from one doctor to another until one provides you with a plausible explanation.
- **recommend strategies to reduce spitting up without correcting overfeeding**—for example, holding your baby upright for 20–30 minutes after a feed, giving smaller, more frequent feeds, or thickening feeds. However, I don't recommend these strategies. While they can be effective in minimizing spitting up, if your baby continues to overfeed, they increase the risk that she will experience intestinal symptoms related to overnutrition, some of which cause discomfort or pain.
- **diagnose a medical condition without consideration of overfeeding.** The symptoms associated with overfeeding are **often** misdiagnosed as colic, acid reflux, lactose intolerance, milk protein allergy or gastroparesis (delayed gastric emptying).

Why overfeeding is overlooked

Health professionals are often taught that babies cannot overfeed, or they may mistakenly believe that only babies who gain excessive amounts of weight are overfed. Consequently, they don't ask parents about their baby's feeding practices.

You need to ask questions to identify overfeeding. If your doctor doesn't ask, for example, how much your baby is eating, how often and how quickly she feeds, the caloric content of her feeds, and whether she's pressured to continue feeding to reach a predetermined volume, then they aren't performing a full assessment. Ezra's case provides an example of what can be missed when questions are not asked.

Ezra

Ezra, aged six weeks, appeared to be an insatiably hungry baby. He guzzled down feeds rapidly, only to have huge vomits soon after feeding. His mother, Victoria, commented that she would change Ezra's and her own clothes at least four times a day, plus clean expelled milk from the sofa and carpet. It was not the vomiting that concerned Victoria the most. Rather, it was the fact that Ezra barely slept and cried often. Victoria believed he was in pain, and she suspected acid reflux was the cause.

She described her observations and expressed concerns about acid reflux with Ezra's doctor. Without being asked a single question about her infant feeding practices, the doctor reassured Victoria that you can't overfeed a baby and that Ezra was eating more to make up for what he lost. He concluded that Ezra's growth was good and, therefore, didn't believe he had acid reflux. His advice to Victoria was to switch Ezra to an anti-reflux (AR) formula, offer small, frequent feeds, hold him upright for 30 minutes after feeds, and provide a pacifier. This reduced large spit-ups to small spit-ups. However, Ezra was no happier. Victoria read online that babies like to eat more often to soothe the pain associated with acid reflux, and she asked the doctor to prescribe medications. He agreed to a two-week trial and prescribed omeprazole. Victoria felt this made little difference.

Initially, Victoria had suspected Ezra's broken sleep was from hunger as a result of losing so much milk. However, he was not losing as much now after following the doctor's recommendations, and yet, he was still not sleeping well. So, Victoria decided to book a consultation with me to discuss ways to improve his sleep.

Questions about Ezra's sleep uncovered a sleep association problem. Ezra had learned to fall asleep while being held in arms, first, in a cradle position, starting from the time of his birth, and later, while held upright after feeds. Victoria felt that sleeping first became problematic when Ezra was about two weeks of age. She claimed that he would wake up crying as soon as she tried to place him in the "pack and play" where he slept during the day so that he would be close to her. At best, he would have three 20-minute naps. He slept solidly at night, waking twice to feed before returning to sleep.

Questions about Ezra's feeding revealed that he was feeding up to 15 times per day. Victoria tried to follow instructions to provide small, frequent feeds, but she claimed he cried so much she felt she had no choice but to offer him more, and so he ended up consuming significantly more over a 24-hour period than had been recommended. He was using a medium flow nipple, which had been recommended because he was now given an AR formula. He wolfed down the recommended volume, draining the bottle in around five minutes, then cried, which Victoria interpret as him wanting more. The flow rate was too fast for a newborn. Speed feeding caused Ezra to swallow a lot of air while feeding. It also meant there was insufficient time for him to experience the sensation of satisfaction before he overfed.

My assessment was that Ezra did not need to eat more to make up for the loss of milk from vomiting or to soothe pain from acid reflux. He was vomiting because he was consuming too much, too often, and too fast. His distress was mostly a result of sleep deprivation caused by overtiredness and overfeeding and not from reflux. I suspected that his sleeping issues were the main reason for overfeeding. While he spit up milk—as do 50 percent of all babies of his age—the extreme vomiting was caused by overfeeding. Victoria was mistakenly attributing fussiness from tiredness as hunger.

Improving Ezra's sleep played a significant role in improving his general contentment and preventing continued overfeeding, but Victoria also had to switch him to a slow-flow nipple to slow down his feeds. I explained ways to differentiate between tiredness and hunger and described signs of satiety. Victoria commented that she was now able to enjoy caring for Ezra for the first time since his birth. Ezra's doctor was agreeable to ceasing the acid-suppressing medications. Victoria decided to switch Ezra back to a non-thickened formula now that the reason for his vomiting was resolved.

Don't expect your baby's healthcare professional to ask questions to identify overfeeding. The reason is because undertaking a feeding assessment may not be within their scope of practice—in other words, not something they are trained to do.

In some cases, health professionals unknowingly trigger the sequence of events that lead to babies being overfed by overestimating their milk needs. If so, they would be even less likely to suspect overfeeding as the reason for the baby's GI symptoms.

"Lexie (aged four months) feeds six times a day at 6, 10, 2, 6, 10, 2. She usually takes between 3.5 and 5 ounces (105 mL–150 mL). The doctor told me she should be able to eat 6 ounces (180 mL) bottles, so 36 ounces (1060 mL) in a 24-hr period. She often only takes 3.5 ounces of the 6 ounces that I prepared. It takes over an hour to make her drink 6 ounces, and she sometimes projectile vomits a bunch of milk. The doctor said she has reflux and prescribed ranitidine, but it's not helping. Do you have any advice?" Hannah

Even when the symptoms of overfeeding should be obvious, as is the case for Lexie, it's not necessarily recognized by the parent or health professional, especially when a baby is drinking **less than expected**. Everyone could be oblivious to the fact that the estimated milk volume exceeds what the baby needs.

My advice to Hannah was to employ baby-led feeding practices and allow Lexie to decide when and how much to eat. If Hanna keeps pushing her to eat 6 ounces each feed, she may find that Lexie develops a feeding aversion, which is a more serious and far more difficult problem to solve compared to overfeeding.

If your baby requires pressure to drink a specific volume and often throws up, you really need to consider the possibility that her milk needs have been overestimated.

Misdiagnosis is common

Parents expect that they will receive an explanation for the cause of the physical signs and behaviors they observe. Generally, they do. However, the explanation won't necessarily be accurate.

Overfeeding will be overlooked if we believe that only fat babies or those who gain excessive amounts of weight are overfed, or if we believe that we know better than a baby how much her body needs, and therefore, fail to consider overfeeding unless she exceeds the estimated volume.

Now that you are aware of the physical signs linked to overfeeding, I am sure you can appreciate just how easy it would be to mistakenly attribute these to a medical condition, such as colic, reflux, milk protein allergy, lactose intolerance, or delayed gastric emptying.

Do medical treatments help?

Parents sometimes state that their baby's symptoms appear to be a little better after medical treatments such as thickening feeds, switching to a lactose-free, soy or hypoallergenic formula, or give baby medications, yet their baby is still upset though less so than prior to treatment. Others claim that medical treatments make no difference or appear to make the situation worse.

Many of the treatments recommended for medical conditions, such as GERD (gastroesophageal reflux disease) and milk protein allergy, will disguise some, but not all, of the symptoms caused by overfeeding. They do this by **enhancing or weakening** the effects of the baby's homeostatic mechanisms. Hence, they have the potential to **improve or hinder** normal bodily functions. See pages 419-420 for an explanation as to why you might see improvements as a result of medical treatments and, additionally, why medical treatments could lead to a baby receiving multiple medical diagnoses.

More woes linked to unidentified overfeeding

The GI symptoms associated with **unrecognized overfeeding** will usually resolve—without the need for thickened feeds, medications, or switching formula—by around two to three months of age, when healthy babies sucking reflex fades or disappears and they are better equipped to stop eating when satisfied. This will happen sooner if parents are made aware of overfeeding and take appropriate steps to remedy the situation.

While the GI symptoms might resolve, unfortunately, the problems linked to unidentified overfeeding don't always end at this stage. New problems can develop if parents and health professionals don't understand why a **previously overfed** baby is now drinking and gaining less than before.

Baby now drinks and gains less

The baby's newfound ability to self-regulate her milk intake may result in her milk consumption dropping. The drop in milk intake can be gradual, starting with one feed, or it can suddenly affect all feeds.

If the baby is permitted to decide how much to eat, she might eat less but she will lose less from vomiting or frequent bowel movements, thus growth may be unaffected.

If the reason for the decrease in her milk consumption is not recognized for what it is—that she can now refuse if not hungry and stop when she has had enough to eat—her parents may start to worry that something is wrong. **If she is not permitted to decide how much to eat,** feeding battles can begin, as parents try to pressure, trick, distract, sleep-feed, or use spoons and syringes to make her eat the volume she was drinking before.

If the baby previously gained at a rapid rate and consequentially, gained extra stores of body fat, causing her weight percentile to climb above length percentile, she might now go through a period of catch-down growth—as her body shape realigns to her genetically preprogrammed path. She may then grow at a much slower rate, and her weight may appear stagnant at times, both of which may be mistaken as slow or poor growth. She will consume less than estimated based on average figures for age and weight as her body converts excess stores of body fat into energy. If the reason for the slowing of her weight is not understood by her healthcare professional, false alarms about growth will be raised and become another reason for her parents to try to pressure her to eat.

Regardless of the reason, repeatedly pressuring a baby to eat greatly increases the chances of her developing a feeding aversion. Rosalie's case provides another example of what can happen when overfeeding is not recognized.

Baby Rosalie

Rosalie was born at term. Her weight and length at birth were in the 3rd percentile. She was classified as IUGR. The reason for her small size at birth was not identified. Genetically, Rosalie would be expected to have been bigger at birth because her mother's height was in the 45th percentile and her father's height was in the 85th percentile. Her pediatrician recommended that Rosalie's mother, Alice, give Rosalie 10 percent extra milk, on top of the average of 2.5 ounces per pound per day (or 150 mL/kg/day) to "encourage" catch-up growth. Alice was able to achieve this for many weeks after birth—a time when Rosalie's sucking reflex was strong—but Rosalie would spit up and poop a lot. However, rather than suspecting overfeeding, Rosalie was diagnosed with acid reflux and milk intolerance, given acid-suppressing medications, and switched to a hypoallergenic formula.

As Rosalie matured she began to resist Alice's efforts to make her eat more than she needed. Distressed by Alice's attempts to make her continue to eat once she had decided to stop, Rosalie ultimately became averse to bottle-feeding and refused to eat. She was hospitalized and diagnosed as "failure to thrive," and put on a feeding tube. I was able to assist Rosalie's parents by teaching them to respond to her feeding cues and allow her to decide when and how much to eat. Over a period of two weeks, she learned to trust her mother to respond to her feeding cues and her aversion to bottle-feeding resolved. She was then weaned from tube feedings and returned to fully feeding orally. She stopped vomiting and slept better once her stomach and intestinal tract were not constantly churning as a result of overnutrition. All medications were ceased, and she was returned to a standard formula.

Circumstances while in the womb—which were out of Rosalie's control—prevented her from growing to her genetic potential. But as a neurologically healthy baby, she was **capable** of self-regulating her milk intake to meet her growth and energy needs. Sadly, she just wasn't given a chance to decide for herself what her body needed. She was overfed from the time of her birth because of the mistaken belief that more food would make her grow faster. But growth cannot be forced. And when you do try to force it, a lot of problems crop up, issues that could easily have been avoided had Alice been encouraged to employ baby-led feeding practices from the time of Rosalie's birth.

As bad as the situation got for Rosalie and her parents, I have seen worse. When someone tells you, "You can't overfeed a baby," don't believe them. Overfeeding is far more prevalent than most parents and health professionals know.

How to prevent overfeeding

As the saying goes, "prevention is better than cure." Being aware of the possibility of overfeeding may help you avoid heading down this path with your baby. If your baby is currently displaying GI signs and behaviors that now seem so obviously related to overfeeding, it's not too late to turn the situation around. You could do so in a matter of days.

A thorough feeding assessment is a good place to start—especially if your baby's growth is good—**before** giving her medications and making dietary changes that she might not need. By assessing and addressing any causes of overfeeding that might be relevant to your baby, you might discover that her GI symptoms can be significantly reduced. If GI symptoms are not reduced, then consider medications or switching formula as a last resort rather than a first.

Prevention and correction of overfeeding involve the same strategies.

It would be easy to think that the solution to overfeeding is to limit the amount of milk you offer your baby. Don't! **Dietary restriction is not an effective solution.** It's not your role to decide how much your baby needs to drink—that's her job! Instead, focus on the reasons that might be causing her to overfeed. As your baby's caregiver, your job is to remove any barriers that may be preventing her from self-regulating her milk consumption.

You can achieve this by going through my Infant Feeding Self-Evaluation Checklist (described on pages 272). Once you can check off all boxes as achieved, you will not only reduce the risk of overfeeding but also all other behavioral feeding problems that commonly trouble healthy babies.

Next

Next, we go to the opposite end of the spectrum to underfeeding. I will cover how to tell the difference between genuine and perceived underfeeding and explore common causes for physically well, typically developing babies to underfeed.

26 Why Won't Baby Eat Enough?

UNDERFEEDING • HOW TO RECOGNIZE IF YOUR BABY IS NOT EATING ENOUGH • CAUSES OF UNDERFEEDING • MYTHS ASSOCIATED WITH UNDERFEEDING

Underfeeding means a baby is either not receiving or not retaining sufficient nutrients to support his growth and energy needs. If you have concerns about the possibility of your baby underfeeding, the first step is to confirm if he is genuinely underfeeding—as opposed to him not willingly eating the daily volume of milk you have been told he needs. There will be clearly observable signs and behavior that point to insufficient nutrition.

If confirmed that he is underfeeding, the next step is to identify the cause. Being aware of the common reasons—both behavioral and physical—for babies to underfeed may help you to recognize the most appropriate course of action. This chapter will help you recognize signs and causes of underfeeding.

Many "underfeeding" fears are unfounded

Often, parents look to me for advice on how they can encourage their babies to **willingly eat more** in the belief that underfeeding is an issue.

These parents have become physically and emotionally exhausted over never-ending battles with their baby at feeding times. They stay awake at night worrying about what might happen if they can't get their baby to eat "enough." They fear dehydration, impaired brain development, and tube feeding or worse could be the outcome.

Some claim to persist for up to two hours each feed trying to reach the recommended amount. Others repeatedly offer feeds, up to 20 times in a 24-hour period. They employ various tactics like coaxing, trickery, distractions, pressure or force, giving milk via a syringe or spoon and feeding their baby while sleeping. All is done in the hope of preventing underfeeding.

In many cases, anxiety could have been averted with some practical advice, as baby is not underfeeding at all. Occasionally, I do see cases of genuine underfeeding; for example, some babies underfeed because of physical problems (described in chapter 33) or medical conditions (see chapter 32). However, in the case of physically well babies, **underfeeding mostly occurs for behavioral reasons** listed in this chapter and described in this book.

Misdiagnosis of underfeeding

While overfeeding is typically overlooked by parents and health professionals alike, underfeeding is often over diagnosed.

An **inaccurate** assessment of underfeeding is typically **based on a single piece of information** given during a brief consultation, such as

- Baby is not gaining average weight = underfeeding
- Baby is not drinking the amount of milk expected = underfeeding
- Baby is not gaining weight quickly enough = underfeeding
- Baby's weight and length are below the 10th percentile = "failure to thrive"

None of these observations are proof of underfeeding. However, they are red flags that signal the need for a comprehensive assessment of the baby's growth and feeding.

It's important for you to be aware that misdiagnosis occurs because it can lead to the development of infant feeding problems.

Poor feeding advice

Regardless of whether underfeeding is genuine or misdiagnosed, many parents will receive poor feeding advice, such as pressuring or forcing their baby to feed, or adopting "quick-fix" solutions—for example, calorie-enhanced feeds, commencing solids too soon, food thickeners, sleep feeding, extra night feeds, and others that are directed at compensating for reduced calories but do nothing to correct the cause of underfeeding.

Without addressing the cause, there is a risk that such strategies will fail to resolve the problem or create new problems at the present time or in the future, or both.

When a healthy baby underfeeds, the most effective solution lies in identifying barriers that prevent him from regulating his milk intake and **not** in finding ways to make him eat more.

How to tell if your baby is eating enough

Numbers can be misleading. A volume of milk consumed by one baby will be too much or too little for another, which is why you need to let your bottle-fed baby decide how much to eat, just like all breastfed babies do.

So how can you tell if your baby is getting enough to eat?

By observation!

Your baby's behavior will indicate if he's happy or unhappy with the amount of food received. Physical signs will also provide clues that let you know if he is or is not receiving enough food. You can tell if your baby is getting enough by

- how he looks;
- his mood and behavior; and
- how often he pees and poops.

Table 26.1 describes signs and behaviors that indicate if a baby is getting enough to eat, not getting enough, or is severely underfed.

Table 26.1: Signs of baby's current nutritional status

	Getting enough	Not getting enough	Severely underfed
Number of wet diapers in 24 hours*	Five or more.	Four or less.	Three or less.
	*Based on frequent diaper changes and milk being the only source of fluids.		
Bowel movements	**Infant formula** Normal frequency–can range from three times a day to once every three days. Consistency–loose, soft, or paste. (A well-fed baby can become constipated for other reasons.)	Infrequent, for example, once every three days or longer. Increased risk of constipation–hard, dry, pebbly stools.	Infrequent. Constipated stools or "starvation stools"–infrequent, green, slimy stools.
	Breast milk Normal frequency–can range between 10 times a day or no bowel movements for 10 days, with sufficient wet diapers.	Infrequent plus low number of wet diapers.	Infrequent, green, slimy stools (starvation stools) plus low number of wet diapers.
Feeding behavior	Demands regular feeds. (Many well-fed babies are content to wait until they are offered a feed.) Appears satisfied at the end of the feed. (Baby might fuss if you try to make him eat more than he wants, or because of an unsatisfied sucking urge or tiredness.)	Demanding feeds earlier than anticipated. (A feeding-averse baby might not demand feeds until ravenous.) Appears unsatisfied at the end of the feed.	Does not demand feeds. Sucking is weak. Might repeatedly fall asleep before finishing the feed. (Newborns and sleep-deprived babies who have developed a feeding-sleep association often fall asleep while feeding.)
Energy levels	Alert, active and energetic.	Alert but not very active.	Listless or lethargic.

Continued...	Getting enough	Not getting enough	Severely underfed
Interest	Inquisitive and interested in surroundings.	May display brief periods of interest when entertained.	Not interested. Wants to sleep.
Mood	Content between feeds except when tired or bored.	Often restless, fretful, or irritable because of hunger. Demands constant attention. Fusses when not held.	Solemn when awake.
Sleep	Sleeps well. (A well-fed baby can have a problem sleeping for reasons unrelated to hunger.)	Has trouble falling asleep and staying asleep because of hunger.	Sleeps for prolonged periods. Difficult to awaken.

Note: These are signs related to your baby's **current nutritional state**. They do not provide information on whether he may have been previously under- or overfeeding.

An absence of one or more signs is not confirmation that he's poorly fed. It's possible that a baby could be well-fed but

- has a low number of wet diapers because he's given calorie-enhanced feeds;
- experiences constipation from the type of protein in infant formula;
- becomes irritable because of sleep deprivation; or
- sleeps poorly because of a sleep-association problem.

You know your baby best. If your assessment was not influenced by numbers or your healthcare professional's opinion, would you consider him to be well-fed? There are only three possibilities: baby shows signs of being well-fed, underfed, or overfed (see pages 325-334 for signs of overfeeding).

Baby shows signs of being well-fed

If your baby shows signs of being well-fed, then he's not currently underfeeding.

A number of situations might cause you to question if your baby is underfeeding or to mistakenly believe that he is.

- Misinterpreting crying as hunger (see pages 74-76);
- Mistakenly blaming wakefulness caused by a sleep association problem on hunger (see pages 292-298);
- Expecting your baby to drink more (see chapter 4 to clarify your expectations); and
- Noticing he is not gaining as much weight as expected. Potential reasons include growth plateau, catch-down growth, or a false alarm due to fluctuations in bodily fluids (how much milk is in his stomach, urine in his bladder, poop in his bowel) at the time he is weighed.

None of these are reliable indicators of underfeeding. Behavior can be attributed to many other reasons, and expectations for milk intake and weight gain can be unrealistic.

*Healthy, skinny, or small, but **not** underfed babies*

Skinny babies, intrauterine growth restriction (IUGR) babies, and small-statured babies are often assumed to be underfed without an assessment of their nutritional state. If a baby is tiny or underweight, it does not mean he's **currently underfeeding**.

- **Genetically lean babies** are often classified as "underweight," and they may be when compared to other babies, but it's because that's their natural body shape and not because they're underfeeding.
- **Genetically small babies** born to small-statured parents are often wrongly classified as "failure to thrive."

Even in cases where the baby was **once** malnourished because of conditions in the womb—as seen in IUGR babies—or past feeding problems, don't assume he's currently underfeeding. Or that he is incapable of deciding how much he needs to eat. It's just as important to assess his **current** nutritional state—by looking for physical and behavioral signs to confirm if he is underfeeding.

Baby shows signs of underfeeding

If you have confirmed that your baby is underfeeding, the next step is to identify the cause. Once you have done this, the solution will be obvious.

There is one point I would like to make clear:

Underfeeding is not the problem.
Underfeeding is a symptom of a feeding problem.

Employing strategies to increase your baby's milk or calorie consumption may mean you're trying to provide a solution to a problem without identifying the cause. Hence, such strategies have a high chance of failing.

> Changing your perspective from 'How can I make my baby drink more or receive more calories?' to 'What is preventing my baby from feeding well?' will prompt a search for the cause. Identifying the cause is far more effective when it comes to figuring out a solution.

If your baby is unwell, the first step is a medical assessment. Consult with his doctor.

If your baby is well, the next step is a thorough assessment of your infant feeding practices—see my Infant Feeding Self-Evaluation Checklist on page 272. This may reveal behavioral causes for underfeeding, like poor positioning, equipment problems, inappropriate responses to behavioral cues, rigid feeding schedules, and chronic sleep deprivation. If there is no room for improvements in your infant feeding management, only then consider physical causes.

Let's look at the most common barriers that prevent healthy babies from consuming sufficient nutrients to meet their needs.

Barriers to effective bottle-feeding

A healthy baby who is physically capable of bottle-feeding might underfeed for a number of reasons, the most common being one or more behavioral causes, such as

- baby chooses to avoid feeding;
- baby is too tired to feed effectively;
- baby has a poor appetite;

- baby is unable to effectively access the milk (breast milk or infant formula); or
- baby is not offered enough milk.

Baby chooses to avoid feeding

A hungry baby might choose to avoid feeding if he finds the feeding experience to be stressful, painful, frightening, or abhorrent because

- he gags, chokes or aspirates. Because the bottle's nipple is too long or too fast, or because he's pressured to suck while crying.
- he fears that something bad will happen. The most common reason for a baby to fear feeding is because he has been repeatedly pressured or forced to feed against his will.
- it is painful for him to suck or swallow. Teething and mouth ulcers may make it painful for a baby to suck. Esophagitis caused by untreated acid reflux or milk protein allergy may make it painful to swallow. (Physical problems causing pain while feeding are described in chapter 32. To assess the possibility of pain, go to pages 409-411).
- he has been switched from breast milk to infant formula or from regular formula to a bitter-tasting hypoallergenic formula and objects to the taste.
- the feel of the nipple in his mouth or the sensation associated with sucking and swallowing is unpleasant due to a sensory processing disorder (see pages 481-482).

Baby is too tired to feed effectively

A baby could become too tired to feed well or too exhausted to wake for night feeds when he is

- sleep deprived because of sleeping problem caused by learned dependence on negative sleep associations (pages 293-294).
- preterm, sick, or severely malnourished. These babies generally sleep a lot. They might lack the strength or endurance to wake and demand feeds or feed to satisfaction.
- too sleepy to feed because of receiving medications prescribed to treat colic, such as antihistamines, antispasmodics, or others, which include any medication that lists drowsiness as a possible side effect.

Baby has a poor appetite

- In illness, poor appetite can be one of the earliest signs before other symptoms become apparent. A baby can lose weight depending on the severity and longevity of the illness. However, once he has recovered, his appetite will return, and he may then experience increased appetite and catch-up growth.
- Vaccinations can cause a temporary drop in babies' milk intake. Reduced appetite can last for three to seven days.

Note: A temporary loss of appetite in an otherwise healthy, happy, and constantly growing baby is considered normal. In general, loss of appetite in babies could be caused during some developmental processes and not necessarily an underlying health issue.

Baby is not able to effectively access the milk

A newborn baby could be physically able to feed, have a healthy appetite, and be willing to eat, but he could be prevented from doing so because of

- **poor positioning** that makes it difficult for him to feed. For example, his neck could be twisted so that his head is turned to the side, making it difficult for him to suck or swallow. The angle at which the bottle is held may make it hard for him to effectively latch and maintain suction.
- **inappropriate or faulty feeding equipment** including issues with nipples being blocked, too short, too slow, or the nipple ring being screwed on too tightly;
- **rigid scheduling** and overlooking or ignoring baby's hunger cues while trying to make him feed at set times;
- **distress.** A ravenous baby can become so distressed that he is unable to calm enough to start to feed when finally offered;
- **disappearance of the sucking reflex**. If a breastfed or tube fed baby has not had repeated experiences feeding from a bottle, he may not know how to bottle-feed.
- **physical problems,** which may affect sucking and swallowing (see chapter 33).

Baby is not offered enough milk

Worldwide—which includes poverty-stricken and war-torn countries—the most common reason for underfeeding is because the baby is not given enough to eat. In affluent countries, a baby is far more likely to be overfed than underfed. However, underfeeding from not being offered enough can occur for the following reasons.

- If you make mistakes when preparing formula, your baby might end up with diluted formula. His belly could become full, and he'd stop feeding, but he may not receive sufficient calories to sustain him for long. This would generally only lead to underfeeding if paired with rigid feeding schedules.
- Demand feeding could be problematic for undemanding babies. Severely underweight babies are often undemanding, and they sleep excessively to reserve energy. Sick, weak, and neurologically impaired babies may not demand feeds.

There is no harm in "offering" your baby more milk in his bottle, especially if he tends to drain it. So long as he is permitted to decide how much he chooses to take, you can offer. Just respect his right to refuse. Don't harass him!

Be wary of "quick-fix" solutions!

Quick-fix solutions include strategies that aim to **compensate for reduced caloric intake** caused by underfeeding **without fixing the problem that causes the baby to underfeed.**

When the reason for underfeeding is not identified, which is usually because the parent is **not** asked questions about their infant feeding practices and behavioral causes are left unexplored, or if it's assumed that the baby is incapable of self-regulating his dietary intake, some health professionals will recommend quick-fix solutions such as

- switching from breastfeeding to bottle-feeding;
- switching from breast milk to infant formula;
- offering enhanced-calorie or thickened feeds;
- starting solids before four months of age;
- sleep feeding;

- syringe or spoon feeding milk;
- feeding more often at night; and
- tube feeding.

Quick-fix solutions can be effective in increasing **some but not all** babies' total daily caloric intake. However, irrespective of whether calories are increased or not, if a feeding strategy does **not** address the cause of underfeeding, there is potential for future problems. For example:

- **Switching from breastfeeding to bottle-feeding.** The baby does not develop oral feeding skills associated with breastfeeding. The risk of overfeeding is increased.
- **Switching from breast milk to infant formula.** Immunity support and other health benefits associated with breast milk are forfeited.
- **Calorie-enhanced or thickened feeds** have associated health risks such as compromised renal function, nutritional deficiencies, electrolyte imbalances and more (see chapter 11).
- **Starting solids before four months of age** is associated with a number of health risks.
- **Sleep feeding** allows a baby to avoid feeding while awake and may eventually result in feeding **exclusively** during sleep. This would severely restrict family life. Many parents feel housebound when their baby refuses to feed awake.
- **Syringe or spoon feeding** is tedious and unsustainable over the long term.
- **Feeding more often at night** encourages a baby to eat less the following day and promotes a reverse-cycle feeding pattern.
- **Tube feeding** reduces the motivation for a baby to feed orally. There are a number of associated problems, such as tube dependence, delayed oral development, and solids refusal—because baby's caloric needs are met via the tube.

Once parents and health professionals head down the path of believing that underfeeding can be fixed by providing more calories, there may be no turning back. Months of trial and error, and numerous health professional appointments, can ultimately lead to, but not end with, tube feeding. Chronic stress related to an unresolved feeding problem is associated with mental health problems in parents, such as anxiety disorders and depression.

> Only use quick-fix solutions for weak or ill babies and babies who are incapable of feeding well.

If your baby has the physical capacity to bottle-feed, **fix the problem causing underfeeding**—see my Infant Feeding Self-Evaluation Checklist page 272—and **not the symptom** (insufficient caloric intake).

What parents fear most

When their baby is not consuming the recommended amount of milk, parents most fear that

- **insufficient fluids** might cause dehydration and threaten their baby's life;
- **insufficient calories** might cause irreversible brain damage; or
- **baby might starve to death** if they don't make him eat.
  Such fears are unfounded in the case of physically well babies.

Is there a risk of dehydration?

> **What is dehydration?**
> Dehydration is "drying out" of the body caused by the loss of water and electrolytes-for example, mineral salts such as sodium, potassium, and chloride—which are essential for normal bodily functions.

Signs of dehydration in babies and young children

Signs of dehydration vary depending on the level of fluid and electrolyte loss—mild, moderate, or severe dehydration—and may include

- six hours without peeing;
- less than five wet diapers in a 24-hour period;
- dry or sticky mouth and tongue;
- cracked lips;
- skin that does not flatten when pinched and released;
- sunken fontanel (soft spot on the top of baby's head);
- listlessness;
- irritability;

- abnormal sleep;
- high fever;
- cold and pale skin;
- racing pulse and rapid breath; and
- sudden weight loss.

If you suspect your baby is dehydrated, call a doctor immediately. Severe dehydration requires hospitalization.

What causes dehydration?

Dehydration occurs when the body loses more fluid than it takes in. Dehydration in babies and children can be caused by **illness or medical conditions,** resulting in either or both

- **inadequate intake of fluids,** which can occur in acute illnesses like colds and flu which cause nausea and loss of appetite, or infections of the mouth or throat—such as a strep throat or tonsillitis; or
- **excessive loss of fluids**, which can occur from vomiting and diarrhea from gastroenteritis or food poisoning, excessive urine output caused by medical conditions such as kidney disease, or heat stroke from prolonged exposure to the sun or high temperatures.

The risk of dehydration to a physically well baby who is capable of bottle-feeding and offered **regular strength** formula or breast milk is extremely low, even in cases of underfeeding.

Breast milk and regular strength infant formula contain around 87 percent water.[145] Solids also contain varying percentages of water. For example, pureed fruit contains around 92 percent water.

The risk of dehydration is increased when a baby receives calorie-enhanced feeds.

Calorie-enhanced feeds

Calorie-enhanced feeds include concentrated formula, fortified breast milk, commercially produced high-energy feeds, thickened feeds—in particular, starch-based thickeners such as baby cereal—and feeds that have added oral nutritional supplements such as carbohydrates or oils.

Increasing the caloric content of a baby's milk between 22 to 30 kcal per ounce (72 to 100 kcal per 100 mL) generally won't cause dehydration, but the risk increases with higher energy concentration. Ultra-high-energy feeds, meaning above 30 kcal per ounce (more than 100 kcal per 100 mL), don't automatically cause dehydration, but they pose a greater risk.

I have seen a number of babies suspected of underfeeding who were given milk feeds that contain up to and over 40 kcal per ounce (134 kcal per 100 mL). This is usually done accidentally because no one has been calculating the caloric concentration of the baby's feeds. Forty kcal is double the number of calories per ounce compared to regular strength formula or breast milk. From the opposite perspective, the baby receives the same number of calories in **half the volume of fluids.**

The only time I have concerns about **physically well babies** becoming dehydrated is when **feeding-averse babies are given ultrahigh-energy feeds.**

When a baby has a feeding aversion, he may only accept feeds when ravenous and consume very little—enough to survive but not thrive. Giving a feeding-averse baby ultra-high-energy feeds means he can resist feeding for much longer periods, and therefore, receives less fluids compared to if he was given regular strength feeds. (Note: Around one third of feeding-averse babies will sleep feed and may take good volumes when asleep.)

Can underfeeding affect brain development?

Some of my clients claim they were told by their baby's doctor, another health professional, or another parent that their baby's brain will not grow and develop normally if he doesn't drink a minimum daily volume of milk specified by a health professional. Such claims are untrue.

Other clients report that because their baby had experienced a hypoglycemic episode shortly after birth, they have doubts about their baby's ability to maintain his blood glucose (blood sugar) levels within a normal range if his milk intake drops. When you understand how babies, and the rest of us, maintain blood glucose levels within a normal range, these concerns can be put to rest.

Glucose and brain development

Your baby's brain requires glucose (a type of sugar) to fuel cell functioning. Because neurons (brain cells) cannot store glucose, they depend on the bloodstream to deliver a constant supply of it.

The amount of glucose in your baby's blood needs to remain within specific parameters considered to be a "normal range". **Hypoglycemia** (a deficiency of glucose in the bloodstream) can be harmful to brain functioning.

Hypoglycemia in the days following birth can occur for various reasons, as a newborn undergoes **huge** physiological changes while adapting to life outside the womb. However, a history of a hypoglycemic episode after birth does not mean the baby is incapable of maintaining his blood glucose levels once he has adjusted to life outside the womb. Your baby's body, like your own, is designed to maintain optimal blood glucose levels.

Your baby's brain monitors and directly or indirectly controls all of his bodily functions, including the maintenance of blood glucose within a normal range, through multiple complex homeostatic mechanisms. Babies, children, and adults receive sufficient glucose to prevent hypoglycemia in three ways:

- food;
- glycogen stores; and
- body fat.

Food

The first line of defense against hypoglycemia is food. The consumption of food—which may solely be breast milk or infant formula— provides nutrients and energy (calories). Acids and digestive enzymes in your baby's stomach and intestinal tract break down the nutrients into tiny pieces, some of which become glucose. Glucose is absorbed through the wall of his small intestine and into his bloodstream, where it becomes blood glucose.

Glucose mostly comes from carbohydrates and simple sugars, like lactose or other carbohydrates found in breast milk, infant formula, and solid foods. Protein and fats can also be converted into glucose.

Glucose is carried via the blood to the cells of the body and brain, where it is used as energy to maintain cell function. As your baby's blood glucose level drops, this triggers the release of a hormone called ghrelin (also known as the appetite-stimulating hormone). This causes him to feel the sensation of hunger, which in turn motivates him to want to eat and the process continues.

A baby's milk intake might not provide for his daily glucose needs for many reasons.

- Baby has a poor appetite or is too weak to feed effectively as a result of an acute infective illness such as a cold, the flu, or gastrointestinal infection.
- Baby loses fluids and nutrients from vomiting or diarrhea.
- A breastfed baby's milk intake is restricted because of a low supply of maternal breast milk or a latch problem.
- Baby may need to fast before a surgical procedure.
- Baby might have self-imposed periods of fasting or limit his milk intake because he has become averse to feeding.

A temporary drop in a baby's milk intake for any of the above reasons could result in a deficit of glucose in the baby's diet but does not cause a healthy baby to become hypoglycemic.

If a baby's diet does not provide sufficient glucose, other homeostatic mechanisms take action to provide a constant supply of blood glucose to support cell functioning and brain development.

Glycogen stores

After your baby's body has used the energy it needs, leftover glucose is stored in little bundles called glycogen in his liver and muscles.[146] They can store enough glycogen to fuel his body in the absence of food for many hours.

If your baby is not eating enough to provide for his glucose needs, his liver then breaks down stored glycogen and turns it back into glucose to maintain his blood glucose level within a normal range.

Body fat

Adipose tissue (body fat) is the body's insurance policy against hypoglycemia. It's used for insulation, cushioning, and energy storage. Our bodies store energy in fat cells as a reserve that can be drawn upon during times of famine and illness. Fat cells expand and shrink as they take on and release energy.

As glycogen stores become depleted, fat cells gradually take over the process of maintaining blood glucose levels. Fat cells release fatty acids and glycerol into the bloodstream, which are converted into glucose and glycogen by the liver. Then, they are released into the bloodstream to maintain blood glucose levels and replenish glycogen stores in the liver and muscles.

If your baby is not eating enough to provide for his daily needs, he will lose a little weight from the shrinkage of fat cells. The longer the deficit, the more energy that is released from fat cells and the greater his weight loss. Once your baby's oral intake improves, fat cells start to store energy once again, they increase in size, and he regains lost weight.

A baby's weight will fluctuate depending on his dietary intake. However, his blood glucose levels will remain within normal parameters, supporting his brain functioning, growth, and development.

A **temporary** reduction in a physically well baby's milk intake will have no detrimental effect on his brain development or long-term growth.

Will baby starve to death?

While your baby has stores of body fat, these will be used as a source of energy. Starvation occurs when a baby's body is devoid of body fat.

Sadly, children starve to death worldwide. Babies can starve in poverty-stricken countries where food is not readily available and where lack of refrigeration and poor hygiene cause food poisoning and gastrointestinal infections that result in further loss of calories from vomiting and diarrhea. The only way starvation occurs in wealthy, developed countries such as our own is through neglect. This is clearly not the case for your baby. Neglectful parents don't read parenting books, and you have the means to offer your baby nutritious food.

Skipping a few feeds or drinking less than expected doesn't cause starvation. While your baby has a healthy layer of fat on his body, he is a long way off from starvation. If he is underweight or severely underweight, this is something that needs to be closely monitored by his doctor, who will decide if the situation is serious enough to warrant a feeding tube or other medical interventions. So rest assured, your much-loved and well-cared-for baby is not going to starve to death.

Next

A behavioral feeding aversion is one of the most common causes of underfeeding. It might require more to fix than the steps outlined in my Infant Feeding Self-Evaluation Checklist. Why babies develop an aversion and how to resolve this common bottle-feeding problem are explained next.

27 Bottle-Feeding Aversion

HOW TO RECOGNIZE A FEEDING AVERSION • WHAT CAUSES A BABY TO BECOME AVERSE TO BOTTLE-FEEDING • WHERE TO FIND A SOLUTION TO A BOTTLE-FEEDING AVERSION

If it feels like you are constantly fighting with your baby to get her to eat, she may have developed a feeding aversion. Or she might be heading down that path. A feeding-averse baby will refuse to eat unless ravenous, and even then, eat very little, but she might feed well in a drowsy state or asleep.

You'd be forgiven for thinking that a "feeding aversion" must be rare; otherwise, most parents and health professionals would know about it. But it's not! It's actually a common cause of feeding refusal, underfeeding, and poor growth. However, many health professionals are unaware because recognizing and teaching parents how to resolve babies' behavioral feeding problems is not within their field of expertise and, therefore, not something they have been taught.

Infant feeding aversions are, in general, poorly recognized, often misdiagnosed, and thus ineffectively managed. Consequently, far too many healthy babies suffer as a result of an unresolved, long-standing feeding aversion.

What is a feeding aversion?

An aversion is avoidance or fear of a thing or a situation. A feeding aversion refers to a situation where a physically well baby—who is fully capable of feeding—repeatedly, partially, or fully refuses to feed despite obvious hunger. The terms "feeding phobia," "feeding strike," or "infantile anorexia" may also be used to describe a feeding aversion.

Babies as young as seven weeks of age can display aversive behaviors toward breastfeeding or bottle-feeding. Older babies can become averse to eating solid foods—not just particular foods but also the process of eating solids. A baby could become averse to one, two, or all three feeding methods, mostly for the same reason: she is pressured to feed. However, there can be other causes.

Oral aversion versus feeding aversion

A feeding aversion and an oral aversion are **not** the same. It's important that you understand this because they have different causes and require different strategies to resolve. In the case of an oral aversion, a baby typically objects to anything in her mouth, including the nipple of a bottle. In the case of a bottle-feeding aversion, the baby is happy to have things in her mouth just so long as it's not the nipple of a bottle—or breast or solids in the case of these types of feeding aversions.

How common is it?

For the past 10 years, infant feeding aversions have dominated my private practice. To date, I have had more than 3,000 bottle-feeding aversion cases. Some of these were tube-fed at the time because of a feeding aversion. I've also seen a smaller number of babies who develop an aversion to breastfeeding and eating solids.

Being repeatedly pressured to feed against their will is the most common of all reasons for babies to become averse to all types of feeding. And yet, pain is the most commonly blamed cause of babies' distressed and avoidant feeding behavior.

Based on the cases I have seen, 100 percent were pressured or forced to feed for periods ranging from 30 minutes to two hours per feed. Around one-third completely rejected feeds while awake but would feed without resistance in a drowsy state or while sleeping.

In around 90 percent of feeding-aversion cases, pressure to eat was the original and only cause of the baby's avoidant feeding behavior. The baby did not, at any stage, show clinical signs that indicated a physical problem.

In the remaining 10 percent of cases, the baby currently, or in the past, displayed physical signs that could point to a physical problem or medical condition. While pressure may or may not have been the original cause of feeding refusal, it was a contributing factor. For example, a baby could initially eat very little because swallowing was painful, and as a consequence, she would be pressured to feed. The baby now had two reasons to fear feeding: pain and pressure. The problem that initially caused pain might resolve naturally or be effectively treated with medications or dietary change. However, her oppositional feeding behavior continued because of fear of being pressured or forced to feed.

Based on my experience, **misdiagnosis of medical conditions** in the case of feeding-averse babies is not just common; it's typical. While only 10 percent of the 3,000+ bottle-feeding aversion cases displayed clinical signs indicating a physical problem, 98 percent had been diagnosed with between one and five different medical conditions to explain their avoidant, distressed feeding behavior—an absolutely staggering statistic.

Signs

A feeding-averse baby will reluctantly eat enough to survive but not willingly eat enough to thrive. Once averse to feeding, the baby will try to ignore her hunger cues for as long as possible. While awake, she'll only agree to eat when she is so hungry she can't resist feeding any longer. She then eats quickly in an agitated state. She'll eat just enough to soothe pangs of hunger but not enough to feel completely satisfied.

Behaviors displayed by feeding-averse babies include

- refusing to eat despite visible signs of hunger;
- consuming less milk than expected for growth and energy needs;
- crying when a bib is placed around her neck, when held in a feeding position, when shown the bottle, or after stopping to burp;
- avoiding eye contact with the parent while feeding;
- rejecting feeds while held in arms;
- only eating in a darkened room or with closed eyes or with eyes covered;
- feeding only while in a drowsy state or asleep;
- eating only when distracted or entertained;
- accepting milk from another source, or enthusiastically eating solid foods after refusing to drink from the bottle.

No baby displays all of the above behaviors. Feeding-averse babies' behavior and its intensity will vary according to age, temperament, how hungry and how alert the baby is when offered a feed, and the lengths their caregivers take to make them eat.

Four behaviors commonly displayed by feeding-averse babies that can cause a lot of confusion are

- reaction for no obvious reason;
- conflicted behavior;
- sleep feeding; and
- accepting water, but not milk, from a bottle.

Baby reacts for no obvious reason

One of the most confusing behaviors displayed by feeding-averse babies is that the distress they show at feeding times appears to be completely unprovoked. At the point the baby reacts, the parent hasn't done anything other than to offer her a feed or calmly hold the bottle while she eats.

Once a baby has developed a feeding aversion, she may react **before** anything has happened. This is because she remembers recent past feeding episodes, and she's expecting a repeat occurrence of the stressful or frightening experience that has caused her to fear feeding.

Feeding is not something a baby can completely avoid except in the case of a feeding tube. As soon as she has eaten enough to soothe pangs of hunger, she could become upset and refuse to eat more. Her refusal to continue eating is done in an attempt to avoid a repeat of the situation she fears.

Conflicted behavior

In my work, I've found approximately four out of five feeding-averse babies display what I call "conflicted behavior" when feeding while awake. This is how it looks.

Baby doesn't seem to know what she wants to do. She is tense and possibly upset but accepts the bottle. She takes a few sucks and turns to the side or arches her back in an agitated state. Within seconds, she turns back and indicates she wants the bottle again. She takes a few more sucks, pulls away upset but quickly returns, wants the bottle, and so on. She could repeat this disjointed feeding behavior throughout the entire feed or until she becomes drowsy, at which time she feeds smoothly.

When a baby displays conflicted behavior, it's clear that she's hungry and wants to eat. However, it appears like something is preventing her. Observers typically suspect it's because she is experiencing pain or having difficulty sucking or swallowing properly.

However, in most cases, it's usually neither of these problems. It's **anticipatory anxiety,** meaning the baby is stressed because she's expecting something bad is going to happen, just like it has during past feeds. Hunger is forcing her to face her fears, but at the same time, she wants to get away before the thing she fears happens again. So, she's in a quandary and swings between eating and rejecting.

Sleep feeding

A feeding-averse baby could complete a full feed without resistance when drowsy or asleep simply because she's unaware she is feeding. Some parents find that their feeding-averse baby will completely reject feeding while awake and **only** feed when drowsy or asleep.

When some parents discover that their baby will accept feeds without resistance while drowsy or asleep, they may no longer try to make her eat while awake. Hence, their baby may no longer become distressed when offered the bottle while awake and instead simply but clearly rejects it by pushing the bottle away.

Accepting water but not milk from a bottle

A tiny percentage of feeding-averse babies are willing to accept water from a bottle but reject milk provided in the same bottle. Parents then believe it's the taste of the milk that is troubling their baby, which is possible. However, it's mostly because, unlike with milk, a baby is not pressured to drink water and therefore doesn't associate the taste of water with a stressful situation.

Causes

A baby could become averse to bottle-feeding if she's felt fear, stress, or disgust while feeding. This could be caused by:

- being pressured or forced to feed, usually because of nonresponsive parent-led parenting practices (described in pages 19-22);
- pain caused by mouth ulcers, a throat infection, acid reflux (chapter 32), functional lactose overload (pages 439-448), or milk protein allergy or intolerance (pages 457-464);
- repeated gagging (page 381-382) or aspiration;
- foul or bitter-tasting milk, plus the fact that the baby is tricked, pressured, or forced into taking it;
- unpleasant-tasting medications if restrained and forcibly given them or tricked into accepting the medication by it being added into milk or given through a nipple-like device;
- trauma from nasal or oral suctioning (in hospital or at home using a nasal aspirator), feeding tube insertion, intubation, or because of stretching exercises recommended following tongue-tie release; or
- sensory processing disorder, which can make the smell or taste of the milk or the sensation of anything in the baby's mouth including the nipple of a bottle objectionable. **Note:** A sensory processing disorder is one of the least common causes of feeding aversion.
- anything that could make feeding unpleasant, frightening, or stressful—for example, an older sibling screeching, banging toys, bumping, poking, smacking the baby while she's feeding, **when often repeated,** can cause a baby to develop a feeding aversion.

Pressure-induced feeding aversion

All of us realize when we're forcing a baby to feed. However, parents and health professionals who are taught, and who teach, **parent-led feeding practices** may not recognize the subtle forms of pressure that these practices involve. "Pressure" includes anything you might do to make your baby accept the nipple into her mouth when she doesn't want to eat or continue eating when she wants to stop. (See pages 275-278 for examples of ways in which a baby might be pressured to feed.)

Once a baby has become averse to feeding, parents continue to pressure or force their baby to eat because they don't know what else to do to resolve the problem of their baby's feeding refusal. They are then trapped by the **fear-avoidance cycle.**

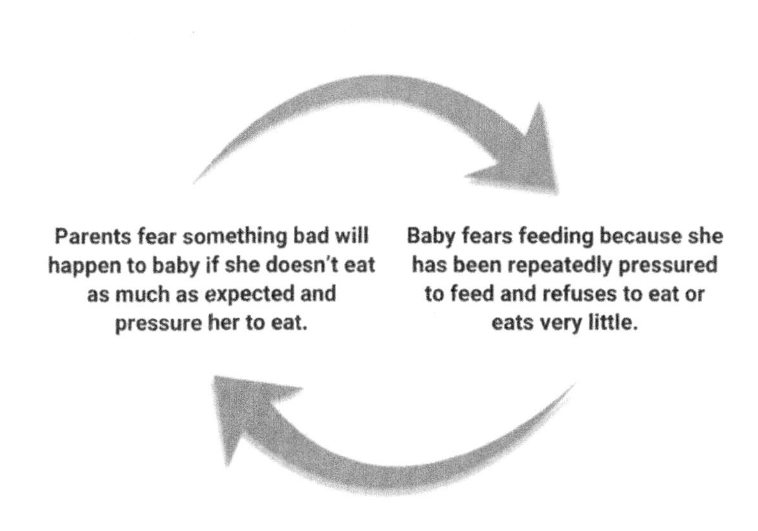

The more the parent pressures, the more stressful the experience is for their baby. The more stressful the feeding experience, the more their baby will try to avoid feeding and the less she eats. The less baby eats, the more anxious parents become. Not knowing what else to do, the longer or more forcefully the parent pressures their baby to eat. And around and around it goes.

The fear-avoidance cycle can spiral downward until the baby completely rejects all feeds offered while awake. Some parents may be able to maintain their baby's growth with sleep feeding … for a while. But sleep feeding tends to lose effectiveness between five and six months of age.

Why parents overlook pressure as the cause

Rarely do parents suspect pressure as the cause before it's pointed out because

- they may be using feeding strategies taught to them by a health professional and therefore believe it's okay;
- their baby's avoidant feeding behavior doesn't occur until their baby is capable of rejecting, which happens once her sucking reflex has faded;
- their baby reacts **before** any pressure is applied because she's learned what to expect, and she's trying to avoid the stress.

Without understanding why their baby becomes so distressed, parents conclude that she's experiencing pain. They discuss their baby's feeding behavior with other parents. The word "reflux" pops up time and time again. They search the internet for more information and find a multitude of vague symptoms such as feeding refusal and back arching, among others. Now somewhat convinced that their baby is suffering from acid reflux, they take their baby to be assessed by a doctor.

Why health professionals overlook the pressure cause

Health professionals suspect pain because the parent strongly believes that. Plus, most are unaware that pressuring a baby to eat can cause the level of distress that parents describe, and so they don't ask. Some health professionals claim babies are too young to develop a feeding aversion, which is not true.

Because pain is believed to be the cause, the baby might initially be diagnosed with acid reflux. If medications don't help, she might be given a hypoallergenic formula.

Confirm that the diagnosis is correct

Don't jump to conclusions about the cause because your baby's distress gives the appearance of pain. Be sure that **all** potential causes for her distressed and avoidant feeding behavior are considered. See pages 409-411 for tips on how to tell if your baby's distress at feeding times is caused by pressure, pain or a sucking problem.

You're the person who knows your baby best. Don't leave it to others to diagnose. If they don't ask you the necessary questions to explore the possibility of a behavioral feeding aversion caused by pressure, they may overlook or misdiagnose feeding aversion.

Misdiagnosis can make the problem worse

Many feeding-averse babies are misdiagnosed with medical conditions to explain their distressed, avoidant feeding behavior. A misdiagnosis can complicate the situation because medical treatments may make the situation even more complex. Here are some examples:

- **Misdiagnosis of acid reflux or milk protein allergy:** The baby may be forced to take medications or accept bitter-tasting formula. Being forced to accept these things risks creating or reinforcing a baby's feeding aversion.
- **Misdiagnosis of oral aversion:** Parents may be advised to place an oro-navigator or oral motor probe—both of which look a little like a rubbery toothbrush with ridges or bumps rather than bristles—into their baby's mouth to stroke her tongue or inside of her cheeks with the goal of "desensitizing" her to the feel of things in her mouth. Placing things into your baby's mouth without permission is more likely to reinforce a feeding aversion caused by being pressured.
- **Misdiagnosis of sucking problem:** A baby with a feeding aversion caused by pressure knows how to suck and may have a history that proves this. She's choosing not to. Following a diagnosis of disorganized sucking, you might be advised to place your finger in your baby's mouth to do "suck training." Doing so without her permission has the potential to reinforce a feeding aversion.
- **Misdiagnosis of tongue-tie:** Creating a raw wound in a baby's mouth and then needing to stick your fingers into her mouth twice a day to stretch the wound to prevent it from reattaching will clearly not help in the case of a baby with a feeding aversion. And in some cases, it can be the reason for the baby to become averse to feeding in the first place.

Many of my clients claim to have spent months and hundreds, if not thousands, of dollars trialing their baby on various bottles and nipples, up to seven different formulas, various combinations of medications, dosage changes, medical and allied health appointments, diagnostic tests, and hospital admissions.

Some clients claimed to have consulted between three and 20 health professionals searching for answers. All the while, pressure or force feeding as the primary or secondary cause of their baby's avoidant feeding behavior was completely overlooked. Most of my clients claim they were **not asked a single question** about their infant feeding practices or their baby's mood or behavior between feeds—questions necessary to differentiate pain from stress—by any of the multiple health professionals they had consulted about their baby's feeding refusal.

How to resolve a feeding aversion

The good news is that it's never too late to fix a feeding aversion, especially while a baby is still feeding orally, albeit unwillingly. However, doing so is not easy. And it's not fast.

Resolving a feeding aversion is not a matter of removing the most obvious cause of a baby's aversive behavior—pressure—and she'll suddenly forget about the past experiences and be willing to eat. You need to remove direct and indirect reinforcements. And you need to regain her trust that she will no longer be pressured to feed, which is something that requires time and patience.

Direct and indirect reinforcements

Direct reinforcements involve the subtle and obvious forms of pressure listed on pages 275-278.

Indirect reinforcements include strategies that enable a feeding-averse baby to avoid feeding from a bottle, or while awake or during the day, including

- giving milk by syringe, spoon, or cup, breastfeeding, or tube feeding;
- feeding while drowsy or asleep during the day;
- offering extra night feeds; and
- giving solid foods as a substitute for bottle-feeding.

Know what to expect

Don't expect your baby to go from loathing to loving feeding overnight. In general, it takes two weeks for a baby to recover from a feeding aversion. A feeding-averse baby has lost trust that her behavioral cues will receive an appropriate response, and you need to earn back her trust. It will take time and repeated feeding experiences where all direct and indirect reinforcements have been removed for her to learn that she is no longer going to be pressured to eat against her will.

Without knowing what to expect, you might give up too soon and revert back to old habits of pressuring her to eat long before she gets the chance to start to enjoy feeding once again.

If you suspect your baby has developed a feeding aversion, my book *Your Baby's Bottle-Feeding Aversion* will provide you with a step-by-step guide to turn your "unwilling feeder" into one who enjoys feeding.

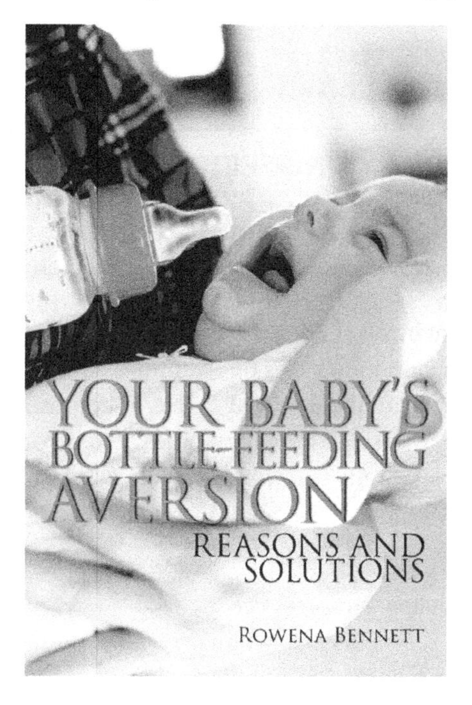

Next

Babies are thinking, feeling, tiny humans with a mind and will of their own. As they mature, they will display many different behaviors while feeding. Next I will provide examples of potential reasons for infant feeding behaviors that cause parents confusion or concern.

28 What's Troubling My Baby?

TOP 25 CONCERNING FEEDING BEHAVIORS • WHY BABIES FUSS OR CRY BEFORE, DURING OR AFTER FEEDS

Becoming a parent involves a steep learning curve. The task of interpreting your baby's behavioral cues can be daunting. At times, your baby will behave in ways that will cause you concern, confusion, or frustration. As you get to know him better, you will learn to recognize the meaning of many, but not all, of his behaviors. To help you fast-track the learning process, I have included the most common reasons for concerning behaviors while feeding or soon after feeding.

1. Baby doesn't show hunger
2. Baby always seems insatiably hungry
3. Baby rejects when offered a bottle feed
4. Baby cries when held in a feeding position
5. Baby turns or arches while feeding
6. Baby spits up or vomits during or after feeding
7. Baby gags or retches while feeding
8. Baby coughs and splutters while feeding
9. Baby feeds in a disjointed manner
10. Baby feeds very slowly
11. Baby feeds very quickly
12. Baby is easily distracted while feeding
13. Baby will only feed while distracted
14. Baby falls asleep while feeding
15. Baby only feeds when drowsy or asleep
16. Baby sucks but doesn't drink
17. Baby fake sucks, chews or plays with the nipple

18. Baby makes clicking sounds while sucking
19. Baby collapses the nipple while sucking
20. Milk pours out of baby's mouth
21. Baby bears down while feeding
22. Baby sucks thumb or fingers while feeding
23. Baby tries to sit up while feeding
24. Baby cries directly after feeding
25. Baby often has hiccups

Once you identify the reason, the solution is clear. Let's look at behaviors your baby might display now or in the future to find out what it means and how to respond.

1. Baby doesn't show hunger

> *"My baby (aged three months) doesn't show signs of hunger. He always has his hands in his mouth, so I can't use that as a sign. I honestly can't tell if he's hungry or not. I think he would go all day without eating if I didn't offer the bottle every three hours. Why doesn't he feel hunger?" Janelle*

Hunger cues indicate a baby is starting to experience discomfort. Janelle's baby accepts the bottle when offered. He would not accept if he was not hungry. Janelle may not be giving him the opportunity to display signs of hunger.

If your baby is healthy and developing normally, he's likely not displaying signs of hunger for one or more of the following reasons.

- **Not given a chance to display hunger cues**. Many parents are diligent at providing feeds for their baby at regular intervals—for example, every three hours—without waiting for him to exhibit behavior that indicates hunger-related discomfort.
- **Temperament.** Babies with an "easy" temperament display hunger in subtle ways, like wanting to be held or with minor fussing. They don't complain if feeds are delayed.
- **Feeding aversion.** A feeding-averse baby could fuss from hunger and yet reject feeds because of fear that something bad will happen if he accepts. His rejection then causes his parents to doubt their ability to accurately recognize his hunger cues.

- **Illness.** Lack of appetite is common during bouts of illness.
- **A severely underweight baby** might have a suppressed appetite. He might sleep excessively as his body tries to conserve energy. He may then appear to be an undemanding baby.

2. Baby always seems insatiably hungry

"Asher is six weeks old and seems like he's constantly hungry. We feed him 5 ounces (150 mL) every three to four hours, and for some reason, after feedings, maybe 30 mins later, he's chewing his hands. He might then take 3 more ounces (90 mL) before falling asleep. He's fussy so often during the day, I worry that my breast milk is not satisfying him." Greta

Many babies, especially newborns, behave in ways that make it **appear like** they have an insatiable appetite. Extreme hunger is usually not the issue; instead, consider the following possibilities.

- **Misinterpreting behavioral cues.** So-called "hunger cues" are actually signs that a baby wants to suck. Babies like to suck for various reasons, such as tiredness, boredom, overstimulation, comfort, and pleasure. (See chapter 7 for how to use time and context to improve accuracy in interpreting behavioral cues.)
- **Newborn overfeeding cycle.** Overfeeding causes abdominal discomfort, which makes the baby want to suck, so he overfeeds, which causes further discomfort and the cycle continues. (See page 333).
- **Feeding-sleep association.** If your baby regularly falls asleep while feeding, he may appear hungry when he wants to go to sleep.
- **Growth spurt.** During a growth spurt, your baby may suddenly be extremely hungry, demand feeds sooner, and drink more milk than usual.

3. Baby rejects when offered a bottle-feed

"Carter, aged four months, has started to completely refuse the morning bottle even after not having fed overnight for the last five hours. I literally can't get anything into him." Emily

You might feel confused if your baby rejects your offer to bottle-feed after giving signals that he's hungry or when you offer at a time that you believe he should be hungry.

Signs of rejection or lack of interest

- closed lips;
- turns his head away;
- pushes the bottle away;
- arches away;
- refuses to latch;
- blocks the nipple with his tongue or hands;
- won't suck;
- pushes the nipple out of his mouth with his tongue;
- chews on the nipple or rolls it around his mouth with his tongue.

All babies will **occasionally** reject feeds when offered. However, if your baby **repeatedly** rejects feeds, the reasons can be different.

Occasional rejections

- **Not hungry.** A baby over the age of three months may not **willingly** accept a bottle feed if he's not hungry.
- **Distracted.** Your baby may be more interested in observing what's happening around him than in eating.
- **Overtired**. When a baby is both overtired and hungry, he may be inclined to reject a feed because he's too upset from physical fatigue to focus on feeding.
- **Illness.** Any illness can negatively affect a baby's appetite.
- **Teething.** A baby may reject offers to feed because he's teething.
- **Vaccinations.** Routine vaccinations are notorious for causing a dip in appetite for periods lasting three to five days.

Repeated rejections

- **Excessive night feeding.** If your baby repeatedly rejects feeds at a predictable time each day—for example, the first feed in the morning—but feeds well at other times of the day, this may indicate that he's feeding more **at night** than he needs at his current stage of development (see pages 314-315).

- **Inexperience.** A breastfed baby might reject bottle feeds simply because he doesn't know how to suck from a bottle (see chapter 19).
- **Feeding aversion.** A feeding-averse baby fears feeding and may reject offers to feed despite obvious signs of hunger (see chapter 27).

4. Baby cries when held in a feeding position

"Elsa, aged four months, has started to scream when I try to put her in a cradle position to feed or get her to sleep." Laura

From around two to three months of age, babies learn to link a sequence of events based on the care they have received in the past. If you repeatedly hold your baby in a certain position for feedings, such as in your arms, or in a specific place, chair, or room, he learns to associate this position or place with feeding. Once he has made this connection, he may then think you're going to feed him every time you hold him in that position or move to the chair where you generally feed him.

Reasons for a baby to cry when held in a feeding position or when moved to a place he has learned to link with feeding include:

- **Hunger.** If your baby is crying in hunger, he's not turning or arching away; he willingly accepts the nipple when placed into his mouth, quickly latches, and starts sucking.
- **Rejection.** Some babies cry in rejection of the feed even before they have seen the bottle. In the case of rejection, the baby will also display other signs of rejection (described in point 3). Crying to indicate rejection usually develops because the baby has learned that subtle signs of rejection, like clamped lips and turning his head away, will be ignored.
- **Feeding aversion.** A feeding-averse baby may cry when placed into a feeding position because he has learned that something bad happens when he feeds (see chapter 27).
- **Discomfort.** A traumatic birth can involve stresses and strains on a baby's muscles and joints caused by hyperextension, excessive traction (pulling), compression or overstretching of the baby's head, neck, spine, or limbs. These injuries may make it painful for a newborn to be held in a particular position.

- **Frustration.** If you feed your baby in the same position that you settle him to sleep, he could be confused about your intentions.

5. Baby turns or arches away while feeding

> *"Hudson often cries if I try to get him to finish his bottle. The doctor asked if he back arches, and when I said yes, he said it's because of acid reflux." Christina*

If Christina's doctor had asked a few more questions, he would have discovered that Hudson stops crying as soon as the feed has ended and that he feeds well in a drowsy state, both of which would not be the case if he was suffering from acid reflux.

Arching of the back is a normal body movement for babies. They will turn and arch back to distance themselves from something they wish to avoid. When accompanied by crying or screaming, back arching is an expression of frustration, anger, or pain. In the case of a physically well baby, pain is the least likely cause. (See pages 409-411 to assess the possibility of pain.)

The intensity of your baby's behavior and whether he displays other behavioral cues at the same time can provide clues for the reason. A baby could be turning and arching:

- in a relaxed manner;
- while crying; or
- while screaming.

Turning in a relaxed manner

- **Finished feeding**. If your baby has stopped sucking and is turning his head or body away, these can be signs that he has had enough to eat.
- **Needs to burp.** He could stop sucking and turn away because he is experiencing minor discomfort from swallowed air.
- **Distraction.** He could turn away if distracted by a noise or movement in his surroundings or simply because it's a new place he has not seen before.
- **Bottle vacuum problem.** If you hear or see bubbles flooding into the bottle after he releases suction, it could be he has learned that by turning away and then returning, it's easier to suck (see pages 301-306).

While crying

- **Temperament.** A "spirited" baby may have finished feeding or be frustrated because of equipment problems and react by crying and arching away.
- **Overlooked signs of rejection or satisfaction.** If a baby has learned that passive cues of rejection or satisfaction are ignored, he might then respond more intensely by crying while arching away in rejection or when he's had enough to eat.
- **Tiredness.** A baby's frustration tolerance is lower when tired. The more fatigued your baby becomes, the more likely he is to reject a feed or fuss during the feed.
- **Lack of head support.** A newborn cannot support the weight of his own head, especially when partially reclined or during the process of placing him into a feeding position. If his head falls back, this triggers the **tonic labyrinth reflex**, a sudden automatic movement that will generally cause him to cry. This reflex will usually disappear by four months of age.
- **Discomfort.** Physical discomfort may cause a baby to cry and arch away.
- **Illness.** A baby's frustration tolerance will be low if he is unwell.

If your baby is crying and arching away, he wants to stop, and you need to let him do so. If you persist despite his opposition, you will stress him more, and he may then start screaming.

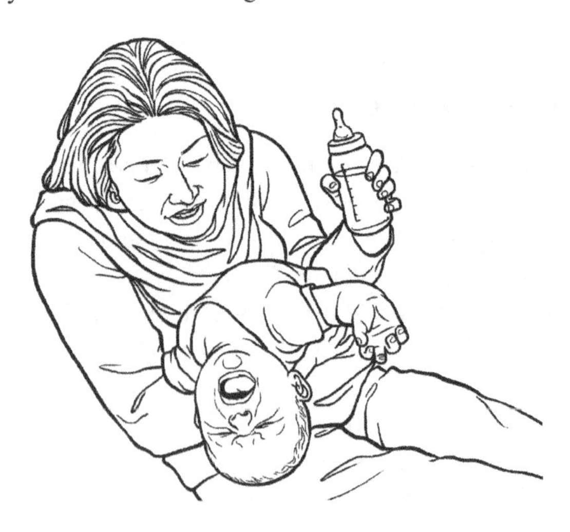

While screaming

- **Overlooking or ignoring signs of rejection** and persisting in trying to make him continue feeding will make it stressful for him.
- **A feeding-averse baby** might scream and arch away even before pressure is applied because he's expecting to be pressured. A baby who is rejecting or averse to feeding **will calm quickly once he realizes the feed has ended**.
- **While pain is typically the first thing parents suspect** when a baby is screaming during feeds, pain fades; it does not suddenly disappear. A baby experiencing pain while feeding **will be distressed and difficult to soothe long after feeding has ended** (see pages 409-411 for more ways to tell if pain is or is not responsible).

6. Baby spits up or vomits during or after feeding

> *"My son is 12 days old, and he vomits a lot after every feeding. Like puddles of milk. When it happened last night, he was inconsolable for three hours after the feeding. This morning he was not upset at all after he vomited. So, I'm not sure if he's in pain or not. What's going on? Am I doing something wrong?" Crystal*

When milk is expelled from a baby's mouth, different terms may be used—such as spitting up, posseting, regurgitation, reflux, or vomiting. Parents often claim their baby is vomiting when, in reality, he is refluxing. The mechanisms triggered by the body when vomiting is **not** the same as those when refluxing. The **causes and treatments for each differ.**

Reflux

Reflux involves a **passive expulsion** of stomach contents. The amount expelled can vary from a small dribble to what appears like the entire feed. It happens suddenly without prior warning. Reflux generally occurs when there is increased pressure within or upon the stomach.

Reasons for reflux include:

- **Gastroesophageal reflux (GER).** This is normal regurgitation commonly experienced by physically well babies (see pages 429-433).

- **Speed-feeding**. If a baby feeds too quickly, the stomach expands rapidly, increasing the risk of reflux. Speed-feeding also increases the risk of overfeeding.
- **Overstretching of the stomach**. Spitting up will be more pronounced if a baby overfeeds.
- **Pressure on a full stomach.** Sitting in a slumped position, having legs lifted to change a diaper, crying, or coughing can all cause a baby who has a full stomach to spit up.
- **Gastroesophageal reflux disease (GERD)** meaning abnormal reflux caused by an underlying physical problem or condition. This is listed last because it's the least likely reason for healthy, thriving babies to reflux stomach contents. Only a tiny percentage of babies suffer from GERD (see pages 451-457).

The nipple that Crystal was using for her baby was too fast, causing him to speed-feed and overfeed. Crystal was also misinterpreting her baby's tiredness cues for hunger, which was another reason he overfed.

Vomiting

Vomiting is the **forceful expulsion** of the contents of the stomach, and sometimes the contents of the small intestine, out of the mouth. The "vomiting center" is located in the brain. **Vomiting is a protective mechanism**. Nausea and loss of appetite often precede vomiting. Baby may also retch after the stomach has been emptied.

Baby might vomit for a number of reasons:

- **Gagging.** A gag could trigger vomiting.
- **Distension of intestinal tract.** Caused by overfeeding or constipation.
- **Food allergy**. An allergic reaction to cow's milk or soy proteins in infant formula can result in vomiting and diarrhea. Other signs of food allergies can include respiratory and skin symptoms such as coughing, wheezing, sneezing, and eczema (see pages 457-458 for more signs.)
- **Medication side-effect.** Many medications given to treat acid reflux have potential side effects, including bloating, nausea, vomiting, and abdominal spasms.
- **Illness.** In particular, a gastrointestinal infection (gastroenteritis) is typically associated with loss of appetite, nausea, and vomiting. Some

other infective illnesses unrelated to the gastrointestinal tract, like respiratory, urinary tract, or ear infections, can also cause vomiting.

- **Food poisoning.** A baby can experience vomiting as a result of food poisoning that occurs if his milk becomes contaminated from inadequate cleaning of equipment, preparation, or storage errors (see chapter 13).

7. Baby gags or retches while feeding

> *"My six-week-old used to take a bottle fine, but lately, he's been gagging quite a bit while eating. He gets really upset, and it seems like he quits eating because it's so hard since he keeps gagging. But he cries and acts hungry when we take the bottle away." Mollie*

The reason I make the distinction between gagging and retching is because visually, the movements of gagging and retching are virtually indistinguishable. However, the triggers are different.

Gagging is a reflex that acts as a natural body defense mechanism to prevent choking. While gagging is more likely to occur when a baby eats solid foods, babies can also gag while bottle-feeding. An **occasional** gag may be of no significance. However, when a baby **repeatedly** gags while bottle-feeding, the reason needs to be identified and addressed.

Retching (also called dry heaving) is making the sound and movement of vomiting without actually vomiting. It is often associated with feelings of nausea and vomiting.

Both gagging and retching can have a physical or psychological cause.

Physical causes

- **Nipple shaft length**. A nipple extending too far back into your baby's mouth can cause him to gag.
- **Bouncing or rocking while feeding.** Accidentally pushing the nipple too far into your baby's mouth while bouncing or rocking him can trigger the gag reflex.
- **Flow rate is too fast.** If your baby has trouble coordinating sucking, swallowing, and breathing because the milk flows too rapidly, milk can pool in his mouth and trigger his gag reflex.
- **Inexperienced bottle-feeder.** An exclusively breastfed or tube fed baby who does not have experience bottle-feeding might gag when the

nipple of a bottle is placed into his mouth because the sensation of a synthetic nipple in his mouth is unfamiliar.

Psychological reasons

- **Anxiety-induced gagging.** Although it isn't understood why anxiety triggers the gag reflex, it is believed that anxiety stimulates the nervous system, which triggers physical reactions to stress. I have observed a number of feeding-averse babies gagging even before the nipple has touched their lips.
- **Bad taste or smell.** A baby could gag if he finds the smell or taste of the milk unpleasant.
- **Force-feeding.** A baby might gag as a way to resist efforts to pressure or force him to accept the nipple into his mouth or continue sucking.
- **Learned behavior:** With positive reinforcement, gagging can become a learned behavior. For example, when a baby is stressed and possibly crying from being pressured to feed against his will, he might gag due to his inability to coordinate sucking and swallowing. The parent responds to his gagging by removing the bottle. When this is repeated, he learns that crying is ignored, but gagging gets his parent to stop. He may then deliberately gag as a way to get his parent to stop. I see this response of deliberate gagging in some feeding-averse babies (and during failed sleep-training attempts). Responsiveness to the baby's early signs of rejection can prevent and resolve this problem.

If you are unable to pinpoint and address the cause of repeated gagging, consult with your baby's doctor for a physical assessment.

8. Baby coughs or splutters while feeding

> *"My son sometimes sputters and coughs when bottle-feeding. It happens more at the beginning of a feed. It can take him five seconds to start to breathe normally again. It scares me every time it happens." Hayley*

Coughing, gagging, and sputtering (making a choking sound) are reflex actions that protect a baby's airways. These reflexes may be triggered by liquid that has moved into the throat before the swallow reflex is triggered.

Triggering of reflexive actions doesn't automatically mean your baby is aspirating fluids into his lungs. However, frequent coughing, spluttering, and delayed breathing while feeding requires an assessment by a speech-language pathologist.

Milk might pool in your baby's throat before he has a chance to swallow for a variety of reasons.

- **Gulping.**

  a) A fast-flowing nipple.
  b) If you follow a schedule and your baby is kept waiting too long, he may be ravenous when offered a feed and will gulp.
  c) A feeding-averse baby will typically refuse to feed until ravenous and may gulp when he's finally willing to accept.

- **Poor feeding position.** If a newborn is poorly positioned (see chapter 15), this can make it difficult for him to coordinate sucking, swallowing, and breathing.
- **Overtired.** A baby could have a poorly coordinated suck-swallow-breathe pattern feeding when overtired (see pages 290-292).
- **Forced to feed when crying.** A baby cannot coordinate sucking if he has milk forced into his mouth, especially if he's crying.
- **Sleep feeding.** Feeding while asleep or drowsy is associated with an increased risk of aspiration (see pages 281-282).[147]
- **Physical causes**. If you have ruled out behavioral reasons—see my Infant Feeding Self-Evaluation Checklist on page 272—consult with your baby's doctor for an assessment of physical causes.

9. Baby feeds in a disjointed manner

> *"When I try to feed my baby, he'll eat for three seconds, pull off crying or whining, and then try to latch on again. Then another three seconds later, he pulls off again. If I remove the bottle completely, he will cry until I give it back to him. It's so confusing. I wonder if it might be reflux." Danielle*

Pain is only one of the reasons a baby might feed in a broken, disjointed, or "conflicted" manner. I recommend you consider all possibilities before assuming your baby is experiencing pain.

- **Pausing.** Baby may be doing his own version of paced feeding.
- **Vacuum problem**. Babies over the age of four months can learn to turn and release the suction when it starts to get too hard to suck. Releasing suction allows air to enter through the hole at the end of the nipple—bubbles then flow through the milk—which temporarily corrects a vacuum problem (see pages 301-306).
- **Distractibility**. A baby might repeatedly pull off each time something captures his attention.
- **Developmental.** When a baby first discovers a new skill, like holding and controlling the bottle, he will want to practice by pulling the nipple in and out of his mouth repeatedly. The novelty of this wears off in a few days.
- **Feeding aversion.** Babies display disjointed feeding behavior I call "conflicted" behavior. He has learned that the bottle will satisfy his hunger, but he has also learned to expect something bad will happen while feeding so he swings between wanting to eat and wanting to stop (see chapter 27).
- **Learned behavior.** Disjointed feeding behavior can become a learned or a conditioned response. In other words, the way in which a baby learns to feed. Learned behavior is reinforced by the parents repeatedly returning the bottle.

10. Baby feeds very slowly

> *"I have twin girls aged six weeks. I feed them individually because I find they don't feed well. The problem is they take so long to eat that even before I have finished feeding both, they are crying from tiredness. I tried using faster nipples, but they get upset because it's too fast." Julie*

The younger the baby, the slower he needs to feed. Julie's baby girls take around 30 minutes each to complete a feed. This is not slow for a newborn. The problem is that Julie is finding it difficult to feed both babies at the same time.

A "slow" feed from a parent's perspective may not be slow from a baby's perspective. Table 28.1 lists the ideal feeding duration for babies of different ages.

Table 28.1: Ideal duration of feeds for age

Age	Ideal feed duration
Birth to 3 months	20–40 minutes
3–6 months	10–20 minutes
Over 6 months	5–10 minutes

Feeding too slow can be problematic for some babies. A newborn could wear out and stop sucking or fall asleep before completing a feed. Babies three months and older could express frustration if it takes too long to feed to satisfaction.

Babies might feed slowly for a number of reasons.

- **Nipple flow rate is too slow**;
- **Vacuum forming in the bottle** (see pages 301-306);
- **Tired baby** (see chapter 22);
- **Blocked nipple;**
- **Fake sucking** if he is not interested in eating.

11. Baby feeds very fast

> *"My eight-week-old is finished in five minutes but still fussing. He uses a level 1 nipple. I am worried that I might overfeed him if I give him more." Sarah*

Five minutes for an eight-week-old baby to complete a full feed is too fast. Sarah is wise to be concerned about overfeeding.

Feeding too quickly (also called speed feeding) is associated with a number of problems such as overfeeding, swallowing large amounts of air, and discontentment directly following thc feed because of an unsatisfied sucking urge. A baby might belch, spit up, or vomit during or after the feed. Aspiration (meaning milk entering into the baby's airways) is a more serious complication that can occur if he is unable to coordinate sucking, swallowing, and breathing caused by the rapid flow rate.

Babies might feed too quickly for a variety of reasons.

- **Nipple flow rate is too fast**. Sarah could try slowing down her baby's feeds by providing a nipple designed for preterm babies. She could also try a different brand of nipple.
- **Damaged nipple**. Wear and tear could cause the hole to become larger and the milk to flow faster.
- **Ravenous baby:** If your baby becomes ravenous, he may be more inclined to suck quickly at the beginning of the feed and then slow down.

12. Baby is easily distracted while feeding

It's normal for babies to become more aware of their surroundings as they get older and therefore become more easily distracted during feeds. Other reasons include

- **temperament**. Some babies are naturally more inquisitive and easily distracted;
- **new environment**. New places will be more stimulating for your baby;
- **lack of interest in eating.** He may not be particularly hungry;
- **getting full.** As your baby becomes satisfied, his sucking will slow down, and he will be more easily distracted.

13. Baby will only feed when distracted

A baby might fuss during feeds or refuse to eat unless distracted or entertained. For example, a young baby might refuse to feed while being held in the parent's arms unless the parent stands and sways or rocks or sits on a yoga ball and bounces. Older babies might refuse to eat unless they are entertained by the television, videos, books, or toys.

Refusing to eat without movement or entertainment is common for feeding-averse babies. However, without other behaviors that point to a feeding aversion (see pages 363-365), it could also be a learned habit. Whether it's a habit or a sign of a feeding aversion, the situation of only eating while distracted or entertained can be changed by following the same steps used to resolve a feeding aversion.

14. Baby falls asleep while feeding

> *"My baby falls asleep before finishing his feed, then naps for 20 minutes and wakes and wants to eat again. He then takes one ounce (30 mL) and falls asleep again."* Rosemary

Most babies, especially newborns, occasionally do this. Repeatedly falling asleep while feeding can be a sign of an underlying feeding or sleeping problem. It can also **be the cause** of feeding and sleeping problems. Baby may fall asleep when eating for numerous reasons.

- **Equipment problems**. If the flow rate is too slow or the bottle is not venting correctly, newborns can tire (see chapter 23).
- **Tired baby.** If a baby is chronically sleep-deprived, this could become a regular occurrence.
- **Feeding-sleep association.** If a baby has learned to link feeding with the act of falling asleep, he will want to feed when tired as a way to fall asleep (see pages 297-298).
- **Combination of reasons.** The reason for a baby to repeatedly fall asleep while feeding could include one, two, or all three of the reasons mentioned.

15. Baby only feeds when drowsy or asleep

> *"I am struggling to bottle-feed my baby because he only drinks while he is sleeping. He refuses to eat while awake. I have to cuddle him until he is drowsy or asleep and then feed him. We can't leave the house because I am afraid that he won't sleep if we are out and then won't eat."* Madison

A baby may reject feeds either passively or aggressively while awake but then accepts the nipple into his mouth and sucks well while in a drowsy state or asleep. This situation can be extremely frustrating to parents and restrictive on family life. There are two reasons a baby may appear to prefer feeding while drowsy or asleep.

1. **Feeding aversion.** A feeding-averse baby might be more receptive to feeding in a drowsy state or asleep because he's not fully aware he is feeding and therefore has his guard down. He will be **drowsy or asleep at the start of the feed**.

2. **Feeding-sleep association.** A baby who has learned to rely on feeding as a way to fall asleep will display a preference for feeding when tired and ready to go to sleep. **He will be awake at the start of the feed,** feed drowsy and fall asleep while feeding.

16. Baby sucks but doesn't drink

> *"I gave my baby a bottle for his last feed, and he was sucking away for more than half an hour and took only 10 mL. If I took the bottle out of his mouth, he'd scream until I gave it back." Vanessa*

A baby could happily accept the nipple into his mouth and make movements that appear as if he is sucking effectively, but he's receiving very little or no milk. Whether your baby appears to be frustrated or relaxed provides additional information to make your assessment. He may suck but not drink because of

- **lack of hunger;**
- **using the nipple as a pacifier;**
- **a blocked nipple;**
- **thickened feed.** The milk might be too thick;
- **a bottle vacuum problem.** The venting system in the feeding equipment may not be working properly (see pages 301-306);
- **poor feeding position** (see chapter 15); or
- **lack of experience**. A baby may not know how to suck from a bottle, especially if he is over the age of three months and has been exclusively breastfed or tube fed in the past.

17. Baby fakes sucks, chews, or plays with the nipple

From around four months of age, a baby has a greater ability to move his tongue to the side of his mouth. He may start to "mouth" (meaning explore with his mouth and tongue) and roll his tongue around the nipple and chomp on it. Basically, he finds it stimulating to play with the nipple in his mouth to see what he can do because he's

- **not hungry;**
- **teething;**
- **inexperienced.** A breastfed baby over the age of three months who is unfamiliar with bottle-feeding won't associate silicone or latex in his

mouth with satisfying his hunger. Basically, he doesn't know what to do with it;

- **feeding tube-dependent.** A baby who has been tube fed for weeks or months might not get the chance to learn how to suck from a bottle, or may forget, or may no longer connect feeding orally with satisfying his hunger.

18. Baby makes clicking sounds while sucking

A clicking or clucking sound indicates a loss of suction as your baby's tongue rolls off the tip of the nipple for any of the following reasons.

- **Equipment.** The shaft of the nipple may be too short for him. It might have been long enough at a younger age but might no longer be suitable as he grows.
- **High palate**. A baby may have a high arch to his hard palate, meaning he has trouble stabilizing the nipple in his mouth and so periodically loses suction. Ask your baby's doctor or health nurse to check his mouth and palate.
- **Poor positioning of the bottle**. If the bottle base is held too high, the nipple will push down on the back of his tongue. If held too low, it will push up against the roof of his mouth. Either way, it will be difficult for him to maintain suction (see pages 203-207).
- **Tongue-tie**. A tongue-tie could prevent a baby's tongue from molding around the nipple and cause a loss of suction. Tongue-tie will be evident from the time he first starts to feed. If your baby only recently started making clicking sounds while sucking, it's highly unlikely tongue-tie is the cause.

19. Baby collapses the nipple while sucking

Latex (brown rubber) nipples are softer than silicone nipples and are more likely to collapse. However, a firm silicone nipple could collapse if your baby has a strong suck. Bubbles flowing into the bottle after a baby releases suction also indicate a vacuum problem. Reasons for collapse include:

- **Nonvented bottles or nipples.** The nipple ring is screwed down too tightly and is preventing air from entering the bottle and replacing the space of the removed milk.

- **Vented bottles or nipples.** A collapsing nipple **while** the baby is sucking or bubbles flooding into the bottle **after** the baby releases suction would indicate that the venting system is not working correctly (see chapter 23).

20. Milk pours out of baby's mouth

Milk may pour out of a baby's mouth for many reasons, for example

- **flow rate is too fast;**
- **poor body or bottle positioning**;
- **nipple is placed under the baby's tongue;**.
- **lack of interest in eating;**
- **tongue-tie or uncoordinated suck-swallow pattern**.

21. Baby bears down during feeds

Baby may bear down and appear like he is going to poop during feeds for a couple of reasons.

- **Gastrocolic reflex:** Sometimes the baby might poop, and other times he won't. If his stools are normal consistency (see pages 435-437), this is normal behavior and nothing to be concerned about. However, **if extreme**, often occurring outside of feeding times, it could be one of a number of signs linked to functional lactose overload (see pages 439-448).
- **Constipation:** If your baby passes hard, dry, pebbly stools, this indicates he is constipated.

22. Baby sucks thumb or fingers while feeding

> *"My daughter keeps trying to wedge her thumb into her mouth while having a bottle! I hold her hand, but she is fighting me to try and get it in her mouth. If I pull her thumb out, then her other hand sneaks up. Does this mean she's teething?" Erin*

Babies have a strong desire to suck. From around three months of age, some will start to suck their fists. And from four months, some suck a thumb or fingers.

The reasons for thumb or finger sucking vary.

- **Before a feed.** This could be a sign of hunger; however, babies also suck their thumb or fingers for reasons unrelated to hunger.
- **When offered the bottle.** If turning away at the same time, your baby might be sucking his thumb or fingers to prevent you from placing the nipple into his mouth.
- **While feeding.** Placing his fingers or thumb into his mouth along with the nipple while feeding could be a sign that he is losing interest in eating.
- **After the feed.** Many babies suck their thumb or fingers to self-soothe or satisfy their sucking urge (see pages 69-71). It does not automatically mean he is still hungry.

23. Baby tries to sit up while feeding

"My baby has recently been pushing himself forward to sit up when I'm giving him a bottle. He now does this almost every time. It makes it difficult to feed him." Naomi

From around six months of age, some babies will occasionally or repeatedly try to sit up during the feed. This makes it difficult to keep milk in the nipple when he is seated in an upright position, and he can't feed effectively.

This happens for a number of reasons.

- **Developmental.** Many babies will try to sit up during feeds from around six months of age. If your baby insists on feeding upright, an angled bottle may make it easier to feed without the risk of swallowing a lot of air.
- **Rejection.** This can be a sign that your baby does not wish to eat or that he has had enough and is ready to move on to other things. Respect his wishes.
- **Distracted.** A baby may sit up to look around if distracted by other children, television, or events taking place in his immediate surroundings.

24. Baby cries directly after feeding

"My four-week-old cries for 15 to 30 minutes after every feed. I don't know why. We keep him upright while burping him for at least 30 minutes after feeding. I've given him gas drops before and during his feed. We have switched his formula a few times. Nothing seems to help." Abbie

Common reasons for this behavior include

- **Unsatisfied sucking urge.** Many babies have an urge to suck that extends beyond feeding (see pages 69-71). A baby will cry to have his sucking needs met.
- **Tiredness.** Tiredness cues are often mistakenly interpreted as hunger or boredom (see pages 288-289). As the baby's level of fatigue increases, he will cry with greater intensity, which is then commonly mistaken as pain.
- **Need to burp.** If your baby has not burped within two to three minutes, his crying is probably not because of swallowed air. Look for other potential causes.
- **Boredom.** Looking into a parent's chest or over the parent's shoulder for 15 to 30 minutes while being held upright following feeds might be boring for babies over the age of three months.
- **Pain.** Pain can, of course, cause a baby to cry. If your baby displays gastrointestinal (GI) symptoms, first check if he is overfeeding (see chapter 25) which can cause functional lactose overload issues (described on pages 439-448). Check out these common problems before assuming colic, reflux, milk protein allergy or intolerance, or other physical problems or medical conditions described in chapter 32 are to blame.

25. Baby often has hiccups

Hiccups are a common condition caused by sudden, irregular contractions, or spasm, of the diaphragm. The contractions cause air to be sucked into the windpipe, and this is followed by a sudden closure of the vocal cords, which produce the characteristic "hic" sound.

We all hiccup at times. However, babies, especially newborns, hiccup often. Hiccupping is rarely a reason for concern.

No one knows for sure why babies frequently hiccup; however, there are a number of different theories. Because hiccups often develop after eating, it is suggested that they may be caused by pressure on the baby's diaphragm from a full stomach or from gulping down formula or breast milk too quickly or from swallowing large amounts of air. But babies will also hiccup for no obvious reason.

The frequency of bouts of hiccups generally decreases with age and has often disappeared by the time a baby is six to nine months old. A baby will normally stop hiccupping within five to 10 minutes. If your baby's hiccups do not stop within a couple of hours, it is important to see a doctor.

Next

Next, I describe when and how to cease bottle-feeding, and reasons why parents might find their baby is resistant to giving up his much-loved bottles. Even if your baby is currently too young to cease bottle-feeding, I recommend you read the next chapter because there may be steps you can take now to make the transition from bottle-feeding to cup feeding occur seamlessly when the time is right.

29 Preparing to Cease Bottle-Feeding

THE BEST TIME TO CEASE BOTTLE-FEEDING • HOW TO PREPARE YOUR BABY FOR THE END OF BOTTLE-FEEDING • WHY SOME CHILDREN DON'T WANT TO GIVE UP BOTTLE-FEEDING • CUPS THAT SUPPORT ORAL DEVELOPMENT

Long before your baby needs to stop bottle-feeding, you can take steps to make it easier for her to switch. Choosing the right equipment, promoting her cup-feeding abilities, and knowing why toddlers resist giving up bottle-feeding will help you decide on the most appropriate course of action.

When to end bottle-feeding

The American Academy of Pediatric Dentistry (AAPD) recommends you wean your baby from bottle-feeding by the time of her first birthday.[148] Others, such as the American Academy of Pediatrics (AAP), recommend you phase out bottles between 12 and 24 months of age.[149]

Prolonged bottle-feeding has health risks, some of which can also occur when drinking from training cups.

Reasons to stop bottles

Prolonged bottle-feeding can be detrimental for a variety of reasons, including the baby's oral and speech development, nutrition, and dental health.

Oral and speech development

Teaching your toddler how to drink from a cup is a precursor to speech development.

The longer a child continues using a bottle, the greater the chance she has of developing a habitual pattern that can impact her speech and sound development and cause a lisp.

Toddlers need to develop a **mature swallow** pattern.[150] In partnership with the skills gained while eating solid foods, a mature swallow learned while drinking from a **suitable** cup is necessary for safe drinking, chewing, eating, swallowing, controlling saliva, and taking medications.

Nutrition

While milk is the most important food for babies before the age of 12 months, solids slowly increase in value from six to 12 months. By 12 months of age, solid foods are more important to a child's diet than milk. If a child continues bottle-feeding and consumes a disproportionate amount of milk compared to solid foods, nutritional deficiencies—in particular, iron deficiency anemia—can result.[151]

Bottle-feeding is associated with more rapid weight gain compared to breastfeeding.[152] Prolonged bottle-feeding beyond 12 months of age may continue the pattern of excessive weight gain.

Teeth

If a child is permitted to run around all day sucking milk, juice, or other sweet-tasting fluids from a bottle or cup, this can cause "baby bottle tooth decay."[153] Tooth decay (dental caries) can occur as early as one year of age.[154] Prolonged bottle-feeding can also cause malocclusion (when the top and bottom teeth do not come together, creating an open bite).[155]

While there is good reason to switch a toddler from bottles to cups, some or all of these problems can also occur when a child uses certain types of sippy cups. Therefore, your choice of cups will be important.

Choosing suitable cups

Sippy cups (also called trainer cups) are not necessary! A normal, healthy baby doesn't need to use a trainer, sippy, or straw cup. Long before sippy cups were invented, babies were taught to drink from an open cup.

Sippy cups are not designed to aid a child's oral development. Their sole purpose is to minimize spillage that often occurs as a child learns to drink independently from a cup. Therefore, they benefit parents more than the child.

Many styles of sippy cups promote similar lip and tongue functions as a baby uses when sucking from a bottle. Hence, they don't promote mature swallowing and instead delay rather than aid drinking, eating skills, and speech development.

What to avoid

- **Training cups with a nipple.** The only difference between this and a bottle is the shape of the container holding the milk. It has the same effect on oral skill development as bottle-feeding.
- **Spouted sippy cups.** Can cause the malformation of a baby's hard palate, leading to malocclusion and crooked teeth.[156]
- **No-spill valves.** Use encourages sucking and does not allow the child to sip, which is the purpose of a training cup. Parents may be inclined to allow their child to self-feed from a no-spill cup whenever she chooses, resulting in frequent bathing of her teeth by milk or sweetened fluids.

Though these cups help with skills like holding a bottle, hand-to-mouth coordination, familiarity with drinking from more than just a bottle, they don't offer much in the way of **oral skills**. They can also cause the same problems associated with frequent and prolonged bottle-feeding, so they are best avoided.

What to use instead

Occupational therapists, speech-language pathologists, and pediatric dentists recommend avoiding sippy cups and providing fluids instead via an open cup and straw cup to encourage a mature swallow.

An open cup allows strengthening of the muscles around the lips to ensure proper closure, which is necessary for a baby to learn how to safely eat, drink, swallow and to decrease drooling. These muscles are also important for certain speech sounds.

Drinking out of a straw cup (with flexible straw) is a good oral motor workout. While aiding oral development, a straw cup should not be exclusively used for fluids; instead, use it in addition to drinking from an open cup.

Barriers to a smooth transition to cups

Switching a child from bottle-feeding to cups is rarely something that just happens, even though some babies appear to do it with ease. It's not an easy transition for all. Others appear to have great difficulty making the switch. They may appear to desperately cling onto bottle-feeding, not only resisting their parents' efforts to encourage them to drink from a cup but exhibiting distress if not given a bottle.

There are four barriers that will make it harder for a child to make a smooth transition from bottle to cup. These include

1. lack of skill development;
2. a bottle-feeding sleep association;
3. an emotional attachment to bottle-feeding; and
4. an aversion toward eating solid foods.

Lack of skill development

The key to success is choosing cups that are appropriate for your child's age and stage of development—for example, at six months, an open cup is a better option than a straw cup. Providing lots of opportunities for your baby to learn to master the skills required to drink from a cup, while at the same time making these experiences fun long before you plan for cups to take over from bottles, will make it easier to make the switch.

Six to 9 months

Start to offer your baby sips of water from an open cup from around **six months of age**. Your baby needs to be in a **fully upright position,** either seated on your lap or in a highchair. Hold the cup, and offer baby tiny sips from the rim. This will train her tongue to start to elevate to the correct position to promote mature swallowing.

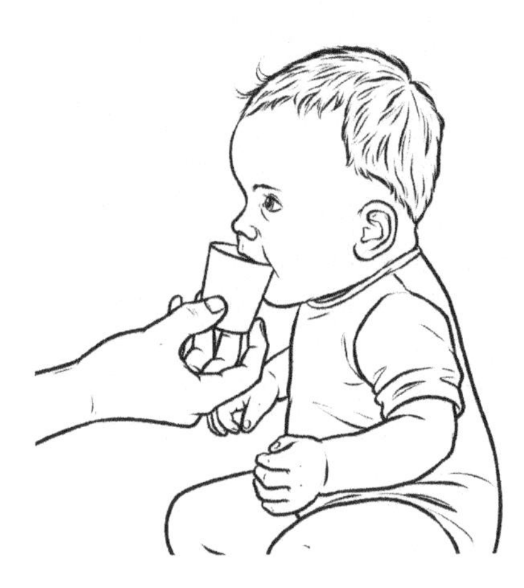

Don't be surprised if your baby treats the cup as if it's a toy at first. Choose a cup without handles for this age group, as handles may make it tempting for her to grab the cup and fling it about. Be patient. It can take a baby several weeks of daily use before she starts to understand how to drink from it.

Nine months+

Around **nine months of age,** encourage your baby to learn to suck from a straw cup (in addition to continued practice with an open cup). Two options can help your baby understand the concept of what a straw does.

1. Place a straw in a glass of water, and use your finger to cover the opening, sealing the water inside. Lift the straw, place the open end in your baby's mouth, and release your finger, allowing the water to fall into her mouth. She should instinctively seal her lips around the straw and begin to suck.
2. Start with a soft-sided straw cup, so you can squeeze the cup to help the liquid move up the straw.

As your baby learns to suck and draw fluids through the straw, move to a straw cup with handles and a weighted base (also called a self-righting cup) so she can practice the hand-to-mouth coordination required to self-feed. Eventually, move to an open cup with no handles, so she learns to hold the cup in her hands. Choose a small cup suitable for tiny hands.

Remember, children develop skills at their own pace. The more opportunities your baby gets to practice, the faster she will learn.

Tip: Use a different color or design of cup for different fluids so your baby can recognize what she is being offered by the appearance of the cup. Increase the variety of cups as soon as your child's skills develop.

When and how to offer

Choose times when she is relaxed and appears interested. Offer, don't force or pressure. Be guided by your child. Be respectful of her right to accept or reject. Demonstrate the same responsiveness to her behavioral cues as you do when offering her the bottle.

Bottle-feeding-sleep association

If your baby uses a bottle **as a way to fall asleep**, don't wait for it to cause problems (see pages 297-298). Teach her to fall asleep in a different way—the sooner, the better.

If you give your baby a bottle as part of her bedtime routine, move the feed forward in the routine so that it becomes one of the first steps and not the last—for example, bottle-feed, then bathe, dress for sleeping, clean teeth, then cuddles and story before bed.

Emotional attachment

Some toddlers are more attached to bottle-feeding than others because of their past feeding experiences and what bottle-feeding represents. It has been a source of nourishment and comfort all of their lives. Most toddlers, but not all, love milk. Some prefer drinking milk to eating solids. Others love to suck from a bottle. It may not matter what's in the bottle. It may be because they have learned to link bottle-feeding with calming, reassuring times cuddled in mommy's or daddy's arms. For whatever reason, they have become emotionally attached to the bottle and may be reluctant to give it up.

If this is the case for your little one, you may need to take steps to help her separate feeding from soothing. Aim to move bottle-feeding from a comforting action to more of a functional one where milk is served at mealtimes only. Find alternative ways of soothing your child.

Are you finding it difficult to let go?

It's not just babies who require time to adjust emotionally. Even if you've been counting down the days until your baby finally stops bottle-feeding, you might be surprised to find that it makes you feel a little emotional.

"No more bottles" represents the end of babyhood. It can be hard to accept that this chapter of your child's life is coming to an end. If you know that this is your last baby, an end to bottle-feeding can bring about a lot of emotions.

Aversion to eating solid foods

If a child has developed an aversion to eating solid foods, this could prevent her from smoothly transitioning from bottle to cup. Usually, it's not an issue with the food itself but the experience associated with eating solid foods. Consequently, she satisfies her hunger by drinking milk. She refuses to drink milk from a cup because it's too slow and too frustrating for her to receive the calories she needs when hungry.

One reason to switch a child from bottle to cup at 12 months is that cup feeding will naturally reduce the amount of milk a child consumes and, in turn, increase her motivation to eat solid foods. Denying the bottle or limiting the milk consumption of a child who has become averse to eating solids will reduce her total daily caloric intake, distress her because of hunger, and may result in poor growth.

If your child has become averse to eating solid foods, you will recognize that something is seriously wrong, but you might not understand why or what to do to fix the problem.

The most common reason for children to become averse to eating solids (meaning the act of eating rather than specific foods) and therefore refuse to eat is that they have been repeatedly pressured or forced to eat in the past.

What to do

If you suspect that your child has developed an aversion toward eating solid foods, this needs to be resolved **before** trying to end bottle-feeding.

Seek individualized advice from an occupational therapist, speech-language pathologist, or feeding therapist **who specializes in feeding aversions**. Be aware that not all health professionals who help with infant and child feeding problems are aware of how to resolve a feeding aversion. Alternatively, go to my website, **Babycareadvice.com,** for professional advice on how to resolve feeding aversions to breast, bottle, and solids.

When it's time to end bottle feeds

As your baby approaches her first birthday you might be thinking about how to transition from a bottle. If you have been teaching her to drink from a straw or open cup from nine months of age or sooner, then by 12 months she has likely developed the skills to enable her to hold a cup and drink from it independently. If you have separated bottle-feeding from sleeping and soothing, and there is no suspicion of her being averse to eating solids, you may find the transition to cup feeding is easy.

The most effective way to break your baby's bottle habit is to wean her off the bottle without her even realizing. Gradual weaning is recommended.

Tips for gradual bottle weaning

The weaning process can be as long as you feel is necessary. A gradual wean could take anywhere between one to six months depending on your baby's age when you start.

These steps should help:

- **Choose the time**. Don't make changes when your child is sick, or if she is experiencing a significant change, like moving to a new house, a new caregiver, starting daycare, or a shift in routine.
- **Make only one change at a time**. For example, switching from formula to cow's milk, or no longer warming her milk. Allow time to adjust before making more changes.
- **Limit her access to bottle-feeds**. Either feed your child or supervise her self-feeding and then remove the bottle as soon as she has finished rather than allow her to walk around holding it. Don't allow her to feed from a bottle in her bed before sleep.
- **Offer solids before milk**. Solid food will fill an empty tummy making it easier to cut down on the use of a bottle.
- **Cease one bottle-feed at a time**. Substitute a cup of milk for a bottle of milk, starting with the middle of the day bottle-feed first, then the morning bottle, and lastly the bedtime bottle. Wait for your child to

adjust and stop asking for a bottle at that time, and then substitute another.

- **Distractions**. If she is asking for a bottle, try to distract her with a fun activity to take her mind off of it.
- **Out of sight, out of mind**. Keeping the bottle out of sight may help her to not ask for it.
- **Positive reinforcements**. Praise or star charts for an older child (2 years or older) could help her transition.
- **Water down milk in the bottle**. Make the milk in the cup taste better by watering down the milk in the bottle by 50 percent, but offering full strength milk from the cup. Then slowly add more water until the entire bottle is water or she has stopped asking for it.
- **Promote cup feeding skills.** Continue to offer your baby **both** open cups and straw cups as she transitions off bottles.

Encourage safe and healthy habits from the start

Keep in mind that your actions will encourage and reinforce your child's habits. Think about the habits you want her to develop. It will be easier to encourage healthy eating habits from the start than it will be to change bad habits.

A substantial number of toddlers experience facial injuries as the result of falls occurring while running and drinking from a sippy cup or bottle.[157] Encourage your child to sit and remain seated while drinking from a cup to prevent injuries. Remove the cup if she refuses to remain seated.

Tooth decay occurs when exposed to sugar, whether the exposure occurs from drinking from a bottle or cup. Discourage snacking. Don't allow your child to be constantly sipping on liquids that contain milk, juice or other sweetened fluids, or go to bed with a sippy cup. Offer these liquids at meals or snack times only. And remove the cup and discard any leftover milk or juice once the meal or snack has ended. Offer water as necessary between meals and snacks.

Don't forget to thoroughly clean the straws using a straw brush and replace the straws as required.

Next

Next, we go to Part G. The chapters in Part G may help you to identify if your baby has a physical or medical problem causing pain, gastrointestinal symptoms, or negatively impacting his ability to suck from a bottle safely and effectively.

PART G:
Physical and Medical Problems

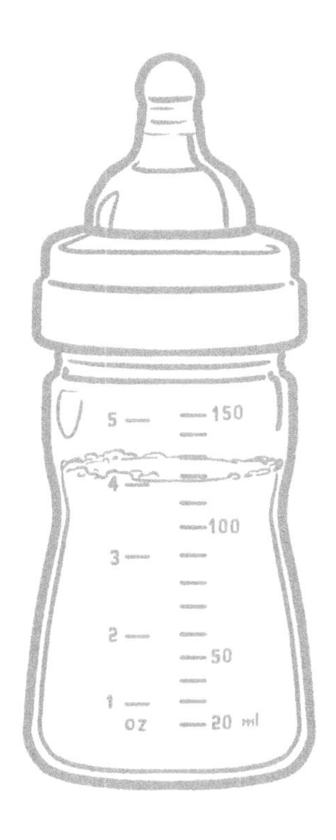

30 Before Going Down the Medical Path

WHY MISDIAGNOSIS OF INFANT FEEDING PROBLEMS IS COMMON • WHAT A FEEDING ASSESSMENT INVOLVES • HOW MEDICAL TREATMENTS COMPLICATE A BEHAVIORAL FEEDING PROBLEM • THE SNOWBALL EFFECT OF OVERLOOKED OR MISDIAGNOSED BEHAVIORAL FEEDING PROBLEMS

When a physically well, normally developing baby spits up often, has unusual bowel movements, cries for unknown reasons, or experiences feeding, sleeping, or growth problems, our first reaction is to suspect that there's something physically wrong with him. Instead, our first reaction should be to check if there's something that we—parents and health professionals—might be doing or not doing to cause this.

Some parents and health professionals have tunnel vision when it comes to finding a solution to their baby care dilemma. They can spend weeks, months, and even years in a fruitless search for a medical solution to what is actually a behavioral (nonmedical) problem.

My experience

When babies experience feeding or sleeping problems or cry for unknown reasons, it is **often assumed** that one or more physical or medical causes is responsible. "Assumed" because behavioral causes have not been considered.

During my career, I have seen literally thousands of mistakes made by parents and health professionals because they were unaware of normal infant development and/or behavioral feeding and sleeping problems that distress normal developing babies or which can cause gastrointestinal (GI) symptoms—such as those described in the chapters of Part F.

Consequently, I don't automatically accept the diagnosis made by others to explain the reasons for a **physically well baby** to experience feeding or sleeping problems. Instead, I make my own assessment by comparing the signs and symptoms associated with commonly diagnosed medical conditions and those caused by behavioral problems to determine the most likely cause.

Typically, there are multiple causes for an individual baby's troubles. In the case of **healthy, normally developing babies**, these are usually **exclusively behavioral** causes. If your baby is physically well, I recommend you assess and address all potential behavioral causes first. If his feeding troubles or GI symptoms persist after all behavioral causes have been ruled out, only then consider medical problems such as colic, reflux, and milk protein allergy or intolerance.

Which babies are more likely to have a physical cause?

Physical reasons for feeding problems are more common with babies who have congenital abnormalities, birth defects affecting their digestive tract, physical disabilities, chronic medical conditions, metabolic disorders or syndromes, who experience neurological impairment due to birth trauma, or who have a strong family history of allergies.

Rarely is the cause of a baby's feeding issues purely physical. Physical and behavioral causes can, and often do, occur simultaneously. Babies troubled by a physical problem or medical condition can also experience behavioral feeding and sleeping problems, which can be the cause of, or add to, their distress. In such cases, feeding or sleeping troubles from **unidentified** behavioral causes could persist long after the physical problem or condition has been resolved or effectively treated.

If your baby has been diagnosed with a physical problem or medical condition, don't overlook behavioral causes that could also be affecting his feeding.

Why assess behavioral causes first?

There are a number of very good reasons to first assess behavioral causes that you might not have thought of.

- Behavioral feeding issues are without exception the most common reasons for physically well babies to cry or develop feeding and sleeping problems. Yet they are the most poorly recognized problems.
- Though physical problems are the least likely to cause a healthy baby's troubles, these are the most commonly diagnosed causes during brief medical consultations.
- A physical or medical condition increases the risk of a baby developing a behavioral feeding or sleeping problem.
- No medication, dietary change, diagnostic test, therapy, or surgical procedure will solve a behavioral problem.
- Medications and dietary changes can create new problems, either at the time or in the future, most of which will not be recognized as being connected to the medications, change in diet, or therapy.
- The most important reason of all is

Health professionals don't suffer from their oversights, poor feeding advice or mistakes. Babies and their families do.

The effect of unrecognized behavioral problems can be devastating for babies and their families.

> *"It's incredibly hard to get Mateo to eat. He's been diagnosed with failure to thrive. Every time he turns down a bottle I panic until the next bottle! I feel like a crap mother because I can't handle my child's feeds. I have major PTSD as a result of his feeding issues. No one understands!! I have decided not to have a second child because I never want to go through this again." Marianna*

Each year, I see hundreds of families who have been suffering emotionally, financially, and socially as a result of unrecognized—and therefore unresolved—infant behavioral feeding problems. For many, the situation was made worse as a result of recommended treatments that were based on misdiagnoses.

One of the first things to identify when a baby is distressed is whether he is experiencing pain.

How to tell if your baby is experiencing pain

Babies experiencing pain are distressed. However, a distressed baby is not necessarily experiencing pain.

The first step involved in figuring out the cause of your baby's tears is to determine if his crying is caused by pain or distress.

It's relatively easy to rule out pain as the cause of a baby's feeding issues by assessing how he behaves or responds in other circumstances. Pain is unlikely to be responsible if baby is

- physically well;
- happy when you stop feeding him;
- feeds well in predictable situations;
- content between feeds;
- sleeps well; and
- has normal bowel movements.

Baby is physically well

When there are no observable physical signs—for example, unusual bowel movements, a nasty diaper rash, sore throat, or an ear infection—identified during a routine medical examination, any comments about the cause of your baby's distress will be based on assumptions. While an absence of physical signs does not rule out pain, it creates doubt.

Baby is happy when you stop feeding him

If your baby is happy as soon as you stop trying to feed him, pain is probably not the cause of his distressed behavior at feeding times. Pain fades. It doesn't suddenly disappear simply because the feed has ended. A baby who is stressed because he's pressured to feed against his will or fears he is going to choke will stop displaying signs of stress as soon as he realizes the feed has ended.

Baby feeds well in predictable situations

If your baby predictably feeds well in certain situations—for example, during the night or while in a drowsy state or asleep—you can probably rule out pain. If pain was responsible for his distress while sucking and swallowing during the day or while awake, you'd expect him to also experience pain while feeding at night or when sleep-feeding. Sleep does not numb a baby to the sensation of pain.

Baby is content between feeds

If a baby is generally content between feeds, the distress he displays at feeding times is unlikely to be from pain. Pain associated with acid reflux, milk protein allergy or intolerance, constipation, or teething is not restricted to feeding times. Your baby will be distressed at random times during the day and night if he's suffering from pain caused by a physical problem or condition.

Baby sleeps well

If your baby sleeps well, you can probably rule out pain as the reason for his feeding problems. Pain due to a physical problem or medical condition will negatively impact a baby's sleep. A baby who is experiencing pain will find it difficult to fall asleep and stay asleep. He will be difficult to sooth and may cry inconsolably—nothing you do calms him.

Many parents mistakenly believe their baby is experiencing pain when in reality their baby is distressed owing to sleep deprivation caused by a sleep-association problem (see pages 292-298). A tired baby can generally be calmed once he receives his sleep associations—provided he's not already reached the point of overtiredness, in which case he may cry inconsolably due to the effect of stress hormones.

Baby has normal bowel movements

When a baby cries for reasons that are not obvious, it's often assumed to be caused by a problem in his digestive tract. While you can't see inside your baby's digestive tract, you can see what comes out in the form of spit-ups and poop. This provides information about what is happening on the inside. (See pages 435-437 for what's normal and what's not.)

Normal bowel movements = normal digestion. Abnormal bowel movements **might** indicate a digestive problem that **might** cause pain or discomfort. As such, this requires further investigation, starting with behavioral causes. First, rule out overfeeding (chapter 25), functional lactose overload (pages 439-448), food poisoning (chapter 13) and side effects of medications.

If, as a result of this checklist,

- **you now have doubts about your baby experiencing pain,** then explore the many behavioral reasons that cause a baby distress or GI symptoms. Ruling out pain doesn't mean he does not have a physical problem or a medical condition. It just means pain is not the reason for his tears or feeding or sleeping problem.
- **you still believe your baby is experiencing pain,** read all chapters in Part F and G, and the cause may be revealed. Perhaps it's something you already suspect or which he has already been diagnosed with, or maybe something you are unaware of. Discuss any concerns with your baby's doctor.

Routine medical examination

When a baby who is physically well cries—which healthy babies tend to do quite often—usually nothing untoward can be seen, heard, or felt during a routine medical examination. If a doctor can't see any signs, they might then do one of four things:

1. Reassure you that your baby is well and inform you that they don't know the reason for his troubled behavior or claim that your baby's behavior is normal. You will probably not be happy about either comment if you believe something is wrong. And you may take your baby to be examined by another doctor.
2. Assume the cause relates to an unobservable occurrence in your baby's digestive tract, and diagnose a condition based on your concern, the physical signs you have observed, and your description of your baby's behavior. For example, if you disclose that you're concerned that your baby is suffering from reflux because he spits up and is often crying, he might be diagnosed with acid reflux. If you claim that your baby is often gassy or has frequent bowel movements and that you're worried

he's not tolerating his milk, he might be diagnosed with milk protein intolerance. Or if he cries for long periods in the evening, he will likely be diagnosed with colic. There are various diagnoses that could made depending on how **you describe** the situation.

3. Order diagnostic tests.
4. Refer your baby to another health professional, perhaps a medical specialist or speech-language pathologist (SLP), occupational therapist (OT), or registered dietician (RD).

What a feeding assessment involves

When it's suspected that a baby has difficulties feeding or is suffering physical discomfort as a result of a feeding-related problem or digestive disorder, a thorough feeding assessment is required to identify the cause. A feeding assessment includes

1. the parent's description of observations;
2. a thorough history, which includes birth, growth, and feeding history;
3. a physical examination of the baby's mouth;
4. an observation of the baby being fed by the parent.

1. Parent's perception and description

When a **physically well baby** is examined, nothing abnormal and nothing upon which a diagnosis can be made can be observed. Hence, a health professional would then need to rely on the parent's description of their baby's behavior and any GI symptoms the parent has observed to make a diagnosis.

Your perception matters! Whether your baby receives a medical diagnosis or not will largely depend on **your description.** Beware! If you've been trawling the internet for answers, you need to know that it's not a reliable source of information on **behavioral problems affecting babies**. By the time you see your baby's doctor, you may already have one or more possible diagnoses in mind. When discussing your concerns and observations with your baby's doctor, you will understandably provide information that backs up your theories, hoping it will help the doctor to make a diagnosis.

Your level of concern will also influence whether your baby receives a diagnosis. How concerned you are will be based on your depth of knowledge about the reasons for certain infant behaviors and GI symptoms and whether you believe what your baby is doing is normal or not.

2. A thorough history

Your baby's birth, growth, and health are all very important. But don't forget about your **baby's feeding history**. For a health professional to gain relevant information on your baby's feeding history, he or she needs to ask you multiple questions; for example, how much milk your baby consumes, the caloric concentration of his feeds, how often he feeds, how fast he feeds, what his behavior is like before, during, and after feeds, equipment type, and your responses to problematic behaviors, to name only a few.

To check for the possibility of the many behavioral problems I have described in Part F, I typically ask the parent to complete a questionnaire consisting of **80 or more questions** and return this before their consultation. These questions are asked to gain details about their baby's birth, growth, physical health, feeding, and sleeping (sleeping affects feeding and vice versa), and most importantly, the parent's infant feeding and settling practices which includes their responses to their baby's feeding cues.

You will know how thoroughly your baby's healthcare professional has considered the possibility of **behavioral problems** by the number of questions asked of you.

No questions asked means little or no consideration has been given to behavioral causes.

If you have not been asked any questions about your baby's feeding and your infant feeding and settling practices, and your baby has not been observed while feeding, then behavioral causes have not been considered. And where there's an incomplete assessment of causes, there's also an increased risk of misdiagnosis. This was the case for Mica.

Baby Mica

Mica was aged eight weeks. His mother, Yani, expressed concern to Mica's doctor that he was often coughing and crying while feeding. Based on this information alone, she was advised to thicken his formula with rice cereal. The doctor didn't do a feeding assessment of potential causes.

The reason for Mica's coughing and crying was caused by poor positioning and a nipple that flowed too fast for him. Yani also overlooked his satiety cues while trying to "encourage him to finish" the bottle, which didn't help.

While the thicker formula gave the appearance of helping because it slowed down the rate of milk flow and reduced coughing episodes, it created new problems. The rice cereal added around 25 percent more calories per ounce. This resulted in Mica drinking less.

An expected reduction in his milk intake as a result of the increased calories was not explained to Yani. Hence, she started to use subtle forms of pressure to get him to drink the volumes he had taken previously before the addition of rice cereal. She was unaware of Mica's signs of satiety (satisfaction from eating), so she unintentionally ignored these cues while she persisted for 60 to 90 minutes each feed to get him to "finish."

Mica's doctor had made feeding recommendations without a feeding assessment. Had Mica been aspirating small amounts of fluids into his lungs—a possible reason for coughing and crying—then the addition of rice cereal could have made the problem worse. Had Yani continued to try to make Mica consume the same volumes he had previously, this could have resulted in feeding refusal owing to a feeding aversion.

3. Physical examination of baby's mouth

If a baby refuses or fusses during feeds, or if sucking or swallowing problems are suspected, a physical examination of his mouth is required to check for any abnormalities. The health professional might use a flashlight and gloved finger and possibly a tongue compressor while looking for abnormalities like oral thrush, mouth ulcers, or lip or tongue-ties. They might also feel the shape of the baby's palate, possibly triggering his sucking reflex to gain a sense of his sucking strength, check if the movement of his tongue matches his stage of development, and assess his gag sensitivity.

If you notice anything unusual, discuss your findings with your baby's doctor. It's important that you don't jump to conclusions about the cause of your baby's feeding issues. Observation of a physical anomaly—for example, tongue-tie—doesn't necessarily mean it is related to the real issue. This is why a thorough feeding history is an essential part of a feeding assessment to identify the cause.

4. Observation of a feed

Observing the baby being fed by the parent provides an ideal opportunity for the observer—who ideally is experienced in educating parents on infant feeding practices—to look for anything that might adversely affect the baby's ability or desire to feed that the parent might not be aware of or has overlooked.

The observer can check for access problems caused by inappropriate or faulty equipment and poor positioning of the baby or the bottle. They can also check the baby's latch and seal around the nipple, his sucking and swallowing coordination, his level of alertness, his behavior, and whether the parent is providing an appropriate response to his behavioral cues or pressuring him to feed.

Be wary of a 5-minute diagnosis

A five-minute diagnosis skips most of the points listed above, with the exception of asking the parent what they perceive is happening. It goes like this. Baby is physically examined. There are no visible signs that indicate illness or a physical problem. A diagnosis is then based solely on the parent's description of their observations. For example:

Crying baby +

- baby spits up = reflux
- baby doesn't spit up = silent reflux
- baby refuses to eat despite obvious hunger = esophagitis caused by acid reflux
- acid-suppressing medications are not helping = milk protein allergy
- blood in baby's stools = milk protein allergy
- baby repeatedly vomits + has poor growth = gastroparesis (delayed emptying of baby's stomach).

I could add 100 or more examples to this list where medical conditions and/or sucking problems are suspected or diagnosed based solely on the parent's description or perception of the problem made in the absence of a thorough feeding assessment and feeding observation. Jackson's case is one of thousands during my career.

Baby Jackson

"Jackson (aged eight weeks) is a little milk monster, but he continuously vomits after a feed and cries till the next feed. I spoke to his doctor about the vomiting, and he prescribed Gaviscon, but he's still vomiting. Do you think I should ask for stronger meds?" Gina

Jackson's doctor didn't ask how much, how often, or how fast Jackson was drinking before prescribing medications (Infant Gaviscon® is an antacid and thickening agent combined). When I asked, Gina commented that Jackson was downing 6 to 7 ounces (180 to 210 mL) seven times a day, in around five to 10 minutes. This was more milk and at a speed that was faster than would be expected for a baby of his age and size.

Given the volume of milk Jackson was consuming, it was not surprising that he was vomiting. He was not feeding too often, and so I suspected the cause was that he had a strong suck and was feeding from a nipple that was too fast for him. So, it was a simple fix to switch him to a slower nipple.

As a result of slowing down the duration of his feeds, Jackson's little body had time to recognize when he had consumed enough, and he had the chance to signal when he was satisfied. Supporting him to self-regulate his milk intake in this way resulted in him consuming less milk than he did previously. This was not a problem since he was no longer vomiting—though he still had occasional tiny spit-ups, which is normal for babies. Less milk consumed resulted in less vomiting and had no negative effect on his growth. Gaviscon was ceased.

I am not claiming that conditions such as acid reflux, milk protein allergy or intolerance, and others don't exist. I am simply pointing out why it might appear like half the babies of the parents you speak with have been diagnosed with one or more of these conditions.

These conditions are **not** common. Rather, they are commonly misdiagnosed—often without clearly observable signs and symptoms typically associated with these conditions—during brief consultations. It's a **huge** leap to go from "baby cries and spits up" to "baby is suffering from acid reflux." Or deciding that because baby's stools contain microscopic traces of blood, he has a milk protein allergy. Doing so bypasses all potential nonmedical (behavioral) causes for fussing, crying, feeding, sleeping and growth problems, and GI symptoms described in this book.

An assessment of sucking or feeding-related problems should not be based solely on the parent's description of their baby's behavior. Without undertaking a thorough feeding assessment or using the aid of diagnostic tests, any diagnosis of the cause of a healthy baby's troubled behavior will be based on a guess. Maybe the guess is correct. But maybe it's not.

If your baby's healthcare professional has not undertaken a thorough assessment of all possible reasons for infant feeding problems, which includes behavioral feeding and sleeping problems described in this book, you will need to do it—with the help of this book—or find someone who can.

Avoid using treatments to make a diagnosis

Health professionals might suggest "treatments" such as

- medications—prescribed or over the counter;
- herbal remedies;
- digestive enzymes and probiotics;
- changes in diet—the baby's or mother's;
- feeding equipment recommendations;
- feeding management advice;
- feeding therapies, such as those to improve sucking coordination; or
- surgical procedures.

If an assessment of behavioral causes hasn't been done and physical signs that point to a medical condition aren't present, I don't recommend any of these. Without evidence of a physical problem or medical condition (see chapters 31 and 32 for signs and symptoms), making random changes—for example, switching equipment, changing formula, or trying different medications and dosages **based on a vague hope that it might help**—risks making the situation worse.

Treat the cause, not the symptoms

> *"My 2.5-month-old has been diagnosed with having gas and reflux and is on medications." Phoebe*

If you have a distressed little baby on your hands, it's important that you understand the difference between a symptom of a problem and the problem that causes the symptoms. Gas and reflux can be normal and completely unrelated to a baby's distress. Or both could be **symptoms** of a problem, condition, or disorder that causes discomfort or pain.

Most medical treatments are directed at reducing or eliminating symptoms and not the actual problem.

To **effectively** resolve a problem, any treatment, strategy, therapy, or feeding recommendation needs to be directed towards **the cause** of the problem, medical condition, or digestive disorder. In other words, treat what's causing the symptoms rather than the symptoms themselves.

Sometimes it's not possible to remedy the cause of a baby's distress—for example, if a formula-fed baby is allergic to cow's milk protein. Removing cow's milk protein from the baby's diet might be as good as it gets.

However, in some cases, it's possible for parents to correct the actual problem that is causing their baby's symptoms by making appropriate changes to their infant feeding and settling practices—for example, when a baby spits up or vomits because of overfeeding, speed-feeding, bouncing, pounding on the baby's back to make him burp, all of these can be corrected without the need for medications or thickened feeds.

It is immensely beneficial to identify the cause of concerning behaviors and physical symptoms—such as gas, spitting up, vomiting, or unusual bowel movements—so you can determine if the cause can be fixed or not rather than merely treating the symptoms.

One problem with treating symptoms and not the cause is that the symptoms will return as soon as the medications wear off. Treatment needs to be ongoing. Another problem with mistaking a symptom, such as "gas" or "reflux," as the cause of a baby's distress is that it discourages further exploration that enables discovery of the cause of gas and reflux. It also limits your chances of finding an effective, **long-lasting** solution. (See chapter 31 for **nonmedical** causes and chapter 32 for **medical** causes for gastrointestinal symptoms.)

Treatment benefits and risks

Medications change the way a baby's body functions. This has benefits and risks.

Medications have side effects. But the secondary adverse effects associated with changing the way a baby's body functions are sometimes more concerning. For example, giving a baby acid-suppressing medication will change the acid balance (pH) in his stomach **and** his intestinal tract. This increases the risk of food or waterborne illnesses,[158] acute gastrointestinal infections and intestinal dysbiosis (an imbalance of gut microbiota associated with an unhealthy outcome),[159] respiratory infections including pneumonia,[160] poor absorption of calcium,[161] food and environmental allergies,[162] and more. Also, switching a baby from breast milk to infant formula means he misses out on all the health benefits that breast milk provides (see page 111).

The benefits of reducing spitting up by adding a starch-based thickener like rice cereal to a baby's milk need to be weighed against the risks of changing the nutritional balance of a baby's diet and other risks associated with this practice (see pages 157-158).

Whether you decide to give your baby medications or make significant changes to his diet ultimately comes down to how confident you are that the diagnosis is correct and whether you believe the benefits of treatment outweigh the risks. To make an informed decision, you need to understand the risks.

Because of the associated risks, medications and dietary changes should only be considered **as a last resort.** This means **after** behavioral reasons for spitting up, crying, feeding refusal, sleep disturbance, unusual bowel motions and poor growth have been assessed and ruled out.

Medication usage can trigger a snowball effect. The more medications a baby is given, the more difficult it becomes to tell which symptoms are linked to the original problem, which are caused by medication side effects, and which occur as a result of secondary adverse effects of changing how a baby's body functions. Further medications are sometimes given to treat the symptoms caused by the side effects and secondary adverse effects of other medications. For example, acid-suppressing medications slows gastric emptying (how fast the food takes to empty from the stomach into the small intestine.[163] Prokinetic medications (also called motility medications) may then be prescribed to speed up suspected delayed gastric emptying.[164]

The Snowball Effect

> *"I can't wait for my baby to grow up. Feeding him has been a nightmare since the start. He has never been a good eater. He has been diagnosed with reflux and CMPA (cow's milk protein allergy). It seems like we no sooner get over one problem and there's another. I am so tired of fighting with him to get him to eat."*
> *Elise*

I suspect that Elise is experiencing the "snowball effect"—a series of escalating problems. This is something I have **often** observed when parents are taught and encouraged to use parent-led feeding practices or when behavioral feeding problems have been overlooked.

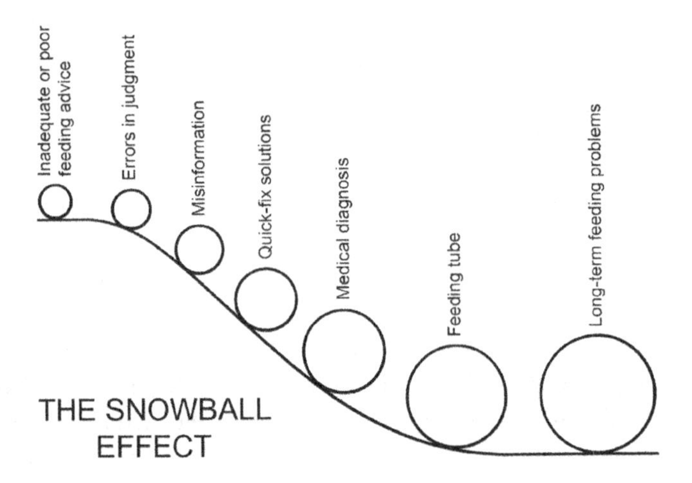

While most infant feeding problems can be prevented or resolved, sadly for many families, they are not. Not because there is no solution—rather, it's because of the snowball effect of unidentified behavioral feeding problems. What begins as a result of limited knowledge about the care of babies can deteriorate in a predictable way through a series of erroneous decisions based on mistaken assumptions, which evolves into increasingly more complex and confusing situations. I will explain.

Inadequate or poor feeding advice

After baby's birth, instead of receiving education to help us (parents) understand our baby's needs and behavioral cues and our responsibilities when feeding a baby, we might receive simplistic advice to "feed on demand" or "feed baby X ounces or milliliters of milk, X times per day or every X hours."

Errors in judgment

Because of limited knowledge of infant development, the needs of babies, and how we influence our baby's behavior through our infant feeding and sleep-settling practices, we make some errors in judgment. Something we all do! We don't understand his behavioral cues, so provide an inappropriate response at times. For example, we mistake tiredness cues for hunger or we persist too long to make baby eat the "recommended amount" or we repeatedly break the feed to burp him or annoy him with our feeding practices. We are unaware that our actions are causing him to express his frustration, anger, or stress. And when he does, we don't recognize that these behaviors occur because of what we're doing or not doing.

Misinformation

Confused by baby's behavior, we become concerned that we might be missing something or making mistakes, so we actively seek answers from others whom we believe have more experience in caring for babies. We might ask our own mother, siblings, or friends for their opinions about why our baby behaves as he does. Without being asked a single question about our infant feeding or settling practices, we might receive reassurances like "You're doing nothing wrong" or "It's normal for babies to fuss." Alternatively, others **take a guess** at what they believe is upsetting baby. "He's hungry," "It's colic," "It could be reflux," "It's probably something you're eating," and more.

Based on the problem we have been told is troubling baby, we then search the internet and are literally swamped by information. Some information is reliable, but it will be wedged between a **lot** of misinformation and old wives' tales—for example, swallowed air causes colic; back-arching, hiccups, wet burps, the appearance of insatiable hunger, or refusing to eat indicates acid reflux; straining indicates constipation. We may also read that any of the concerning behaviors we observe while baby is feeding or after feeding (described in chapter 28) mean something they don't.

Without the ability to discern the difference between reliable information and misinformation, we risk taking actions that further frustrate baby, such as constantly breaking the feed or spending too long trying to get him to burp. Or we may cause a feeding problem like overfeeding based on false claims that it's not possible to overfeed a baby. Or we create a situation where baby experiences both feeding and sleeping problems because we're told it's natural for babies to fall asleep while feeding, so we allow him to do so. There are countless other possible scenarios when actions are taken based on misinformation.

Witnessing that the situation is getting worse rather than better prompts us to make an appointment to discuss our concerns with baby's primary healthcare professional.

Quick-fix solutions

Baby's healthcare professional might recommend a quick-fix solution. Quick-fix solutions include feeding strategies or recommendations that **treat the symptoms of a problem but not its cause.**

Quick-fix solutions are generally recommended by health professionals when they believe an infant feeding problem can't be fixed, as can occur with some medical conditions. Or when the cause of the problem is not identified, as can occur when a health professional doesn't know about behavioral causes for infant feeding and growth problems. Some of the **quick-fix solutions** provided to parents for feeding-related problems include

- burping baby every ounce to expel swallowed air;
- holding baby upright for 30 minutes after feeds to reduce spitting up;
- thickened feeds to reduce spitting up;
- calorie-enhanced feeds to increase calories received;
- giving baby solids before the age of four months to increase calories received.

Quick-fix solutions can be effective to treat symptoms, such as bloating, milk regurgitation, or poor growth, experienced by babies who suffer as a result of a physical problem or medical condition that affects feeding. However, in the case of healthy babies who are troubled by a behavioral problem, instead of helping, quick-fix solutions risk creating new problems. An example of the types of problems they can create include

- burping every ounce is likely to frustrate a hungry baby;
- holding upright for 30 minutes can create a sleeping problem as a result of baby learning to depend on sleeping in his parent's arms;
- thickened feeds, in particular, starch-based thickeners like cereal or flour, can negatively affect the nutritional balance of a baby's primary source of nutrition;
- calorie-enhanced feeds merely reduce the volume of milk consumed by healthy babies who regulate their milk intake according to the calories;
- giving solids before four months of age, causes unfavorable changes in a baby's intestinal microbes.

In the case of **healthy babies**, quick-fix solutions are more likely to perpetuate rather than halt the snowball effect as a result of these additional problems. If quick-fix solutions fail to resolve a baby's feeding or growth issues, he may then receive a medical diagnosis, or two, or more.

Medical diagnosis

Baby is physically examined. No abnormal physical signs can be observed—as will be the case when the source is behavioral. No questions are asked about our infant feeding or settling practices. No feed is observed. A diagnosis of the cause is based solely on our description of baby's distressed behavior or GI symptoms observed. When nothing can be observed during a routine medical examination, it's assumed that something within his digestive tract is responsible.

Baby may be diagnosed with colic, reflux, milk allergy or intolerance to explain his distress or GI symptoms. Consequently, he may be prescribed medications or dietary change. (The benefits and risks associated with giving a baby medications and making changes in diet are described in chapter 32).

Feeding tube

If quick-fix solutions and medical treatments fail to resolve baby's feeding problem, the final solution offered may be a feeding tube. Feeding tubes are lifelines for babies who are incapable of safely feeding orally. When used for babies who have the physical capacity to safely feed orally but who refuse to do so for reasons that have not been identified, they are another example of a quick-fix solution. Sure, they are an effective way to improve a baby's growth. However, they do nothing to fix the problem of feeding refusal and instead increase the chances of complete feeding refusal.

Feeding tubes also continue the snowball effect because even a small overestimation of a baby's milk needs will remove hunger and thus remove the incentive for a baby to want to eat orally. In doing so, tube feeding can indirectly reinforce a behavioral feeding problem that may have caused the baby to require tube feeding in the first place. Logan's case is an example.

Baby Logan

"My eight-month-old refuses to eat, and his doctors admit they cannot explain why. They told us they have done every test there is. All have come back completely normal. He has been diagnosed with reflux, CMPA, gastroparesis, and visceral hypersensitivity. The OT thinks he might have a sensory disorder. He's on Neocate (an amino acid-based hypoallergenic formula) and has been given every medication they know of to try to solve his feeding issues. He had a tongue-tie snipped at four months and has weekly feeding therapy with the OT. Nothing has helped. His doctors are happy with his growth since he's been tube fed and say that he can get off the tube once he's eating enough solids. I am really worried because he's starting to refuse to eat solids as well. I am afraid that he's going to be stuck tube feeding forever. What is so frustrating is that I know he can feed. He bottle-fed until he was three months old." Olivia

Logan did not have these multiple medical diagnoses or a sensory disorder. He had a behavioral feeding aversion owing to being pressured to eat. The numerous health professionals (12 in total) whom Olivia consulted about Logan's feeding issues had done every known diagnostic test and trialed him on every medication and infant formula they could think of. And yet, **not one asked her about her infant feeding practices**. Therefore, they did not unveil that the original reason for Logan's partial feeding refusal and poor growth, which prompted the need for tube feeding at three months of age, was the result of a behavioral feeding aversion. Hunger was the only incentive he had to eat around 50 percent of his feeds back then. Once he was tube fed, he was no longer hungry and completely refused oral feeds within a few days.

While the doctors had claimed Logan would eventually eat solids and tube wean, there was no guarantee that this would happen. He was already showing signs of developing an aversion to eating solids for the same reason—being pressured to eat. Even without an aversion, it's unlikely that he would suddenly start to eat lots of solids while all of his caloric needs were provided via the tube.

After five months of complete feeding refusal, it took just seven days to get Logan to return to willingly eating orally once again, once I provided Olivia with a tube-weaning plan that included calorie reduction and feeding strategies to resolve his feeding aversion. Similar strategies were used to encourage him to eat solid foods. With his pediatrician's consent, he was eventually weaned off the many medications he was given and switched to regular infant formula.

Long-term feeding problems

At some point, we may come to the realization that the health professionals we have consulted so far are unable to help. Upon doing so, we either search elsewhere for solutions, which is what Olivia did, or resign ourselves to the fact that we have no further options available other than to continue to do what we have always done. Unaware that doing what we have always done may be the very reason that baby's feeding issues have persisted for so long.

During my career, I have seen thousands of families at various points on this scale, many babies with feeding tubes and children with feeding problems that commenced in infancy and have persisted for years. The stress that these families endured was because parents are taught and encouraged to use **parent-led feeding practices**—which is a major reason for babies to experience behavioral feeding problems—and consequently the resulting problems were not identified or not effectively managed.

When will this end?

Not all babies experience feeding problems. And of those who do, many of their families are fortunate to receive reliable advice that remedies the problem early. But sadly, some don't. The reason it's not resolved is that no one identified that the original cause that started the ball rolling—which more often than not is parent-led feeding practices—continues, usually because no one has asked the parent questions or observed the parent's infant feeding practices or believed that such feeding practices are responsible. They merely made assumptions about the cause and offered advice and treatments based on an incomplete assessment of the situation.

If you were to do nothing but be swept along, many, but not all, babies would eventually "outgrow" a **dietary regulation problem** such as overfeeding and underfeeding.

Overfeeding will generally resolve naturally between three and six months of age as a baby gains greater ability to self-regulate his dietary intake. And some cases of underfeeding, in particular those linked to access problems, will resolve as the baby matures and gains the physical strength to voluntarily move his body and therefore be better able to access the feed.

The resolution of dietary regulation problems between three and six months of age—which occur with advancements in a baby's development—may give a false impression that whatever treatments are employed at the time are finally starting to help.

Not all behavioral feeding problems will spontaneously resolve. Babies don't "outgrow" a feeding aversion. This is because the baby's avoidant feeding behavior is reinforced by parent-led feeding practices, and baby's behavior intensifies with increased maturity. If the cause is not corrected, the problem of feeding refusal will persist.

You can end the snowball effect

If you suspect that your baby is heading down this path, **the good news is it's never too late to solve a baby care problem.** At any one of these listed points, a behavioral feeding problem can be resolved. However, the health professionals you have consulted with so far may **not** be familiar with behavioral feeding problems. So, it may be up to you to take charge rather than be led by others in the management of your baby's feeding issues.

- **Step 1.** Finish reading all chapters of this book. After doing so, you will know more about behavioral feeding problems than most health professionals. Awareness of behavioral feeding problems will enable you to recognize misdiagnoses and poor feeding advice.
- **Step 2.** Babies can be troubled by both physical and behavioral feeding problems at the same time. While behavioral problems are the most common cause of feeding issues for physically well babies, don't overlook the possibility of a physical cause. If you have any concerns, discuss them with your baby's doctor. A head-to-toe physical examination is necessary.
- **Step 3.** If you have concerns about your baby's sucking and swallowing abilities, read chapter 33. If still concerned, ask your baby's healthcare professional for a referral to a speech-language pathologist (SLP) for a professional assessment of your baby's sucking abilities.
- **Step 4.** Regardless of whether your baby receives a medical diagnosis or not, cover all bases by completing your own assessment of potential behavioral causes. Go to page 272 to complete my Infant Feeding Practice Self-Evaluation Checklist. You might discover the cause and recognize the solution.
- **Step 5.** Go to my website, www.babycareadvice.com, to book a consultation with a health professional or parenting educator who has been trained to assess and advise on infant and toddler behavioral feeding problems.

Next

Next, let's look at common but poorly recognized **nonmedical** causes for GI symptoms such as spitting up, vomiting, extreme intestinal gas and diarrhea. Reading about nonmedical causes may help you recognize if your baby requires medications or dietary change, or simply for you to make appropriate changes to your infant feeding practices.

31 Baby Spits-Up, Farts a Lot and has Runny Poop!

WHEN REFLUX IS NORMAL • WHY BABIES SPIT UP • HOW TO MINIMIZE SPIT-UPS • BOWEL MOVEMENTS—WHAT'S NORMAL • HOW TO TELL IF YOUR BABY IS CONSTIPATED OR HAS DIARRHEA • INTESTINAL GAS—WHAT CAUSES IT • FUNCTIONAL LACTOSE OVERLOAD

When a baby cries for reasons that are not obvious, we will look for signs that might provide clues as to the cause.

Without awareness of what's normal for a baby, we might mistake gastrointestinal (GI) symptoms as a sign of a problem, when it's not. Alternatively, when we identify **unusual** GI symptoms, we might suspect a medical condition—especially if the baby displays signs of distress—because we don't know what else could cause such symptoms.

This can be the case when a baby spits up or farts **a lot**, has frequent loose, watery bowel movements, or stools that contain mucus or blood. Such signs don't automatically mean the baby has a physical problem or medical condition that requires medical treatments. In the case of normal healthy babies, GI symptoms can be linked to the parent's infant feeding and childcare practices, and relieved by a few simple, but appropriate, changes in the care provided.

In this chapter, I describe nonmedical reasons—meaning no medical treatment is required—for a baby's GI symptoms, and steps you can take to minimize any distress these might cause.

Spitting up is normal

Spitting up, chucking up, spills, reflux, "wet burps", and posseting, all of which are alternative names for gastroesophageal reflux (GER), is a normal occurrence for healthy, thriving babies at some stage during their first year.

GER refers to the backward flow of milk (or food) from the stomach into the esophagus. This could exit from the mouth or be swallowed. GER is caused by normal bodily functions, does not harm babies or cause complications.

GER differs from GERD (gastroesophageal reflux **disease**). GERD refers to the situation when the regurgitation of stomach contents **causes complications** such as esophagitis (inflammation or ulceration of baby's esophagus), respiratory problems, or poor growth. GERD is described in pages 451-457.

GER is one of the most misunderstood of all infant behaviors. When a baby cries for unknow reasons, it's **often assumed** that she's suffering pain because of acid reflux, irrespective of whether she spits up or not (called "silent reflux").

How common is GER?

Spitting up is common during infancy. The prevalence peaks at four months of age, with two-thirds of babies regurgitating at least once daily[165] and approximately 40 percent regurgitating with most feedings.[166] The percentage of babies who spit up drops to 14 percent by seven months of age and to less than 5 percent between 10 and 14 months of age.[167] Further decline in the incidence of regurgitation occurs during the second year of life.[168]

All adults, children, and babies periodically experience so-called "silent reflux," where we regurgitate milk or food that travels **partially** up into the esophagus before being pushed back by muscular contractions in the esophagus. Mostly we are unaware when it happens. Sometimes you might observe your baby swallowing regurgitated stomach contents back down, but most times, there will be no observable sign that she has silently refluxed.

What is regurgitated is not always acidic. Even when it is, acid reflux seldom causes problems such as heartburn or esophagitis. Only a tiny percentage of babies who have very frequent or forceful spitting up, crying, coughing, distress, or weight loss have GERD.

What are the signs of normal reflux?

Milk typically comes out of the baby's mouth, but when spit-ups are large and forceful, milk can also come out of her nose. Baby could spit up during, after, or between feeds or while she's sleeping. The spit-up could appear to be "curdled" because it is partially digested.

Spit-up size varies considerably. It could be a tiny milky dribble, a "wet-burp," or a large projectile spit-up that lands many feet away. The size of the spit-up is not diagnostically significant if growth is within a healthy range. In other words, it can't be said that a baby has "severe reflux" simply because she has large projectile spit-ups.

Why do babies spit-up?

Pressure within the stomach can cause spitting up. Babies are susceptible to spitting up because they drink large volumes of milk in relation to their size. The volume a newborn baby consumes at a single feed in proportion to body size would be like you drinking half to three-quarters of a gallon (2.8 liters) of milk in one sitting. Extreme spit-ups can be linked to overfeeding. But of course, overfeeding is not the only reason for babies to spit up. Speed-feeding, where baby feeds too quickly, and swallows large amounts of air are also common reasons for increased intragastric (within the stomach) pressure that can cause spit-ups.

Outside **pressure on the stomach,** which can occur from sitting in a slumped position, lying over a parent's shoulders, having legs pulled up to change a diaper, crying, and coughing, will also increase the risk of spitting up.

In general, babies spend a lot of time lying down. This makes it easier for the backward flow of milk from the stomach. Sleeping on her back, elevated or not, is the safest position for a baby if she was to spit up while sleeping, as it means the milk will flow below her trachea (opening to her airways).

My baby is an "unhappy spitter"—should I be worried?

Parents are often told that if their baby is a "happy spitter" who is growing well, it points to GER and therefore does not require treatment. While this claim is true, it is misleading because it is then assumed that an "unhappy spitter" is suffering from acid reflux or GERD, which is rarely the case. It's normal for babies to spit up. It's also normal for babies to cry. The two are seldom related. A baby could spit up or not spit up **and** cry, feed or sleep poorly for a multitude of unrelated reasons—many of which have been described in this book.

Whether your baby spits up or not, often cries, or refuses to eat doesn't prove that reflux is the cause of her distress. It also doesn't provide evidence of acid reflux or esophagitis.

Does acid reflux cause problems?

In healthy babies, children and adults, acid is refluxed into the esophagus many times every day. Mostly we are unaware when this happens. Regurgitating acidic stomach contents doesn't usually cause harm or pain because our bodies have homeostatic mechanisms that provide protection against acid in the esophagus.

Acid does not sit pooling in a baby's stomach. It's secreted from cells in the stomach wall during the gastric phase of the digestive process. It also exits from the stomach, along with the partially digested food, as the stomach contents empty into the small intestine. There is very little acid left in the stomach once it has emptied. The incidence of GER lowers as the stomach empties.

Milk has a neutral acid balance that buffers the effect of stomach acid.[169] So spitting up during or directly after feeds is not acidic, as there would not be enough time for acid secretions to drop the pH (acid balance) to a level where it could cause pain. During infancy gastric acidity is low, especially so in the newborn period.[170] This low acidity together with the high buffering capacity of milk is unlikely to cause esophagitis.

It takes around 1.5 to 2 hours after a feed for the pH to drop to a level where it could burn.[171] Even if the baby was to reflux acidic stomach contents into her esophagus, homeostatic mechanisms would protect her esophagus from harm. These include

- the esophagus' muscular wall contracts and pushes food and fluid toward the stomach. Any refluxed stomach contents will be pushed back into the stomach within a matter of seconds;

- a mucosal lining of the esophageal wall protects the underlying tissues against brief episodes of acid exposure; and
- saliva, which naturally contains bicarbonate, a chemical that helps to neutralize acid. In the esophagus, saliva serves to neutralize refluxed acid and thereby restore esophageal pH (acid balance) to a normal level.[172]

In most cases, when healthy babies reflux acidic stomach contents, the worst thing they experience is a bad taste in their mouth for a few seconds.

Crying occurring around the time the baby refluxes could be caused by fright—as there is usually no forewarning before reflux occurs—or discomfort caused by a hyperextension of the stomach or a multitude of unrelated reasons. Alternatively, crying itself can increase pressure on the stomach and result in GER.[173]

The reality is that the cause of most healthy babies' crying, feeding refusal, or sleeping problems is **not** linked to reflux or pain due to heartburn or esophagitis. See pages 409-411 for how to tell if your baby is experiencing pain and read the chapters of Part F for other reasons for infant feeding and sleep problems that can cause distress that gives the appearance of pain.

How to minimize spit-ups

Ways in which you can minimize the incidence of your baby's spitting up include

- Confirm that your baby is not overfeeding (see chapter 25).
- Check that she's not feeding too quickly (see page 184).
- Support her to self-regulate her milk intake by following her lead and allowing her to decide when and how much to eat. (See chapter 16 for how to respond to feeding cues).
- Feed her in a semi-reclined or upright feeding position.
- Provide a "burp break" during the feed, but don't keep her waiting too long before returning the bottle. She could start to cry due to frustration related to the feed being halted. If she has not burped within two minutes, return to feeding.
- Avoid pressure on her stomach after feeding. Avoid having her seated in a slumped position, and change her diaper before feeding rather than

after. If needing to change after, when her stomach is full, roll her from side to side rather than lifting her legs.

- Hold her upright after feeds, but don't persist if she fusses due to boredom or looks like she is going to fall asleep on your shoulder.
- Ensure she gets plenty of sleep. Lack of sleep is the most common of all reasons for babies to become distressed, which may then be mistakenly attributed to acid reflux.

You will not completely eliminate the incidence of spitting up. Accept that GER is normal for healthy babies and don't allow the fact that your baby spits up blind you to the many behavioral reasons for crying, feeding and sleeping problems.

Intestinal gas

In most cases where parents worry about gas causing infant crying, the amount of gas their baby is passing is normal. However, some babies do suffer as a result of painful abdominal cramps or spasms, and they can be **very** gassy. This is usually for reasons unrelated to swallowed air—something that most people erroneously believe is the cause of intestinal gas. So let's start by looking at what's normal.

What's normal?

The amount and odor of flatulence produced in your baby's intestinal tract are largely related to the type and amount of carbohydrates in her diet. A healthy baby could fart up to 20 times a day. Her farts could be small and silent, noticed only as a tiny rumble in her diaper when you're holding her. Or they could be loud and plentiful, heard from the other side of the room. They could have no odor or emit a smell that clears the room. All types can be normal.

If there are **no signs such as diarrhea or constipation,** it's unlikely that your baby is suffering from painful abdominal cramping. And in this case, the volume and smell of her fluctuance are normal and have no connection with the reason or reasons for her tears. In these cases, I find that any distress the baby might display is usually caused by sleep deprivation as a result of a sleep association problem (see chapter 22).

What's not normal?

Extreme flatulence can be normal, or it can be a **symptom** of an underlying problem. In other words, something is causing excessive production of intestinal gas. **Gas is not the actual problem.** It's important to make this distinction about gas being a symptom and not the problem because anti-gas treatments will do nothing to resolve the actual cause of excessive gas production. The solution lies in identifying and correcting the cause.

Extreme flatulence could be a symptom of the following problems.

- **Functional lactose overload.** Incomplete digestion of lactose can cause an excessive production of intestinal gases (see pages 439-448).
- **Milk allergy or intolerance.** A digestive disorder can also cause excessive gas production in the intestinal tract because of inadequate digestion of one or more of the major nutrients in milk—protein, carbohydrate, or fats). Protein is the main reason for milk allergy and carbohydrates are the main cause of food intolerances. (See pages 457-464 for other signs and symptoms of milk allergy an intolerance.)
- **A side effect of a prescribed or over-the-counter medication or herbal remedies.** Check the leaflet provided with the medication for side effects.
- **A viral, bacterial, or fungal gastrointestinal (GI) infection.** Baby will appear unwell and have diarrhea, among other symptoms.

If your baby **has diarrhea,** and the amount of gas she's passing is extreme, it could be related to one of the problems listed above. However, the gas isn't responsible for the baby's distress when suffering from these problems. Distress is from pain caused by **intense intestinal contractions**. The extra gas that might be produced because of the problems listed above is simply along for the ride.

If you're burping your baby in the belief that this will prevent swallowed air from causing intestinal gas and abdominal cramps, you're wasting your time. Other strategies such as tummy massages, warm baths, bouncing on a yoga ball, holding baby upright, or giving her herbal teas or medications to make her burp more readily might help her to expel some of the gas but **will not fix the problem** causing abdominal cramping and an excess production of intestinal gas. You need to **target the cause, not the symptoms**.

Extreme intestinal gas—meaning beyond normal production—occurs when a baby has constipation or diarrhea. If you suspect your baby is "gassy" the next step is to identify if her bowel movements are normal or not. If bowel movements are normal, then the amount of gas your baby expels is also normal and not the reason for crying.

Bowel movements—what's normal?

In order to tell if there is a problem within your baby's intestinal tract it's necessary to know the normal frequency, color and consistency of babies' stools. You need to know what's normal to be able to recognize what is not.

Normal stools

Depending on whether your baby receives breast milk, infant formula or a combination of the two, her stools will be quite different. Table 31.1 describes what's typical.

Table 31.1: Typical stools for babies receiving breast milk or infant formula

	Breast milk only	Infant formula
Frequency	Breastfed babies usually poop a lot—up to 10 times per day—before they reach the one-month mark. After the first month, breastfed babies often have fewer bowel movements than before. On average ranging three to four times per day. No bowel motion for seven days can also be normal **provided the baby shows signs of being well fed** (see page 42).	Three times per day to once every three days, and anything in between.
Consistency	Watery or loose-scrambled-egg consistency. Stools might contain white milk curd flecks that look like seeds.	Sloppy, paste, or semi-formed. Stools might be watery when given hypoallergenic formula.
Color	Yellow to mustard. May sometimes be green.	Yellow-brown, tan-brown or greenish-brown.

Variations from those described in the table could be normal for individual babies related to their physical condition, mother's diet, the type of infant formula, solid foods consumed, or medications received. If unsure, it's best to check with your baby's doctor.

Constipation

A baby is considered to be constipated if she has difficulty passing **hard, dry, pebbly stools**! If your baby's poop is fluid, soft or paste consistency, she's not constipated.

Constipation is a common problem for formula-fed babies and for both formula and breastfed babies once they start to eat solid foods. It's rare for a baby receiving **only breast milk** to become constipated as breast milk contains natural laxatives.

Constipation can cause abdominal discomfort, poor appetite, reduced milk intake, crying, fussy feeding behavior, feeding refusal, and wakefulness. If your baby is constipated, treatment may be required to soften the stools and provide relief from discomfort before she will return to feeding well. It's important that she's not pressured to feed when constipated, or you risk upsetting her further.

Prevention is better than cure. Common reasons for formula-fed babies to become constipated are one or more of the following: casein-dominant formula, lactose-free formula, medications that slow down gastric emptying time such as acid-suppressing medications, antibiotics, thickening agents in particular cereal and starch, concentrated formula, and rarely, milk allergy.

Decreased stool frequency

You might become concerned that your baby is constipated if she does not poop for a number of days. More so, if she also happens to be irritable or not eating as much as usual.

Constipation is **not** about the frequency of your baby's stools. It's about the consistency!

There are circumstances when decreased frequency of bowel movements need to be expected. For example, around four to six weeks of age the frequency of stools of both breastfed and formula-fed babies decreases. Formula-fed babies could go up to three days and breastfed babies up to seven days without a bowel movement without being constipated.

I often see parents providing constipation treatments simply because their baby has not had a bowel movement for a number of days. They are unaware that some medications given to treat constipation work by increasing intestinal contractions and cause discomfort.

Straining

Parents often suspect constipation when their baby strains. Straining is normal behavior for babies. It's not a sign of constipation unless her stools are like pellets.

During the early weeks of life, straining is involuntary. Newborn babies will often stop sucking, grimace, bear down at some point while feeding, pass gas, or poop, or expel nothing for the effort. The straining action—which is triggered by the gastrocolic and defecation reflexes (see pages 67-69)—enables a baby to use her abdominal muscles to help move stools through her intestines.

Straining while having a bowel movement or passing gas is commonly seen in babies around four to six weeks of age. It is at this age your baby is becoming more aware of her body sensations and she is learning to gain some control over her body that will eventually be necessary to voluntarily control bowel movements in the future. As your baby strains she is also learning which muscles do what and how much effort is needed to poop. She might use a little more effort than necessary to begin with, but after a few weeks of practice she will become a "poop master" and straining will settle.

Straining can also occur at times when your baby is learning to pass a larger or slightly thicker consistency stool than she's used to. Thicker stools can occur if a baby's diet is changed such as switching from breast milk to infant formula or when she first starts eating solid foods. This is also normal.

Diarrhea

Diarrhea is characterized by **abnormally** frequent watery stools. If your baby's stools **suddenly** become more frequent and waterier, she may have diarrhea.

Diarrhea sometimes, but not always, contains mucus or blood and may have a foul smell. It can be mild, moderate or severe.

Diarrhea scale

- **Mild:** 3 to 5 watery stools per day.
- **Moderate:** 6 to 9 watery stools per day.
- **Severe:** 10 or more watery stools per day.

Diarrhea can be **acute** which means it occurs suddenly and lasts for less than four weeks or **chronic** which means it lasts for longer than four weeks.

Causes of diarrhea

Diarrhea is a symptom of an underlying problem or condition. There are numerous reasons why babies and children develop diarrhea, most are not serious and will pass on their own or can easily be treated by a change in diet. Potential causes include

- overfeeding;
- functional lactose overload;
- food allergy;
- food intolerance;
- medications to treat constipation—especially when the baby was not actually constipated;
- medication side effect—for example, antibiotics or acid-suppressing medications;
- gastrointestinal infection (gastroenteritis);
- food poisoning;
- a metabolic disorder;
- gastrointestinal surgery.

If your **baby is well**, check for signs of overfeeding (chapter 25) and functional lactose overload (described later in this chapter).

If your **baby is unwell**, it's important to have her examined by a doctor.

Because most episodes of diarrhea are short lived, it's not always possible to discover the cause.

When frequent watery stools are normal

The stools of a **breastfed baby** are often frequent and watery, and it can be difficult to tell the difference between normal stools and diarrhea. A healthy, thriving breastfed baby could have three to 10 watery bowel motions per day without it being diarrhea.

A **formula-fed baby** can also experience brief episodes of diarrhea from time to time for no identifiable reason. Without other physical symptoms, loose watery bowel movements don't necessarily mean a baby is ill or that she has a digestive disorder.

While there can be several causes for frequent watery or sloppy bowel movements, I recommend you start with the most common of all, which is functional lactose overload.

What is functional lactose overload?

Lactose (the main carbohydrate in milk) needs to be broken down into single sugars (glucose and galactose) by the **digestive enzyme lactase** to be absorbed into the bloodstream and used by the body as energy.

The digestion of lactose normally occurs primarily in the small intestine. In the case of **functional lactose overload,** the body makes enough lactase to adequately digest **most, but not all,** of the lactose received. Undigested lactose cannot be absorbed into the blood stream.

Undigested lactose makes it to the colon (large intestine or bowel), where lactose-digesting bacteria, normally present in the bowel, ferment the lactose. This generates short-chain fatty acids, lactic acid, and hydrogen gas. The colon will absorb some of the extra acids, gases, and water. Gases not absorbed are pooped out.

Undigested lactose draws in water through the intestinal wall and the intestine expands, and this increases the intensity of intestinal contractions.

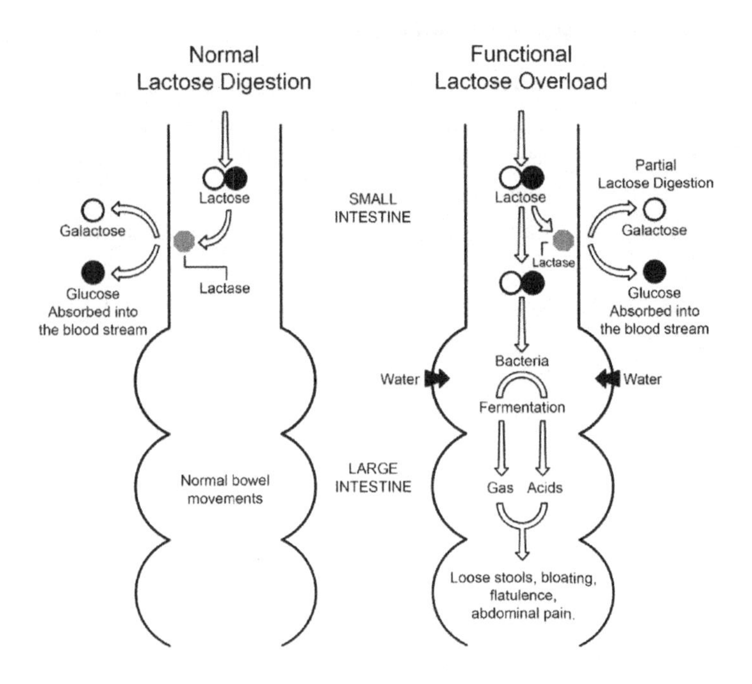

Symptoms

Small amounts of undigested lactose might cause no symptoms. But larger amounts entering into the baby's colon are more likely to cause symptoms. The signs and symptoms come and go and vary from mild to severe. Most newborns will display mild symptoms every so often. Whether the symptoms are present, remain mild, or intensify largely depends on what you do in response.

I will describe what's happening inside your baby's body, the signs you will observe, and how some parents interpret and respond to these signs.

Mild to moderate

Baby's bowel movements will either be very frequent (six or more times per day) or there could be one or two massive explosions each day, with poop leaking out of her diaper and up her back. The consistency of her stools will be sloppy if she consumes formula or watery in the case of breast milk. She will fart a **lot** from an abundance of intestinal gas. You might suspect her farting is caused by swallowed air. It's not! It's gas that is produced in her colon during the fermentation process.

The bearing-down movements associated with the **gastrocolic reflex** (see page 67-68) will be more frequent, obvious, and extreme. This is caused by increased intestinal contractions related to the fermentation process. You might also notice that your baby often grunts, primarily in the early hours of the morning, because of an accumulation of gas.

Nursing mothers might blame their diet, but dietary restrictions will have **no effect on lactose overload** as lactose is produced in the mother's breast irrespective of her diet. Parents might switch between brands of infant formula, but if the new brand contains the same amount of lactose—typically 7 percent—it will make no difference.

When uncomfortable, the baby will be fussy, want to be held, and will search for something to suck on to soothe. You might interpret her fussiness and desire to suck as hunger, and in doing so, take steps to increase the amount of milk or calories she receives. Nursing mothers might give their baby bottles of breast milk or infant formula in addition to breastfeeding. Bottle-fed babies may be pressured to drink more. Unbeknownst to the parents, such steps will increase the lactose load and only make things worse.

Moderate to severe

Your baby will display the symptoms described above, only more extreme and intense, plus other signs. The stools of a formula-fed baby will be sloppy. The stools of a baby receiving breast milk will be watery and occasionally green in color. If she poops as you're changing her diaper, you might notice her stools appear frothy.

When lactose overload is extreme, stools can contain mucus and blood.[174] Cells lining her intestinal wall secrete mucus as protection from the effects of lactic acid and as a defense against harmful pathogens. When exposure to lactic acid is severe or prolonged, the mucus shield can no longer protect the intestinal wall, and bleeding can occur. The baby's stools might contain specks or streaks of blood, or blood may be microscopic, only detectible via a **fecal occult blood test (FOBT).** Acidic stools could burn her little bottom, causing a nasty, red, and inflamed diaper rash around her anus.

The cumulative effect of extreme gas, bloating, intense intestinal contractions, inflammation of her intestinal wall, and acidic stools would understandably distress a baby. Baby's distress is rightly identified by parents as pain; however, the symptoms of lactose overload are **often** erroneously attributed to a medical condition.

Why misdiagnosis occurs

Based on GI symptoms alone, it's easy to see why functional lactose overload might be misdiagnosed as colic, reflux, milk protein intolerance, or lactose intolerance. To add to the confusion, babies experiencing GI symptoms linked to functional lactose overload may return positive results for some lab tests used to diagnose lactose intolerance and milk protein allergy. Plus, some treatments will reduce the GI symptoms caused by functional lactose overload. I will explain.

- **Colic:** Most over-the-counter medications have minimal or no effect. Prescribed medications—including muscle relaxants, antihistamines, and sedatives—allow more time for lactose digestion to occur and thereby reduce, but don't completely eliminate, symptoms associated with functional lactose overload.
- **Reflux:** Thickened feeds, recommended as a treatment for reflux, slow down the intestinal motility rate and may have some effect on reducing GI symptoms related to functional lactose overload.
- **Lactose intolerance:** Stool tests for lactose intolerance, which check for lactic acid and undigested lactose and other sugars in the stools, will provide a false-positive result in the case of functional lactose overload.
- **Milk protein intolerance:** Stool tests checking inflammation in the intestinal tract, called fecal calprotectin, and fecal occult blood test (FOBT) may also be positive in cases where the GI symptoms linked to functional lactose overload are severe or prolonged.

Basically, **diagnostic tests are inconclusive.** A diagnosis based on these tests or solely on your description of your baby's GI symptoms might result in her being switched to a lactose-free formula, soy infant formula, extensively hydrolyzed infant formula, or an amino acid-based infant formula.

An absence of lactose in these formulas will relieve many of the symptoms associated with functional lactose overload. No lactose = no functional lactose overload symptoms! But they won't deal with the cause.

A baby could still show signs associated with overfeeding—a major cause of lactose overload—or other physical or behavioral problems. Hence, why parents often only see a partial improvement in their baby's general level of contentment after switching her to an baby formula that contains no lactose.

A reduction in the baby's GI symptoms will bring a sense of relief and give the impression that the diagnosis was correct. However, medications and dietary changes have the potential to create problems at the time or down the road (explained in chapter 32). They are not required in the case of functional lactose overload.

Understanding the causes of functional lactose overload will help you identify the most appropriate steps to relieve your baby's symptoms. You don't need medications or dietary changes!

Causes

Reasons why babies experience difficulty digesting lactose include

- limited lactase production;
- overfeeding;
- increased motility rate;
- low numbers of acid-digesting bacteria—such as Bifidobacterium and Lactobacillus.

Each of these will impact how effectively lactose is digested and absorbed.

Reduced lactase production

Primary lactose intolerance (or congenital lactose intolerance)—where a baby does not produce lactase from birth—is rare. However, it is common for newborn babies to experience a temporary type of lactose malabsorption called **transient lactase deficiency** (also known as functional or developmental lactase deficiency). This relates to incomplete lactose absorption, which is a normal phenomenon in the first few months of life.[175] It's a reflection of an immature digestive system and is more common in preterm babies—before they have reached their expected date of birth.[176]

Babies with transient lactase deficiency produce some lactase, but not enough to digest the amount of lactose contained in the volumes of milk they need to consume for healthy growth. (The younger the baby, the faster she grows, and the more milk she needs in relation to her body weight.) Lactase deficiency usually lasts only for a few months after birth. As the baby matures, the production of lactase increases, growth rate naturally declines and the volume of milk required **in proportion to the size of her body** decreases.

Other reasons for lactase deficiency include gastroenteritis, food allergy, or long-term use of antibiotics; these can temporarily impair the production of lactose.

Overfeeding

Most healthy babies born at term will produce sufficient lactase necessary to digest the lactose received in **normal volumes of milk**—meaning the amount they need to support healthy growth. However, they don't produce enough to digest an **excess of lactose**, as can occur in cases of overfeeding and an oversupply of breast milk.

- **Overfeeding:** Newborn bottle-fed babies are susceptible to overfeeding. In chapter 25, I explained how easy it is for babies, especially those under the age of eight weeks and those who learn to rely on feeding as a way to go to sleep, to be overfed.
- **Oversupply of breast milk:** Healthy babies regulate their dietary intake according to the calories and not the volume. When the fat content of breast milk is low, as can occur when a mother has an overabundance of breast milk, the calories per ounce or milliliter may be lower. Consequently, her baby will drink higher volumes, thereby being exposed to more lactose. See pages 117-119 for more on oversupply.

Increased intestinal motility transit rate

Motility is a term used to describe the contraction of the muscles that mix and propel contents through the intestines. An increased intestinal motility rate means there is less time for lactose digestion to occur in the baby's small intestine. What increases intestinal motility?

- **Volume:** The volume of milk in the intestinal tract affects the speed at which it will pass through the small and large intestines. The greater the volume, the more intense the intestinal contractions and the faster it travels.
- **Fat content:** The fat content of milk affects motility rate. Fat takes longer to digest. If a baby consumes milk with a lower fat percentage, as can occur when a mother has an oversupply of breast milk, milk can rush through the small intestine faster than lactose can be digested.[177]
- **Prokinetic medications:** These are given to increase motility rate for suspected delayed gastric emptying (called gastroparesis). They not only speed up the time milk takes to empty from a baby's stomach but also increase intestinal contractions and therefore reduce the length of time that milk remains in the baby's small intestines, limiting the digestion of lactose.
- **GI infections:** When we experience gastroenteritis or food poisoning, intestinal contractions increase, causing diarrhea; this is the body's way of attempting to expel harmful pathogens.

The amount of **undigested lactose** entering the baby's colon will be increased for any of the reasons mentioned. For some babies, there can be more than one cause.

Low numbers of acid-producing bacteria

Intestinal microbiomes play an important role in the fermentation of carbohydrates in the large intestine. The simplicity of a baby's microflora (the balance between good and bad bacteria in the intestinal tract) limits fermentation capacity for complex carbohydrates.[178]

Babies naturally have **reduced numbers of lactose-digesting bacteria,** such as Bifidobacterium and Lactobacillus, because of immaturity. It takes time for these helpful bacteria to colonize in a baby's intestinal tract. The numbers of lactose-digesting bacteria will take much longer to establish in the intestinal tract of babies born by cesarian section compared to a vaginal birth.[179] The numbers will remain lower in babies who are given infant formula[180] in particular lactose-free formula, which includes soy and hypoallergenic formula[181] compared to babies who receive breast milk. They will also be lowered when a baby receives solid foods, which includes cereal in a baby's milk, before the age of six month.[182] And significantly altered when a baby receives acid-suppressing medications[183] or antibiotics.[184]

Why newborns are especially vulnerable to lactose overload

Symptoms related to lactose malabsorption caused by functional lactose overload are most likely to occur in the first three months. However, some babies continue to be troubled until up to six months of age. Newborns are at increased risk because

- they have an immature digestive tract, and beneficial intestinal microbes have not been established;
- they grow at a faster rate than older babies and, therefore, require larger volumes of milk **in relation to body weight.** Consequently, they receive a greater lactose load;
- they are more likely to overfeed because of an active sucking reflex; and
- nursing mothers often have an oversupply of breast milk in the early months.

How lactose overload compares to other digestive disorders

If your baby is healthy and thriving, her GI symptoms are more likely caused by functional lactose overload rather than other digestive disorders such as milk protein allergy or intolerance, or lactose intolerance. Such disorders are associated with **poor growth** while untreated. In the case of functional lactose overload, the baby is generally gaining weight at a normal or accelerated rate.

How to reduce or relieve symptoms

If your baby has lactose overload symptoms, discuss this with her doctor **before** giving her medications or switching to lactose-free, soy, or hypoallergenic formulas. Try the following steps first.

- **Step 1.** Correct overfeeding (see chapter 25). This step alone may be sufficient to relieve GI symptoms for many babies. If not, there are additional steps to try.
- **Step 2.** If you are pumping volumes of breast milk that are **well in excess** of your baby's needs, reduce oversupply.
- **Step 3.** A number of studies have demonstrated that adding lactase drops—brands include Colief™ or Lacteeze™—in into pumped breast milk or infant formula is helpful in reducing intestinal gas and crying.[185]
- **Step 4.** Increase the percentage of good bacteria in your baby's intestinal tract by giving pre- and probiotics—developed specifically for babies. Probiotics containing strains of Bifidobacterium and Lactobacillus aid the digestion of lactose and reduce lactose malabsorption symptoms.[186]
- **Step 5.** Reassess the need for acid-suppressing and prokinetic medications and avoid giving antibiotics to treat viral respiratory infections. (Antibiotics have no effect on viral infections and reduce the number of good bacteria in your baby's digestive tract.)
- **Step 6.** If necessary, reduce the lactose load by giving a formula-fed baby a **lactose-reduced** formula, which is not the same as lactose-free formula—such as those advertised as "gentle on baby's tummy" or "helpful to prevent colic."[187] Compare the lactose content between brands, and go for the lowest.*
- **Step 7.** Remember, a baby can experience more than one problem at a time. Consider the possibility of distress occurring as a result of birth trauma, sleep deprivation, and behavioral feeding problems, and take appropriate steps to address these problems.

Avoid lactose-free formula

Lactose in milk supports the growth of helpful lactose-digesting bacteria in a baby's intestinal tract. So avoid lactose-free formulas if possible. Lactose withdrawal results in a reduction of lactose-digesting bacteria, which might lower the threshold for intolerance symptoms if lactose is reintroduced into your baby's diet.[188] Plus lactose—which is broken down into glucose and galactose—may be a baby's only course of galactose. Galactose supports healthy brain development.[189]

With **effective management,** you could expect to witness subtle signs of improvement in your baby's GI symptoms within 24 hours and further improvement as the days progress. Bear in mind that it will take longer than a few days, possibly up to a few weeks, for your baby's intestinal tract to fully heal if the symptoms have been severe.

If these strategies fail to resolve the GI symptoms of a **thriving baby,** only then consider switching to a lactose-free or hypoallergenic formula.

Note: There is no one-size-fits-all approach to the management of an oversupply of breast milk. You might need an individualized assessment and feeding or pumping advice from a lactation consultant.

Next

Now you are aware of what are normal and unusual GI symptoms that can be improved or resolved by making simple changes to your baby care practices. In the next chapter, I describe medical conditions that are often diagnosed when babies cry for unknown reasons, experience feeding or sleeping problems, or display gastrointestinal symptoms. Included are behavioral reasons for the same signs and symptoms.

32 Commonly Diagnosed Medical Conditions

SIGNS AND SYMPTOMS OF GERD, MILK ALLERGY AND INTOLERANCE, COLIC AND OTHERS • WHAT ELSE CAN CAUSE THE SAME SIGNS AND SYMPTOMS • BENEFITS AND RISK OF MEDICAL TREATMENTS

If your baby is not a good feeder or sleeper, you might worry that he has a physical problem or medical condition. I want to reassure you that over 95 percent of babies who present to doctors because of concerns about crying for unknown reasons have no medical problems.[190] Yet the number of **healthy but irritable** babies who are diagnosed with colic, acid reflux, milk protein allergy, and other conditions is astounding.

If your baby's situation has not improved despite medical treatment, your baby's doctor could be missing something. Maybe it's a physical problem. But it's more likely to be an overlooked behavioral problem.

In this chapter, you'll read about the physical signs and behaviors typically associated with commonly diagnosed medical conditions, plus the behavioral causes for the same or similar signs and symptoms.

A medical condition is seldom responsible for crying

Unexplained infant crying is one of the most common reasons parents seek an assessment and advice from health professionals. Twenty percent express concerns about infant crying or irritability in the first three months.[191] But studies show less than 5 percent of healthy, thriving babies who cry and are irritable have an underlying physical cause.[192]

Only 6 to 10 percent of babies diagnosed with faltering growth (also called "failure to thrive") have an underlying medical condition affecting their growth.[193]

If your baby is physically well and therefore not in need of urgent medical attention, make sure you rule out normal developmental and behavioral problems—the reasons for 90 to 95 percent of babies' troubled behavior—before giving your baby medications or making changes to his diet.

What a doctor might diagnose

When trained under the traditional medical model of care, a doctor will physically examine your baby, looking for signs that might fit with a medical condition. If none can be observed during a routine medical examination, you might be told that your baby's behavior is "normal." Alternatively, your baby might be diagnosed with a medical condition based on your description of his behavior.

The most common physical problems or medical conditions blamed for healthy, typically developing babies' unexplained crying, problematic feeding behavior, sleep disturbance, gastrointestinal (GI) symptoms, or poor growth include

- gastroesophageal reflux disease (GERD), in particular, acid reflux;
- milk allergy or intolerance;
- colic;
- gastroparesis;
- visceral hypersensitivity;
- teething; and
- oral thrush.

For each of these problems and conditions, there can be alternative developmental or behavioral reasons to explain the same or similar physical signs and concerning behaviors.

My experience with infant **behavioral problems** means my perspective of the most prevalent reasons for crying, feeding, sleeping, and growth problems affecting **physically well babies** might be very different from that of your baby's doctor and other health professionals you have consulted. A different perspective may be the very thing you need to find an effective solution to your baby care dilemma.

GERD (gastroesophageal reflux disease)

"Reflux" is the commonly used abbreviation for gastroesophageal reflux. When a health professional or others use the term reflux, it's often interpreted to mean acid reflux. However, reflux merely refers to the regurgitation of stomach contents back into the esophagus and can fall into two categories:

1. gastroesophageal reflux (GER); and
2. gastroesophageal reflux disease (GERD).

Many people use the term GER when they are actually referring to GERD, which causes confusion. They're similar, but not the same.

GER relates to normal bodily functions and is not associated with complications. If you have not yet read about GER in chapter 31, I recommend you do. You need to know what's normal before you can tell what's not.

Only in a **tiny percentage** of cases is reflux associated with complications, in which case it's then referred to as GERD.

GERD is abnormal reflux of gastric contents that is associated with complications such as:

- **esophagitis** (inflammation or ulceration of the esophagus) caused by repeated acid reflux;
- **poor growth** because of extreme vomiting;
- **respiratory problems** from refluxed stomach contents entering the airways.

GERD reflects **ineffective homeostasis**. If a baby was to experience these complications, it would mean that one or more of his homeostatic mechanisms (called defense mechanisms) are not functioning as they should or that they have been overwhelmed.

Who is at risk?

Esophagitis (also called heartburn) caused by acid reflux is a relatively common problem experienced by adults. Hence, we might assume that it's common in babies. It's not! Adults have an increased risk of acid-induced esophagitis because of diet and lifestyle factors, including pregnancy, obesity, smoking, overeating, poor diet, fatty and fried foods, large coffee consumption, alcohol, medications for asthma, blood pressure or depression, and underlying medical conditions. Apart from overfeeding, and seldom, obesity, most of these factors do not apply to healthy babies.

GERD is more commonly seen in preterm babies before reaching their expected date of birth because of the immaturity of their digestive and nervous systems, as well as babies who have an underlying physical condition—for example, chronic lung disease, Down syndrome, neuromuscular disorders, cerebral palsy, trachea-esophageal fistula, pyloric stenosis, intestinal malrotation or vagus nerve compression caused by birth trauma. Nasogastric tube feeding is also associated with increased risk of GERD.

Signs and symptoms

- spitting up or vomiting—which may contain blood;
- gagging and choking;
- breath holding;
- frequent coughing;
- respiratory problems—such as aspiration, recurrent pneumonia, noisy breathing or wheezing;
- Sandifer syndrome—abnormal back arching where the baby's neck is twisted to the side plus involuntary muscle spasms that can give the appearance of a seizure;
- weight loss or inadequate weight gain;
- refusing to eat;
- prolonged periods of crying and fussiness during, after, and between feeds;
- sleep disturbance, brief naps, and frequent waking at night.

Most of these symptoms are nonspecific and can either mimic or be caused by other physical and behavioral problems. For example, a baby with GER—normal, uncomplicated reflux—could display some of the same signs and symptoms for reasons that are unrelated to reflux.

What else could it be?

Many of my clients claimed to have been on a crusade that has lasted weeks or months to find the right medications or dosages to "get baby's reflux under control." But "reflux" was not the reason for their baby's distress, hence their inability to find the right medication.

The following table outlines physical signs and behavior that are often attributed to acid reflux and alternative reasons for the same signs and behavior.

Table 32.1: GERD signs and symptoms and alternative explanations

GERD Physical signs	Other possibilities	Read more
Baby spits up.	Normal physiology (GER)	Pages 429-433
Projectile vomiting.	Overfeeding. Speed-feeding. Food poisoning.	Chapter 25 Page 78 Pages 174-178
Blood-stained vomiting.	Maternal blood from a cracked nipple.	
Slow weight gain or weight loss.	"Catch-down" growth. Underfeeding. Overfeeding, which can cause poor growth in some cases.	Page 47 Chapter 26 Chapter 25
Repeated respiratory infections.	Viral infections.	
Behavioral symptoms	**Alternative explanation**	**Read more**
Crying and irritability.	Sleep deprivation. Functional lactose overload.	Pages 290-292 Pages 439-448
Feeding refusal.	Feeding aversion.	Chapter 27
Choking and gagging.	Inappropriate or faulty feeding equipment, poor positioning, or incorrect parental response to infant behavioral cues.	Chapters. 15, 21 & 23

Aspiration causing respiratory problems.	Same as above.	Chapters. 15, 21 & 23
Sandifer syndrome.	Normal back arching a baby will do when frustrated and upset or to distance himself from something he wishes to avoid.	
Repeated coughing.	Equipment, poor feeding position, environmental allergies.	Chapters 15 & 23
Broken sleep. Sleep deprivation.	Sleep association problem. Misinterpreting tiredness cues.	Pages 292-298 Pages 288-289

Parents often consult with me about two baby care problems above all others. These are "screaming newborns" and "avoidant feeders." I find these babies are highly likely to have already been diagnosed and medicated for acid reflux. Inevitably the treatments didn't help, which is why they ended up booking a consultation with me to explore behavioral causes.

Screaming newborns

In my experience, the most common reasons for newborn babies to cry inconsolably for long periods of time are because of four regulatory problems I call the **Big Os: overtiredness** (pages 290-292), **overstimulation, oversupply syndrome** (pages 117-119), **and overfeeding** (chapter 25).

A healthy baby could experience one, two, or three of these problems at the same time. The cumulative effect of each problem adds yet another layer of distress. Get three or four problems occurring at once, and you have an extremely distressed little baby on your hands.

Avoidant feeders

When an obviously hungry baby over the age of eight weeks displays distressed and avoidant feeding behavior while awake, acid reflux is typically the first thing blamed. My experience is that in most cases, the cause of a hungry baby's avoidant feeding behavior is a **behavioral**

feeding aversion caused by being repeatedly pressured or forced to feed (see chapter 27).

What are the odds?

The incidence of GERD is estimated at 1 in 300 babies.[194] And yet, between 5 and 9 percent of babies receive a diagnosis of GERD,[195] indicating a high incidence of misdiagnosis.

Ask yourself which of these scenarios is more likely.

1. Your neurologically and physically healthy, typically developing baby has a physical problem that is negatively impacting the effectiveness of his homeostatic mechanisms; or
2. You and your baby's doctor are missing something.

While it is possible that your baby has developed a physical problem causing symptoms of GERD, the odds are very low. If the behavioral causes listed in table 32.1 have not been considered, there's a good chance that the true cause of your baby's distress has been overlooked.

Think twice before giving your baby medications

Medications should be the **last option** for healthy babies after all other causes for their distress—developmental and behavioral—are ruled out. And not as a "Let's try this and see if it helps" method of eliminating acid reflux as the cause.

Antacids and acid-suppressing medications are so readily prescribed for crying babies that you would be forgiven for believing they are harmless. They are not! While there are side effects, that's not usually the main cause of harm. It's changing the pH (acid balance) of a baby's gastrointestinal (GI) tract that is associated with negative health outcomes.

Stomach acid is not a mistake of nature! It provides many health benefits. Neutralizing or suppressing the production of stomach acid via the use of medications can leave the body vulnerable to a number of diseases and health complications.

Stomach acid functions

Stomach acid plays a crucial role in multiple digestive processes. Here are a few examples. Stomach acid

- acts as a major defense mechanism that kills most food- and waterborne bacteria and viruses;
- activates the protein-digesting enzyme pepsin in the stomach, which works with stomach acid to break apart protein molecules;
- triggers the release of pancreatic secretions in the small intestines;
- aids the absorption of certain vitamins and minerals, such as vitamin B12, iron, zinc, calcium, and magnesium;
- helps to close the lower esophageal sphincter, situated where the esophagus joins the stomach, which reduces the regurgitation of stomach contents;
- helps to activate the pyloric sphincter, situated between the stomach and small intestine, to enable the passage of stomach contents into the small intestines, so it doesn't remain in the stomach longer than necessary;
- influences the pH in the intestinal tract, thereby supporting the growth of friendly bacteria.

Risks associated with low stomach acid

Low levels of stomach acid increase a person's vulnerability to a number of health problems, such as

- food allergies[196] owing to impaired gastric digestion of proteins;[197]
- vitamin and mineral deficiencies;[198]
- respiratory infections;[199]
- Clostridium difficile infection;[200]
- gastrointestinal infections including gastroenteritis;[201]
- intestinal dysbiosis—the imbalance of gut microbiota associated with an unhealthy outcome;[202]
- delayed gastric emptying;[203] and
- rebound stomach acid hypersecretion—an excessive secretion of stomach acid.[204]

Acid-suppressing medications undoubtedly benefit the tiny percentage of babies who **genuinely suffer from esophagitis caused by acid reflux.** In such cases, the benefits gained are greater than the risks.

> Giving acid-suppressing medications to a **healthy, thriving baby** simply because you don't understand his crying and behavior risks causing more harm than good.

Pediatric gastroenterologist Eric Hassell has been arguing for years that doctors overprescribe medications for GERD. I recommend you read his paper "Over-prescription of Acid-Suppressing Medications in Infants: How It Came About, Why It's Wrong, and What to Do About It" in the Journal of Pediatrics,[205] available online.

Milk allergy and intolerance

Milk allergy and intolerance are separate conditions with different causes. Food allergy relates to the immune system, whereas food intolerance is confined to the digestive tract. Food intolerances are more common than food allergies, but an allergy is a more serious problem.

Both conditions will cause similar GI symptoms, so people often confuse the two. A study of 381 babies exhibiting a possible adverse reaction to cow's milk found that 243 of them (64 percent) were **mislabeled** with cow's milk protein allergy (CMPA).[206]

If you are concerned that your baby has a digestive disorder, make sure you understand the difference between the two because each involves different management.

Milk protein allergy

Milk protein allergy happens when your baby's immune system, which normally fights infections, reacts to specific proteins in milk as if they were toxic. This leads to an allergic reaction—a response from the immune system in which chemicals like histamine are released into the bloodstream and spread through the body. Once released, histamine produces many varied effects throughout the body.

Symptoms

A true food allergy causes an immune system reaction that affects numerous organs in the body. Australasian Society of Clinical Immunology and Allergy (ASCIA) state symptoms of a food allergy are usually obvious.[207]

- **Digestive system:** vomiting, nausea, diarrhea, abdominal pain, extreme gas, blood and mucous in stools, and, rarely, constipation.
- **Respiratory system:** symptoms that are like hay fever, such as shortness of breath, coughing, sneezing, and wheezing.
- **Skin:** itchy skin, rashes, hives, or eczema;
- **Swelling** of lips, mouth, tongue, face, or throat.
- **Poor growth:** failure to gain weight or weight loss.
- **Anaphylaxis:** a life-threatening allergic reaction is rare for milk allergy.

Most babies with CMPA develop symptoms before one month of age—often within one week after the introduction of cow's milk-based formula.[208]

Incidence of milk protein allergy

- In babies receiving **infant formula:** 2 to 3 percent, approximately 1:50.[209]
- In babies receiving **breast milk:** 0.5 percent, or 1:200.[210]
- Most babies who are allergic to cow's milk will also be allergic to goat's milk.[211]
- Fifty to 80 percent of babies who are allergic to cow's milk will also be allergic to soy.[212]
- The risk of food allergy is moderately higher for babies if one parent has food or environmental allergies, and there is a higher risk if both parents do.[213]

Treatment

An allergic reaction can be triggered by the **tiniest** amount of a problematic food protein. **Complete avoidance** of the protein is necessary. In the case of cow's milk, goat's milk, and soy protein allergy, this may mean a **formula-fed baby** is given an extensively hydrolyzed infant formula (EHF) or amino acid-based infant formula (AAF). Or a **mother producing breast milk** for her baby may need to undergo dietary restrictions. You need to avoid problematic food proteins, including those hidden in other foods like bread, cake, deli meats, and many packaged and processed foods.

Milk intolerance

An intolerance does not involve the immune system or cause allergy-type symptoms. A food intolerance response takes place in the digestive tract. It occurs when a person's digestive tract is unable to properly break down the food. This could be caused by enzyme deficiencies, sensitivity to food additives, or reactions to naturally occurring chemicals in foods.

Symptoms

Food intolerance symptoms include bloating, excessive intestinal gas, and diarrhea. When symptoms are severe, stools can contain blood and mucous, and the combination can cause abdominal pain.

An intolerance is a "dose-related" condition, meaning that while a little of the food might cause no symptoms at all, a lot can. People with food intolerance may not have symptoms unless they eat a large portion of the food or eat the food frequently.

Incidence of milk intolerance

It's estimated that between 5 to 15 percent of babies display GI symptoms consistent with food intolerance.[214] This includes all food intolerances, which can include proteins, fats and carbohydrates—such as lactose, corn syrup, sucrose and others, and micronutrients.

What else could cause the same symptoms?

Babies can display GI symptoms for a host of other reasons, which are described in Table 32.2. These are often mistakenly attributed to milk allergy or intolerance.

Table 32.2: Signs and symptoms of food allergy or intolerance and other possible reasons

Food allergy and intolerance signs	Other possibilities	Read more
Diarrhea.	Frequent, watery stools can be normal for a baby receiving breastmilk. Functional lactose overload. Food poisoning. Gastrointestinal infection. Medication side effect.	Pages 435-437 Pages 439-448 Pages 174-178
Blood in or on stools.	Functional lactose overload. Gastrointestinal infection. Small tear in rectum from passing constipated stools.	Pages 439-448
Green stools.	Functional lactose overload. GI infection. Iron-fortified formula can cause a khaki (army green) or dark green color.	Pages 439-448
Mucous stools.	Some mucous in stools is normal. Functional lactose overload.	 Pages 439-448
Vomiting.	Overfeeding. GER—physiological reflux. GERD—pathological reflux.	Pages 326-327 Pages 429-423 Pages 451-457
Hard, pebbly, constipated stools.	Casein-dominated formula. Solid foods. Medication side effect. Food thickeners added to baby's milk.	
Abdominal distension or bloating.	Normal appearance of full stomach. Hyperextension of baby's stomach from overfeeding. Medication side effect.	

Extreme intestinal gas.	Gas produced during normal digestion. Functional lactose overload. Medication side effect.	Pages 433-435 Pages 439-448
Respiratory symptoms such as coughing, sneezing, wheezing.	Irritation from milk regurgitation into nose. Airborne allergens, such as pollens, dust mite, animal hair, or mold.	
Rashes or eczema	Baby acne. Heat rash. Contact dermatitis.	
Poor growth.	Perceived rather than genuine poor growth. Underfeeding, Overfeeding can result in poor growth in some cases.	Chapter 26 Chapter 25

Behavioral symptoms	**Alternative explanations**	
Crying.	Misinterpreting behavioral cues. Overtiredness. Overstimulation.	Pages 290-292
Trouble falling asleep.	Overtiredness. Absent sleep associations.	Pages 290-292 Pages 292-298
Broken sleep.	Absent sleep associations.	Pages 292-298
Fussy feeding behavior.	Out-of-sync parent response to behavioral cues.	
Feeding refusal.	Feeding aversion.	Chapter 27

Milk protein allergy is a popular diagnosis to explain why a baby is distressed or has feeding and sleeping issues. Countless numbers of distressed babies have been switched to a hypoallergenic formula **without any physical signs** that point to milk protein allergy or intolerance.

Are diagnostic tests reliable?

Present-day diagnostic tests are inconclusive as a means to test for milk allergy or intolerance in babies. They can provide some helpful information on what is happening inside a baby's body but cannot pinpoint the cause.

- **IgE (immunoglobulin E) blood tests** may be ordered to check if there are antibodies indicative of an allergy. The absence of IgE does not exclude the possibility of milk allergy.
- **Skin prick test** is unreliable for babies under the age of 12 months.
- **Fecal calprotectin** is a sensitive, noninvasive marker for intestinal inflammation. But it does not provide an indication of what is causing the inflammation. High fecal calprotectin levels, especially in the first month after birth, are normal.[215]
- **Fecal occult blood test (FOBT)** used to check for microscopic blood can also be positive for an intestinal infection and functional lactose overload.
- **Reducing substances stool test** designed to check for lactose intolerance will also be positive for functional lactose overload.

The lack of specificity of these tests in identifying the cause means none provide conclusive evidence of milk protein allergy or intolerance, which is why, if you suspect an allergy or intolerance, you need to ensure a comprehensive feeding assessment is undertaken.

Positive test results need to be considered within the context of the big picture. Something that involves a thorough assessment of **all possible causes**—physical and behavioral.

Don't switch baby to hypoallergenic formula "just in case"

The American Academy of Pediatrics (AAP) recommends that the use of EHFs and AAFs should be limited to babies who have **physical signs** associated with milk allergy.[216] A change of formula won't help if your baby has no clearly observable GI signs that indicate he has milk allergy or intolerance.

If your baby receives breast milk

Babies are never allergic to breast milk but can be allergic to food proteins eaten by the mother. Before going down the path of what could be needless dietary restrictions, first rule out all other potential causes for your baby's GI symptoms. Don't overlook the following possibilities

- functional lactose overload, pages 439-448,
- oversupply syndrome, pages 117-119, and
- overfeeding, chapter 25.

If, after ruling out these common problems, you believe dietary restrictions are necessary, seek guidance from a registered dietitian (RD) to pinpoint the problematic food protein and ensure that neither you nor your baby's health is compromised as a result of limiting your food options.

If your baby receives infant formula

Don't switch your baby to a hypoallergenic formula without considering and ruling out alternative causes of GI symptoms, skin and respiratory problems, crying, feeding, and sleeping problems.

There are advantages and disadvantages to giving a baby a hypoallergenic formula. For the tiny percentage of babies genuinely suffering from a milk protein allergy—who are **not** currently breastfed or receiving breast milk—the advantages of improved comfort, health, and growth from switching to a hypoallergenic formula outweigh disadvantages.

Disadvantages include the nutritional balance, taste, and cost. The hydrolyzation process changes the nutritional value of the formula. Lactose is removed and replaced with other sugars. EHFs and AAFs smell foul and have a bitter taste. Hypoallergenic formulas are expensive, usually around three times the cost of regular formulas. (In some countries, national health schemes or insurance companies will cover some of the costs if prescribed by a doctor.) AAFs are often very thin and may require thickeners, which have their own risks (see pages 157-158).

If your baby's doctor thinks it's necessary for you to switch him to a hypoallergenic formula, discuss ways to minimize the negative impact on his intestinal microbiome—for example, whether giving probiotics may be helpful.

If switching to hypoallergenic formula

If your baby is older than eight weeks, expect some refusals and a temporary drop in his milk intake because of the unpleasant taste. Initially, he might refuse, eating only a little when ravenous. It could take many days for him to willingly accept and for his milk intake to return to the volumes he consumed previously.

A gradual transition (described on pages 138-139) might minimize the risk of refusal. If met with refusal, **don't pressure him to eat.** It's understandable that he would not be happy about receiving food with an unpleasant taste. Allow time for him to adjust. If you pressure him to eat, you run the risk of causing him to develop a feeding aversion.

Colic

The main symptom of infant colic is nonstop crying that lasts three hours or more, usually in the evenings, at least three days per week for a period of three weeks or longer. The baby is healthy and gaining weight. He displays no **unusual** signs that point to a physical problem.

Colic is not a condition!

Colic was once the most popular of all diagnoses given as the reason for unexplained crying displayed by healthy newborns. Colic is not a specific condition; rather, it's a term used to describe "long periods of inconsolable crying in a healthy, thriving baby." In other words, colic describes how a baby behaves rather than what a baby has. What a health professional's diagnosis of colic really means is, "Your baby is healthy, and I can see no obvious reason for his crying."

What's really going on?

Everyone has a theory about why 20 percent of healthy newborn babies have episodes of inconsolable crying that fit the criteria for colic. Theories include swallowed air, immature digestive tract, immature nervous system, baby's diet, foods eaten by nursing mothers, baby's temperament, and more. You can't test any of these theories or prove them, for that matter, so I'm skeptical of all such theories.

When a parent consults with me for any baby care problem, I ask about their baby's birth, physical health, growth, diet, feeding equipment, how long feeding takes, volumes consumed per feed and per day, baby's feeding pattern, his behavior while feeding, how much sleep he gets, how he is settled to sleep, the frequency and appearance of his bowel movements, when he cries, how long he cries for, what actions the parent takes in response to his crying, and more. Yes, it takes a while!

Following this assessment, which can take me over an hour, I have found that the most common reasons for "colicky" behavior displayed by physically well but distressed newborns are the Big Os: overtiredness, overstimulation, oversupply syndrome, and overfeeding. The same four problems are also often misdiagnosed as acid reflux and milk allergy.

Gastroparesis

The vagus nerve helps manage complex processes in the digestive tract, including signaling the muscles in the stomach to contract. This helps in the mechanical breakdown of food in the stomach and moves partially digested food from the stomach into the intestines. Ordinarily, the muscular contractions of the stomach are strong but not painful.

Gastroparesis, which means delayed gastric emptying, occurs when the vagus nerve is compromised or damaged. The normal spontaneous movement of the muscles in the stomach is weak, causing the stomach to take too long to empty its contents into the intestinal tract.

Symptoms include acid reflux, nausea, bloating, vomiting, abdominal pain, and poor appetite.

Diagnosis

A gastric-emptying scan can be used to diagnose gastroparesis and rule out physical conditions that may cause similar symptoms. A doctor won't necessarily order a scan. Instead, he or she might prescribe medications based on

1. Poor growth linked to extreme spitting up.
2. Suspected poor appetite owing to baby not consuming the "recommended" volume of milk.

3. Infant distress that has not resolved after baby has been trialed on multiple different acid-suppressing medications.

Medical Treatments

Prokinetic medications (also called motility agents), such as metoclopramide, domperidone, bethanechol, and erythromycin (which is an antibiotic), may be prescribed to help strengthen the lower esophageal sphincter and speed up gastric emptying and transit time in the small and large intestines. This will reduce the risk of milk regurgitation and shorten the time for acid reflux to occur.

Prokinetic medications can have a high incidence of unwanted side effects compared to many other drugs, for example, headaches, bloating, abdominal cramping, and diarrhea.[217] They won't fix the cause of gastroparesis, which relates to the vagus nerve. They just treat the symptoms.

Complementary therapies

A chiropractor, osteopath, or craniosacral therapist may be able to correct **vagus nerve compression** caused by birth trauma.

Other possibilities

Alternative reasons for spitting up, poor growth, and failure of acid-suppressing medications include

- **misdiagnosis.** Acid-suppressing medications will fail to resolve a baby's distress if acid reflux is not the cause of his distress.
- **overestimation of a baby's milk needs.** A baby won't consume as much milk as expected if expectations exceed what his body needs. Overestimation could be related to calories and not volume in the case of calorie-enhanced feeds.
- **overfeeding.** Too much milk or formula can result in vomiting and poor growth in some cases (see chapter 25).
- **speed-feeding.** When the stomach expands too quickly, vomiting can result.
- **delayed protein digestion.** Gastroparesis can be a side effect of acid-suppressing medications, in particular, proton pump inhibitors (PPIs).[218]

- **High-fat feeds.** The higher the fat content, the longer the stomach takes to empty. Adding oil to a baby's milk to increase the number of calories per ounce or milliliter will delay gastric emptying time.
- **Medication side effects.** Vomiting is a common side effect of many medications.

Visceral hypersensitivity

Visceral hypersensitivity is a newcomer to the list of popular medical diagnoses given to explain infant distress for unknown reasons.

Visceral hypersensitivity (or visceral hyperalgesia) is the term used to describe the experience of pain within the inner organs (viscera) at a level that is more intense than normal. Normally, when we eat or drink, the stomach and intestines stretch to accommodate the meal with no discomfort whatsoever. But in the case of visceral hypersensitivity, the mere act of filling the stomach or intestine with a small amount of fluid or food triggers the nerves in the stomach or intestines to respond as if something painful has been introduced.

Diagnosis

There are no tests to diagnose visceral hypersensitivity. A child can tell others if he is experiencing pain. A baby can't. A baby might be diagnosed with visceral hypersensitivity based on the belief that his distress while feeding is from pain. It is typically diagnosed after treatments for GERD, milk protein allergy, and gastroparesis have been ineffective in resolving the baby's distress.

Note: The potential for a misdiagnosis of visceral hypersensitivity is significantly increased if behavioral causes of distressed and avoidant infant feeding behavior—such as those described in the chapters of Part F—have been overlooked.

Treatments

Treatments might include specific antihistamines, antispasmodics, and antidepressants. These drugs affect the function of the nerves in the intestinal tract and block pain messages between the GI tract and the brain, thereby reducing visceral hypersensitivity pain.

What else could it be?

It's important to differentiate between stress and pain (see pages 409-411). Common reasons for babies to display distress or experience pain **while feeding** include

Stress

Baby may be stressed if he

- is receiving an inappropriate response to behavioral cues, in particular being pressured or forced to feed against his will;
- has a feeding aversion (chapter 27). An unidentified feeding aversion is typically why a baby will be misdiagnosed with visceral hypersensitivity; or
- is chronically sleep deprived.

Pain

Baby may be in pain caused by one or more of the following

- functional lactose overload;
- GERD;
- milk protein allergy or intolerance;
- gastroparesis;
- side effects of medications.

Of course, babies can experience distress or pain **outside of feeding times** for many reasons.

Teething

Teething refers to the time when a tooth is breaking through the gum surface. When a baby is teething, his gum may become red, shiny, and swollen. You can see or feel the hard points of his tooth close to or broken through the gum surface. If you cannot see or feel an emerging tooth, he's not teething.

While it's possible for a baby's first tooth to appear around three months of age, the average age is six months. Many babies won't get their first tooth until much later.

Can teething adversely affect feeding?

Many parents and doctors will blame teething pain for fussy feeding behavior or feeding refusal. It doesn't make sense that a teething baby would willingly chew on teething rings and toys but then shy away from the nipple of a bottle when hungry because sucking (not chewing) from a nipple would cause him pain.

Based on many years of professional experience advising parents on infant feeding problems, I would say that teething can cause fussiness and reduced appetite for a period of around three to five days. How upset a baby becomes **while feeding** during teething episodes will be influenced by the extent that the parent goes to try to make their baby consume the amount he would usually eat.

I generally find there are other reasons causing the baby's distress, like the parent providing an out-of-sync response to their baby's behavioral cues, pressuring him to eat, sleep deprivation, or feeding aversion.

Oral thrush

Thrush is the term used to describe an overgrowth of a strain of a yeast-like fungus called Candida albicans. Other names for thrush include yeast infection, fungal infection, candida, candidiasis, or moniliasis.

Signs of oral thrush

White or cream-colored patches resembling milk curds can be seen on the roof of the baby's mouth, inside his cheeks, and on his tongue. These may be surrounded by red areas, or his entire tongue may have a solid white coating. If the baby sucks his thumb or fingers, he may also develop a yeast infection around his fingernails.

Yeast overgrowth can sometimes involve a baby's entire intestinal tract. He might also have a thrush infection causing an angry, red diaper rash surrounding his anus. A yeast diaper rash can cause considerable pain when he pees or poops and when you clean his little bottom.

When it's not thrush

Milk residue left after feeding is often mistaken for thrush. It's usually only thin and found on the tongue, and it can be wiped or rinsed out of the mouth easily.

Can oral thrush cause feeding issues?

Oral thrush, unlike anal thrush on a baby's bottom, **is not usually painful** and therefore not a reason for feeding problems. Fussing, unsettled behavior during feeding from a sore mouth is rare and generally only occurs if an infection is severe, meaning it reaches the stage of causing mouth ulcers, something that seldom occurs in babies with a healthy immune system.

Unless your baby has mouth ulcers, you can probably rule out oral thrush as the cause of any feeding issues he might have.

Other medical causes

Other medical reasons for poor appetite and fussy feeding behavior include

- **anemia,** either an iron deficiency or pernicious anemia (a vitamin B12 deficiency). Lethargy, loss of appetite, and poor growth can be signs of anemia.
- **urinary tract infections** (UTIs) in infants are common. In babies, the symptoms of a UTI include fever, irritability, poor feeding or refusal to eat; cloudy, foul-smelling urine; or blood in the urine. Fever is typically present with a UTI, but not in every case. The incidence of babies with UTI without fever is unknown.

Look beyond physical causes!

> *"Milo (aged four months) hates feeding. He screams whenever I try to feed him when he is awake. He has been exclusively dream-feeding for weeks. I'm still not 100 percent sure his reflux is under control. He's on omeprazole and famotidine for reflux. He's also on Alimentum (a hypoallergenic formula), which I thicken with rice cereal. I'm worried the GI doctor (gastrointestinal specialist) is missing something. Should I see another GI?" Sonya*

Most conditions that affect babies, such as those listed in this chapter, can be treated or managed. Once effectively treated, these problems and conditions will cause a baby no further distress. Given that Milo screams when offered a feed while awake, yet will feed in his sleep, Sonya and Milo's doctor may have overlooked behavioral reasons, such as feeding aversion, for Milo's refusal to feed while awake.

Why medical treatments fail

If medications and dietary change fail to resolve your baby's distress, feeding issues, or sleeping issues, there are three potential reasons:

- misdiagnosis;
- combined reasons; or
- ineffective treatment.

Misdiagnosis

If your baby displays no physical signs or behavioral symptoms associated with the diagnosed condition, the true cause of his troubles may have been overlooked or misdiagnosed.

Your baby's doctor is the best person to advise on medical treatments, but **not** necessarily the best person to identify and advise on the management of behavioral (a.k.a. nonmedical) feeding problems.

Your childcare practices will have the strongest influence on your baby's behavior and how well he feeds and sleeps, and may even influence if he experiences gastrointestinal symptoms. So look for areas where you may need to make changes to your infant feeding and settling practices. Read all chapters in this book from start to finish to discover if you have been missing something. Remember to go through my Infant Feeding Self-Evaluation Checklist (page 272) to be sure you are fulfilling all of your infant feeding responsibilities.

Combined causes

If your baby has a diagnosed medical condition, either confirmed by diagnostic tests or based on an assessment of all causes that your baby's health professional is aware of, he might still suffer from behavioral problems—which are causes that many health professionals are unaware of.

Broaden your perspective of reasons for your baby's crying, feeding, or sleeping problems and cover developmental and behavioral causes as well as physical causes.

Ineffective treatment

Ineffective treatment is the least likely cause of treatment failure, though a possibility. Present-day medications are highly effective in treating the conditions they are developed to treat.

If you have ruled out all other causes, in particular the many described in this book, the condition may remain and continue to cause pain. Or baby may have another physical problem. After ruling out all possible behavioral causes, consult with your baby's doctor.

Next

Next, I will discuss sucking and swallowing problems, the signs and symptoms, and where to find help if you suspect your baby has a sucking problem.

33 Sucking and Swallowing Problems

WHY SOME BABIES EXPERIENCE SUCKING AND SWALLOWING PROBLEMS • HOW TO TELL THE DIFFERENCE BETWEEN A SUCKING PROBLEM AND A BEHAVIORAL FEEDING PROBLEM

If your baby often coughs, sputters, chokes, or aspirates while feeding, this will understandably cause you a great deal of concern. Is she physically incapable of sucking or swallowing safely? Or might something be preventing her from feeding safely? How can you be sure?

Various strategies and therapy options are recommended for sucking and swallowing problems. For some babies, the solution lies in a change of equipment or feeding position. Others might require thickened feeds, medications, surgical procedures, or tube feeding to ensure safe feeding.

Treatments could resolve the problem, make no difference, make the problem worse, or create new problems. Therefore, if you suspect sucking or swallowing problems, ensure your baby gets a **comprehensive feeding assessment** and is observed while feeding to decide on the most appropriate treatment.

What is dysphagia?

Dysphagia describes difficulty with feeding, eating, or swallowing. Other terms, such as an uncoordinated suck-swallow-breathe pattern or a weak, disorganized, or ineffective sucking pattern, might be used as these are more descriptive.

Dysphagia is a symptom, not a disease.

Some babies are at risk because they have a physical condition that negatively impacts their strength, stamina, or ability to suck or swallow. Babies at risk of dysphagia include those with

- head or neck malformations—for example, cleft palate or jaw abnormalities;
- congenital cardiac disease, chronic lung disease, and gastrointestinal disorders;
- complications associated with prematurity;
- neurological conditions or syndromes—for example, cerebral palsy, Down syndrome;
- birth trauma causing muscle weakness in the face and neck; and
- medications that may cause lethargy.

Approximately 1 percent of children without an underlying physical cause will experience swallowing difficulties.[219] Diagnosis requires an assessment from a number of health professionals from different fields—and therefore different areas of expertise—to

- examine the baby for physical abnormalities and order diagnostic tests;
- complete a thorough feeding assessment (described on pages 412-415);
- assess the baby's sucking and swallowing function; and
- investigate behavioral causes.

While a health professional could be an expert in one area, they won't necessarily be experienced in all areas.

Questions that aid assessment

Questions need to be asked of the parent by a health professional to determine

- if the baby has a physical problem that adversely impacts her sucking and swallowing abilities,
- if her ability to effectively and safely feed or her desire to suck and swallow might be negatively affected by an access problem, and
- if the parent is responding appropriately to the baby's behavioral cues.

The following are examples of questions I would ask.

1. **At what age did your baby first start to bottle-feed?** This question is helpful to determine if she is an experienced bottle-feeder. If she only started to be offered bottle-feeds after her sucking reflex had disappeared—around three months of age—she may not have learned how to suck from a bottle.
2. **When did the problematic behavior first become apparent?** Dysphagia because of a physical cause will be evident from the time your baby first starts to bottle-feed, whereas the appearance of sucking problems with behavioral causes tend to become more noticeable around or after eight weeks of age as a baby's sucking reflex starts to fade.
3. **Has the problem become worse or better over time?** Sucking and swallowing difficulties with physical causes generally go in one of two directions: They either remain the same or improve with maturity. Feeding problems from behavioral causes tend to get worse as a baby gets bigger, stronger, more aware, and better able to express frustration, anger, and stress.
4. **Are all feeds affected equally?** Physical problems will affect all feeds with only small variations. The behavior displayed because of a behavioral feeding problem noticeably varies depending on the baby's level of hunger, tiredness, and awareness.
5. **How well does baby feed in a relaxed, slightly drowsy state or when asleep?** Feeding better when drowsy or asleep provides an indication that the sucking issue is related to a baby's anxiety—her guard is down when feeding drowsy or while asleep. If your baby demonstrates coordinated sucking while feeding drowsy or asleep, she is physically capable of doing the same while awake. There are other reasons for the appearance of uncoordinated sucking while awake.
6. **How much sleep does she receive?** Sleep deprivation can severely impair a baby's sucking coordination and frustration tolerance. Lack of sleep is a common reason for poor feeding.
7. **How fast does she normally feed?** Feeding too quickly is a common reason for an uncoordinated suck-swallow-breathe pattern, and consequently, coughing and spluttering, especially in the case of newborns.

8. **Are you trying to feed your baby while she's crying?** A baby cannot coordinate sucking, swallowing and breathing while crying. While a hungry baby could cry, she will quickly stop crying and start to suck once the nipple is in her mouth.
9. **Have there been any recent changes made related to feeding?** These changes could be in equipment, medications, or milk type or taste. Did the behavior only start, or does it only occur when the baby is fed a particular baby formula?

These are just basic questions to help rule out physical causes for sucking and swallowing problems. If the baby has not been observed while feeding—ideally while being fed by the parent—there would be **many** more questions that need to be asked to identify access problems and the parent's responsiveness to their baby's behavioral cues.

Observational feed

Observing the baby while she's feeding is valuable because it allows the observer to check for access problems caused by inappropriate or faulty equipment and poor positioning of the baby or the bottle. It also enables the observer to check the baby's latch and seal around the nipple, her sucking and swallowing coordination, her level of alertness, her behavior, interest in feeding and the appropriateness of the parent's response to her behavioral cues.

A speech-language pathologist (SLP) might use a number of pediatric feeding and swallowing assessment tools to assess the baby's sucking and swallowing abilities and explore functional problems affected by nerve damage or poor muscle tone.

Visually, it can be difficult to tell the difference between a baby who is unable to suck and swallow effectively from a baby who is unwilling to eat. The appearance of an uncoordinated suck displayed by feeding-averse babies can be misdiagnosed during an observational feed because a feeding-averse baby will react in anticipation of being pressured, and this might not be recognized as being linked to the parent's feeding practices; or the parent will understandably be less likely to apply the same level of pressure while knowingly being observed compared to when feeding their baby in private.

Hence, a proper assessment will include knowing more about the baby's history, including her feeding history.

Diagnostic tests

Diagnostic tests can be used to check for physical problems that might adversely affect swallowing function and detect aspiration.

Some tests involve a scope with a camera inserted through the baby's mouth or nose and down her esophagus while she is under anesthesia to see if there are any physical abnormalities in her throat, larynx (vocal cords), or esophagus. Tissue samples may also be taken using the scope if anything unusual is identified.

Other tests may involve getting the baby to drink milk containing barium. This means the milk will be visible via X-ray videos. This allows observation of what's happening inside the baby's body as she swallows. It also enables the identification of aspiration.

I won't go into the details of these tests as this book is for healthy babies, and as such, your baby is unlikely to require diagnostic tests. If, by chance, she does, the details will be explained to you by her healthcare professionals.

Popular diagnoses for babies' sucking difficulties

I see many babies who have or appear to have sucking and swallowing issues that are attributed to the following problems:

- lip and tongue-tie;
- laryngomalacia;
- hypersensitive gag reflex;
- aerophagia (gulping air);
- oral aversion—as opposed to feeding aversion;
- sensory processing disorder.

Read on to find ways to identify if these problems are causing or contributing to your baby's feeding troubles.

Tongue-tie

A tongue-tie means the underside of a baby's tongue is tethered to the base of her mouth by a thin membrane of skin. This could prevent her from fully lifting her tongue or extending it over her bottom gum or moving it from side to side.

Feeding difficulties related to a tongue-tie will be present from the time your baby first starts to feed orally. And all feeds will be affected. If she fed well during a period of her life, or she feeds well now at certain times—for example, at night or while in a drowsy state or asleep—then tongue-tie is unlikely to be the reason for her troubled feeding behavior.

Tongue-tie was once a poorly recognized problem. In recent years, the number of babies being diagnosed with tongue-tie and undergoing a **frenectomy** (release of tethered oral tissue by cutting with sterile surgical scissors or laser) has skyrocketed. Tongue-tie has become a popular diagnosis to explain troubled feeding behavior exhibited by both breastfed and bottle-fed babies.

When a baby demonstrates feeding difficulties and also has a tongue-tie, don't assume that the two are connected. Many babies, children and adults have a tongue-tie, yet not all experience feeding difficulties—or speech problems. Many of the symptoms associated with tongue-tie also occur with other physical and behavioral causes already mentioned.

Most health professionals can identify if a baby has a tongue-tie provided they know what to look for. Ear, nose, and throat specialists (ENTs) and pediatric dentists are unquestionably experts in the anatomy of a baby's mouth and are unlikely to miss a tongue-tie. They can also assess any abnormal tongue shape and movement. However, they are not experts in infant feeding or trained to identify the many behavioral reasons for infant feeding problems, such as equipment problems, feeding position errors, and mismatched responses to a baby's behavioral cues. And neither are doctors. Therefore, they cannot confirm if a tongue-tie is responsible for a baby's troubled feeding behavior prior to completing a frenectomy—which then fixes the baby's feeding problem, or it doesn't.

A hasty assessment leading to a misdiagnosis of the cause of feeding difficulties and **an unnecessary frenectomy can make the situation worse**. A tongue-tie release will do nothing to improve a baby's sucking abilities if there is an access problem. Nor will it improve a feeding-averse baby's desire to feed. Any distress caused by a frenectomy or the stretching exercises that follow can cement her determination to avoid feeding.

If you are concerned about the possibility of a tongue-tie affecting your baby's ability to feed, first consider when feeding troubles started and whether all feeds are affected.

If she has always fed poorly and does so for all feeds, have her assessed by an SLP, who can complete an observational feed and decide whether it's impacting her sucking abilities.

Laryngomalacia

Laryngomalacia is best described as floppy tissue above the vocal cords (larynx) that falls into the airway. Babies with laryngomalacia have intermittent noisy breathing when inhaling, called **inspiratory stridor.** The telltale breathing sounds caused by laryngomalacia are often present at birth or occur within the first 10 days.

In 90 percent of cases of laryngomalacia, the problem will resolve without treatment by the time the child is 18 to 20 months old.[220] In most cases the problem is mild or moderate, which means the baby will have no significant airway obstruction. If mild, there are **no associated feeding difficulties** or other symptoms besides the inspirational stridor. If moderate, the baby may have some **associated feeding difficulties without it negatively impacting on growth**. Severe laryngomalacia is associated **with feeding difficulties, poor weight gain,** and breathing difficulties and may require surgical repair.

Diagnosis can be confirmed by **laryngoscopy,** where a small, flexible tube with a camera is inserted through the nose or mouth to examine the upper airway and vocal cords. It's performed by a pediatric ENT surgeon. Your baby's pediatrician won't necessarily refer your baby to an ENT for a laryngoscopy if mild or moderate laryngomalacia is suspected.

Babies experience feeding difficulties and poor growth for many reasons! A mistaken assumption about the source of a baby's feeding difficulties being from laryngomalacia can increase the risk of surgical intervention or, alternatively, create a sense of powerlessness. In reality, you can do many things about equipment or your feeding practices to resolve your baby's feeding troubles.

Aerophagia

People with aerophagia gulp in so much air that it produces uncomfortable gastrointestinal symptoms such as bloating, belching, flatulence, and abdominal pain. **Aerophagia is a rare disorder in children.**[221]

Aerophagia is a functional gastrointestinal disorder. It **should not** be confused with extreme swallowed air that can happen because of faulty feeding equipment, speed-feeding, or poor positioning.

A diagnosis of aerophagia is sometimes made **incorrectly** when a healthy baby often belches because of swallowing large amounts of air or when irritable babies burp frequently during a single feed, which is normal for some babies.

Hypersensitive gag reflex

Sensitive or hypersensitive gag reflex means the gagging is triggered more readily than would normally be expected for the baby's stage of development. (The location where a gag is triggered moves back in the baby's mouth as she matures, see page 67).

Other reasons for the **appearance** of a hypersensitive gag reflex include

- normal for stage of development;
- stress;
- unpleasant taste;
- head tilted too far back;
- nipple is too long—which can be the case for small for age babies or when parents use a faster nipple than recommended for age because they are thickening the baby's feeds;
- milk flow rate too fast; and
- gastroesophageal reflux (GER).

To differentiate a hypersensitive gag reflex and gagging or retching from other causes (see pages 381-382), you need a comprehensive history and feeding observation.

The distinction between a hypersensitive gag reflex and gagging or retching from other causes is important because physical and behavioral triggers that cause gagging are different, so the solution also differs.

Get the diagnosis wrong, and the treatment, therapy or management may also be wrong.

Oral aversion

When a baby has an **oral aversion**, she does not want **anything** to come near her mouth, including the nipple of the bottle. This can be caused by unpleasant or invasive medical procedures such as nasal or oral suctioning, feeding tube insertion, intubation, or stretching exercises after tongue-tie release.

Rest assured, once these events pass, any reluctance to feed **caused by these procedures** will also pass within days or weeks. That is, provided the baby is not pressured to feed, in which case she could develop a feeding aversion and continue to reject feeds.

A **feeding aversion** is specific to feeding. The most common cause is being pressured or forced to feed. But there can be other causes, such as pain while swallowing or choking. In the case of a feeding aversion, the baby is happy to have most other things—pacifier, toys, or security blanket—in her mouth but appears to reject the nipple of a bottle—or mother's breast or solids from a spoon in other types of feeding aversion. However, she might reluctantly and nervously accept feeds when ravenous and appear to willingly accept feeds in a drowsy state when her guard is down. (See chapter 27 for more on bottle-feeding aversion.)

Sensory processing disorder

Babies who are troubled by a sensory processing disorder perceive sensations differently than others and become upset by situations and things that don't trouble most other babies. They may find a particular smell, taste, or feel of certain foods or the feel of the nipple of a bottle and other objects in their mouth objectionable. Or they may be less aware of, or hypersensitive to, the sensation of hunger.

Babies **formally diagnosed** with sensory processing disorder—based on specific types of behavior that point to this problem—may benefit from treatment provided by an occupational therapist (OT) who has undergone specialized training specific to this problem. When a baby is believed to be troubled by the sensation of having the nipple of a bottle in his mouth, treatment may include putting an oro-navigator or oral motor probe tool—

both look a little like a rubbery toothbrush with ridges or bumps rather than bristles—into the baby's mouth to desensitize her to the feel of things in her mouth.

A sensory processing disorder is **one of the least common causes** of feeding refusal. It's not possible to accurately diagnose a sensory processing disorder based on a baby's avoidant feeding behavior **before** behavioral feeding aversion therapy—such as the process described in my book *Your Baby's Bottle-feeding Aversion*—has been implemented and **given sufficient time** to reverse negative emotions that the baby might have learned to connect with the act of feeding.

Get the diagnosis right!

Misdiagnoses of sucking and feeding problems can occur. How often this happens largely depends on the experience of the person assessing the situation—whether they are aware of physical and behavioral causes that affect a baby's ability **and willingness** to feed. It also depends on how thoroughly they assess the situation—whether they undertake a comprehensive feeding assessment or merely guess at what they believe could be the cause. A guess is associated with increased risk of misdiagnosis.

Recommendations **based on a misdiagnosis** will do one of three things.

1. **Fail to resolve the problem.** If you are not addressing the cause, the problem will continue. A baby could undergo months of weekly or fortnightly feeding therapy without any sign of improvement.
2. **Make the problem worse.** Placing anything—for example, the nipple of a bottle, the therapist's or parent's fingers, or rubbery implements used for feeding therapy—into a baby's mouth without her permission, especially if it upsets or stresses her, can create or intensify a behavioral feeding aversion.
3. **Create new problems.** Tube feeding, while resolving the problem of poor growth, does not fix a feeding problem. Instead, it can remove hunger and thus the motivation to feed orally. It's also associated with a risk of tube feeding dependence, delayed oral skill development necessary to breastfeed, bottle-feed or eat solid foods, and delayed speech development.

Steps to take if you suspect a sucking problem

- **Step 1.** Discuss your concerns with your baby's doctor. A head-to-toe physical examination is necessary. If nothing untoward is identified, ask for a referral to an SLP who specializes in treating children with feeding and swallowing disorders.
- **Step 2.** Whether a possible physical cause is identified or not, complete your own assessment of potential **behavioral causes.** While you may not be able to check your baby's mouth, and identify if her sucking and swallowing is normal, you know more about your baby than anyone else. Therefore, you are in the best position to identify behavioral feeding problems. Go to page 272 to complete my Infant Feeding Practice Self-Evaluation Checklist. You might discover the cause is behavioral or that a behavioral problem is complicating the situation. If this is the case, an effective or complete solution to your baby's feeding issues might lie in your hands.
- **Step 3.** If you have been unsuccessful in identifying or resolving the cause of your baby's sucking or swallowing problem, have your baby assessed by an SLP.

Where to find help

There are a number of health professionals who may be able to assist you with infant feeding problems—your baby's doctor, medical specialists, speech-language therapist, occupational therapist, feeding therapist, pediatric dietician and/or lactation consultant. Try your local health service providers first—you may need to consult with more than one. If you discover they are unable to provide you with an effective solution to your baby's feeding or sleeping problems, go to my website www.babycareadvice.com, where you will find health professionals and parenting experts hand-picked and trained by me to use my assessment methods and feeding recommendations.

Baby Care Advice consultants allocate **2 hours** for a comprehensive feeding assessment and video-chat discussion with parents to provide parenting advice and formulate a care plan—which includes **nonmedical** (behavioral) strategies to resolve well-baby care problems, promote your baby's contentment and your enjoyment and confidence in caring for your little one. Rest assured that all possible causes will be considered, and not even the smallest of detail related to feeding will be overlooked. Options are also available to receive daily email support and guidance until your baby's care problems are resolved.

Endnotes

[1] Shepard DN and Chandler-Laney PC. "Prospective associations of eating behaviors with weight gain in infants". *Obesity.* 2015;23:1881-1885.
[2] Dev DA, Speirs KE, Williams NA, et al. "Providers perspectives on self-regulation impact their use of responsive feeding practices in child care". *Appetite.* 2017;118:66-74.
[3] Hurley KM, Cross MB, and Hughes SO. "A systematic review of responsive feeding and child obesity in high-income countries". *The Journal of Nutrition.* 2011;141(3):495-501.
[4] Black MM and Aboud FE. "Responsive feeding is embedded in a theoretical framework of responsive parenting". *The Journal of Nutrition.* 2011;141(3):490-494.
[5] Lindsay AC, Sitthisongkram S, Creaney ML, et al, "Nonresponsive feeding practices, unhealthy eating behaviors, and risk of child overweight and obesity in Southeast Asia: A systematic review". *International Journal of Environmental Research and Public Health.* 2017;14(4):436.
[6] Black MM and Aoud FE. "Responsive feeding is embedded in a theoretical framework of responsive parenting". *The Journal of Nutrition.* 2011;141(3):490-494.
[7] Jagannath A, Taylor L, Wakaf Z, et al. "The genetics of circadian rhythms, sleep and health". *Human Molecular Genetics.* 2017;26(2):128-138. Laposky AD, Bass J, Kohsaka A, et al. "Sleep and circadian rhythms: key components in the regulation of energy metabolism". *FEBS Lett.* 2008;582(1):142-151. Serin Y and Acar Tek N. "Effect of circadian rhythms on metabolic processes and the regulation of energy balance". *Annals of Nutrition and Metabolism.* 2019;74(4):322-330. Voigt RM, Forsyth CB and Keshavarzian A. "Circadian rhythms: a regulator of gastrointestinal health and dysfunction". *Expert Review of Gastroenterology and Hepatology.* 2019;13(5):411-424.
[8] Kim TW, Jeong JH and Hong SC. "The impact of sleep and circadian disturbance on hormones and metabolism". *International Journal of Endocrinology.* 2015. https://www.ncbi.nlm.nih.gov/pmc/articles/PMC4377487/. Assessed 1 June 2022.
[9] Kennaway DJ, Stamp GE and Goble FC. "Development of melatonin production in infants and the impact of prematurity". *Journal of Clinical Endocrinology and Metabolism.* 1992;75(2):367-369. Bolt RJ, van Weissenbruch MM, Lafeber HN et al. "Development of the hypothalamic-pituitary-adrenal axis in the fetus and preterm infant". *Journal of Pediatric Endocrinology and Metabolism.* 2002;15:759-769.
[10] Larson MC, White BP, Cochran A, et al. "Dampening of the cortisol response to handling at 3 months in human infants and its relation to sleep, circadian cortisol activity, and behavioral distress". *Developmental Psychobiology.* 1998;33(4);327-337.
[11] Sheldon SH, "Development of sleep in infants and children". In Sheldon SH, Ferber R, Kryger MH and Gozal D, editors. *"Principles and practice of pediatric sleep medicine*". 2nd ed. 2024. (pp 17–23).

Elsevier Saunders.
[12] Fox MK, Devaney B, Reidy K, et al. "Relationship between portion size and energy intake among infants and toddlers: evidence of self-regulation". *Journal of American Dietetic Association.* 2006;106(1):77-83.
[13] Theander-Carrillo C, Wiedmer P, Ceftour-Rose P, et al. "Ghrelin action in the brain controls adipocyte metabolism". *The Journal of Clinical Investigation.* 2006;116(7):1983-1993.
[14] Abdalla MMI. "Ghrelin—Physiological functions and regulation". *European Endocrinology.* 2015;11(2):90-95.
[15] Cummings DE, Purnell JQ, Frayo R, et al. "A preprandial rise in plasma ghrelin levels suggests a role in meal initiation in humans". *Diabetes.* 2001;50(8):1714-1719.
[16] Abdemur A, Slone J, Berho M, et al. "Morphology, localization, and patterns of ghrelin-producing cells in stomachs of a morbidly obese population". *Surgical Laparoscopy Endoscopy & Percutaneous Techniques.* 2014;24(2):122-126.
[17] Friedman JM and Halaas JL. 'Leptin and the regulation of body weight in mammals.' *Nature.* 1998;395(6704):763-70.
[18] Considine RV, Sinha MK, Heiman ML, et al. 'Serum immunoreactive-leptin concentrations in normal-weight and obese humans.' *New England Journal of Medicine.* 1996;334(5):292-295.
[19] Little TJ, Horowitz M and Feinle-Bisset C. 'Role of cholecystokinin in appetite control and body weight regulation.' *Obesity Reviews.* 2005;6(4):297-306.
[20] Wang Y, Chandra R, Samsa LA, et al. 'Amino acids stimulate cholecystokinin release through the Ca2+-sensing receptor.' *American Journal of Physiology - Gastrointestinal and Liver Physiology.* 2011;300(4):528-537.
[21] Liddle RA, Goldfine ID, Rosen MS, et al. 'Cholecystokinin bioactivity in human plasma: Molecular forms, responses to feeding, and relationship to gallbladder contraction.' *The Journal of Clinical Investigation.* 1985; 75(4):1144-52.
[22] Wells AS, Read NW, Fried M, et al. 'Effects of a specific CCK-A antagonist, Loxiglumide, on postprandial mood and sleepiness.' *Journal of Psychopharmacology.* 1997;11(3):241-246.
[23] Johnson SL and Birch LL. 'Parents' and children's adiposity and eating style.' *Pediatrics.* 1994;94(5):653-661. Fisher JO and Birch LL. 'Restricting access to foods and children's eating.' *Appetite.* 1999;32(3):405-419.
[24] Lampl M, Veldhuis JD and Johnson ML. "Saltation and stasis: a model of human growth". *Science.* 1992;258:801-803.
[25] Scheer FA, Morris CJ and Shea SA. "The internal circadian clock increases hunger and appetite in the evening independent of food intake and other behaviors". *Obesity (Silver Spring).* 2013;21(3):421-423.
[26] "Infant Feeding Guidelines; information for health workers". *National Health and Medical Research Council.* 2012. Pg 79. https://www.nhmrc.gov.au/about-us/publications/infant-feeding-guidelines-information-health-workers. Accessed 1June 2022.
[27] Consolini DM. "Nutrition in infants". *Merck Manual.* 2021 https://www.merckmanuals.com/professional/pediatrics/care-of-newborns-and-infants/nutrition-in-infants#v1076566. Accessed 1 June 2022.
[28] "Formula milk: common questions". *National Health Service (NHS), UK.* https://www.nhs.uk/conditions/baby/breastfeeding-and-bottle-feeding/bottle-feeding/formula-milk-questions/. Accessed 1June 2022.

[29] "Factsheet on weaning your baby". *British Nutrition Foundation.* 2016. Pg 3. https://www.nhs.uk/ipgmedia/National/British%20Nutrition%20Foundation/assets/Weaningyourbaby.pdf. Accessed 1 June 2022.
[30] Weaver LT and Steiner H. "The bowel habit of young children". *Archives of Disease in Childhood.* 1984;59(7);649-52.
[31] Banner B and Levinger L. "Love and Discipline". (1983) Pg 32. *Ballantine Books.*
[32] "The Zuckerman Parker Handbook of Developmental and Behavioral Pediatrics for Primary Care". (2010). Pg 18. *United Kingdom: Wolters Kluwer/Lippincott Williams & Wilkins Health.*
[33] Saudino KJ. "Behavioral Genetics and Child Temperament". *Journal of Developmental and Behavioral Pediatrics.* 2005;26(3):214-223.
[34] Brazelton TB. "The Brazelton Neonatal Behavior Assessment Scale: introduction". *Monographs of the Society for Research in Child Development.* 1978;43(5-6):1-13.
[35] Woodhouse SS, Scott JR, Hepworth AD, et al. "Secure Base Provision: A new approach to examining links between maternal caregiving and infant attachment". *Child Development.* 2020;91(1):249-265.
[36] "Can less-than-perfect parent be enough?" *Circle of Security; International.* April 2017. https://www.circleofsecurityinternational.com/2017/04/03/can-less-than-perfect-really-be-enough/ Accessed 1 June 2022.
[37] Ackerman S. "Discovering the brain". *National Academies Press (US) Washington D.,* 1992. Pg 86.
[38] van de Rijt-Plooij H and Plooij F, 'The Wonder Weeks: How to stimulate your baby's mental development and help him turn his 10 predictable, great, gussy phases into magical leaps forward". (5th Ed) By Frabs X Plooij and Hetty van de Rijt. Kiddy World Publishing. BV, The Netherlands 2017.
[39] As above.
[40] OECD. "Understanding the Brain: The birth of a learning science". *OECD Publishing, 2007.* Pg 165.
[41] Plotnik R and Kouyomdijan H. "Discovery Series: Introduction to Psychology". *Belmont, CA: Wadsworth Cengage Learning.* 2012. p 208.
[42] Deacon C. "Boost Your Baby's Development: Teach Yourself". *United Kingdom, John Murray Press,* 2010.
[43] Erikson EH. "Childhood and society". *United States: WW Norton,* 1993.
[44] Waters E, Wall SN, Blehar MC and Ainsworth MDS. "Patterns of Attachment: A psychological study of the strange situation". *United States: Taylor & Francis,* 2015.
[45] Livingstone V. "Too much of a good thing. Maternal and baby hyperlactation syndromes". *Canadian Family Physician.* 1996;42:89-99.
[46] Nommsen LA, Lovelady CA, Heinig MJ, et al. "Determinants of energy, protein, lipid, and lactose concentrations in human milk during the first 12 months of lactation: the DARLING Study".
American Journal of Clinical Nutrition. 1991;53(2):457-465.
[47] Kent JC, Mitoulas LR, Cregan MD, et al. "Volume and frequency of breastfeedings and fat content of breast milk throughout the day". *Pediatrics.* 2006;117(3):387-395.
[48] "Food Allergies and Breastfeeding". *Le Leche League International.* https://www.llli.org/breastfeeding-info/allergies/. Accessed 1 June 2022.
[49] Host A and Halken S. "Cow's milk allergy: Where have we come from and where are we going?" *Endocrine, Metabolic Immune Disorders – Drug Target.* 2014;14(1):2-8.

[50] "Food allergies and breastfeeding". *Le Leche League International.* https://www.llli.org/breastfeeding-info/allergies/. Accessed 1 June 2022.

[51] Office on Women's Health U.S. Department of Health and Human Services. "The healthy woman: A complete guide for all ages". *Government Printing Office.* 2014. Pg 200.

[52] "Foods - for nursing parents". *Le Leche League International.* https://www.llli.org/breastfeeding-info/foods/. Accessed 1 June 2022.

[53] "Baby formula: evaluating the safety of new ingredients". *Institute of Medicines, Washington, DC, National Academies Press.* 2004. Pg 43.

[54] "Choosing an infant formula". *American Academy of Pediatrics. Healthychildren.org.* https://www.healthychildren.org/English/ages-stages/baby/formula-feeding/Pages/Choosing-an-Infant-Formula.aspx. Accessed 1 June 2022., "Infant Feeding Guidelines: information for health workers". *National Health and Medical Research Council (NHMRC) Australia,* 2012, https://www.nhmrc.gov.au/about-us/publications/infant-feeding-guidelines-information-health-workers. Accessed 1 June 2022. "Food and Nutritional Guidelines for Healthy Babies and Toddlers (0–2 years)". *New Zealand Ministry of Health.* http://www.moh.govt.nz/foodandnutrition Accessed 1 June 2022.

[55] Jung TH, Hwang HJ, Yun SS, et al. "Hypoallergenic and physicochemical properties of A2 β-casein fraction of goat milk". *Korean Journal for Food Science of Animal Resources.* 2017;37(6):940–947.

[56] De Noni I, FitzGerald RJ and Korhonen HJT. "Review of the potential impact of β-casomorphins and related peptides". *Scientific Report of EFSA.* https://www.healthline.com/nutrition/a1-vs-a2-milk#a1-concerns Accessed 1 June 2022.

[57] Restani P. "Goat milk allergenicity". *Journal of Pediatric Gastroenterology and Nutrition.* 2004;39(4):323-324.

[58] "Cow's milk (dairy) allergy". *Australasian Society of Clinical Immunology and Allergy (ASCIA)* https://www.allergy.org.au/patients/food-allergy/cows-milk-dairy-allergy. Accessed 1June 2022.

[59] Merritt RJ and Jenks BH. "Safety of soy-based baby formulas containing isoflavones: The clinical evidence". *Journal of Nutrition.* 2004;134:1220-1224.

[60] "Infant Feeding Guidelines: information for health workers". *National Health and Medical Research Council (NHMRC) Australia,* 2012, https://www.nhmrc.gov.au/about-us/publications/infant-feeding-guidelines-information-health-workers. Accessed 1 June 2022. "Food and Nutritional Guidelines for Healthy Babies and Toddlers (0–2 years)". *New Zealand Ministry of Health.* http://www.moh.govt.nz/foodandnutrition Accessed 1 June 2022.

[61] "Phytoestrogens and health". *Committee on Toxicity of Chemicals in Food, Consumer Products and the Environment (2003).* https://cot.food.gov.uk/sites/default/files/cot/phytoreport0503.pdf Accessed 1 June 2022.

[62] Y Vandenplas, J Ziffer Lifshitz, S Orenstein, et al. "Nutritional management of regurgitation in babies". *Journal of the American College of Nutrition.* 1998;17(4),308-316.

[63] Guarino A, Ashkenazi S, Gendrel D, et al. "European Society for Paediatric Gastroenterology, Hepatology, and Nutrition/European Society for Paediatric Infectious Diseases evidence-based guidelines for the management of acute gastroenteritis in children in Europe". *Journal of Pediatric Gastroenterology and Nutrition.* 2008;46:81-184.

[64] Coelho AI, Berry GT and Rubio-Gozalbo ME. "Galactose Metabolism and Health". *Current Opinion.* https://www.researchgate.net/publication/283726200_Galactose_metabolism_and_health. Accessed 1 June 2022; Fynn A. "Nutrition and Health: Galactosemia". *Reference Model in Food Science.* 2016. https://www.sciencedirect.com/science/article/pii/B9780081005965009707 Accessed 1 June 2022.
[65] Wu SL, Ding D, Fang AP, et al. "Growth, gastrointestinal tolerance and stool characteristics of healthy term infants fed an infant formula containing hydrolyzed whey protein (63%) and intact casein (37%): A randomized clinical trial". *Nutrients.* 2017;9(11):1254.
[66] Puntis JW. "Gastro-oesophageal reflux in young babies: who should be treated?". *Archives of Disease in Children.* 2015;100:989-993.
[67] Aggett P, Agostoni C, Goulet O, et al. "Antireflux or antiregurgitation milk products for babies and young children: a commentary by the ESPGHAN Committee on Nutrition". *Journal of Pediatric Gastroenterology and Nutrition.* 2002;34:96-498.
[68] As above
[69] Bongers M, de Lorijin F, Reitsma JB, et al. "The clinical effect of a new infant formula in term infants with constipation: a double-blind, randomized cross-over trial". *Nutritional Journal.* 2007;6:8.
[70] Taitz LS and Scholey E. "Are babies more satisfied by casein based formulas?" *Archive of Disease in Children.* 1989;64(4):619-621.
[71] "Types of formula milk". *National Health Scheme (NHS).* https://www.nhs.uk/conditions/pregnancy-and-baby/types-of-infant-formula/. Accessed 1June 2022.
[72] Burnham MM, Goodlin-Jones BL, Gaylor EE, et al. "Nighttime sleep-wake patterns and self-soothing from birth to one year of age: a longitudinal intervention study". *Journal of Child Psychology Psychiatry.* 2002;43(6):713.
[73] "A guide to infant formula for parents who bottle-feed. A health professional's guide". *Unicef. United Kingdom.* https://www.unicef.org.uk/babyfriendly/wp-content/uploads/sites/2/2016/12/Health-professionals-guide-to-infant-formula.pdf. Accessed 1 June 2022. "Types of formula milk". *National Health Scheme (NHS).* https://www.nhs.uk/conditions/pregnancy-and-baby/types-of-infant-formula/ Accessed 1 June 2022.
[74] "Infant Feeding Guidelines: information for health workers". *National Health and Medical Research Council (NHMRC) Australia,* 2012, https://www.nhmrc.gov.au/about-us/publications/infant-feeding-guidelines-information-health-workers. Accessed 1 June 2022.
[75] New York University. "Toddler formulas and milks—not recommended by health experts—mislead with health claims". *Science Daily.* https://www.sciencedaily.com/releases/2018/02/180205113039.htm. Accessed 1 June 2022.
[76] "The Baby Friendly Initiative". *Unicef United Kingdom.* https://www.unicef.org.uk/babyfriendly/?item=47 Accessed 1 June 2022.
[77] Jasani B, Simmer K, Patole SK, et al. "Long chain polyunsaturated fatty acid supplementation in infants born at term". *Cochrane Systematic Review.* Version published: 10 March 2017 https://www.cochranelibrary.com/cdsr/doi/10.1002/14651858.CD000376.pub4/full. Accessed 1 June 2022. Pluymen LPM, Dalmeijer GW, Smit HA, et al. "Long-chain polyunsaturated fatty acids in infant formula and cardiovascular markers in childhood". *Maternal & Child Nutrition.* 2018 Apr;14(2):e12523. doi: 10.1111/mcn.12523. Accessed 1 June 2022.

[78] Wang L, Liu J, Lv H, et al. "Effects of nucleotides supplementation of infant formulas on plasma and erythrocyte fatty acid composition: a meta-analysis". *PLoS One*. June 23, 2015 https://doi.org/10.1371/journal.pone.0127758. Accessed 1 June 2022.

[79] European Food Safety Authority (EFSA). "Safety, bioavailability and suitability of lutein for the particular nutritional use of infants and young children". *The EFSA Journal*. 2008;823:1-24.

[80] Chassard C, de Wouters T and Lacroix C. "Probiotics tailored to the infant: a window of opportunity". *Current Opinion Biotechnology*. 2014;26:141-147.

[81] "Probiotics may ease constipation". *Harvard Health Publishing*. https://www.health.harvard.edu/blog/probiotics-may-ease-constipation-201408217377 Accessed 1 June 2022. Infante D, Segarra O, Redecillas S, et al. "Modification of stool's water content in constipated infants: management with an adapted infant formula". *Nutrition Journal*. 2011;10:55.

[82] Vandenplas Y, De Greef E and Veereman G. "Prebiotics in infant formula". *Gut Microbes*. 2014;5(6):681-687. Ashley C, Johnston WH, Harris CL, et al. "Growth and tolerance of infants fed formula supplemented with polydextrose (PDX) and/or galactooligosaccharides (GOS): double-blind, randomized, controlled trial". *Nutrition Journal*. 2012;11:38.

[83] "ASCIA Guidelines - Infant feeding and allergy prevention". *Australian Society of Clinical Immunology and Allergy*. https://www.allergy.org.au/hp/papers/infant-feeding-and-allergy-prevention. Accessed 1 June 2022

[84] As above.

[85] American Academy of Pediatrics. "Lactose intolerance in babies, children, and adolescents". *Pediatrics*. 2006;118(3):1279-1286.

[86] Sampson HA, James JM, and Bernhisel-Broadbent J. "Safety of an amino acid–derived baby formula in children allergic to cow milk". *Pediatrics*. 1992;90:463-465.

[87] DJ Barker. "The fetal and baby origins of adult disease". *British Medical Journal*. 1990. doi: https://doi.org/10.1136/bmj.301.6761.1111 Accessed 1 June 2022.

[88] Elenberg Y and Shaoul R, "The role of infant nutrition in the prevention of future disease". *Frontiers in Pediatrics*. 2014;2:73.

[89] C Agostoni, T Decsi, M Fewtrell, et al. "Complementary feeding: a commentary by the ESPGHAN Committee on Nutrition". *Journal of Pediatric Gastroenterology and Nutrition*. 2008;46(1):99-110.

[90] "ASCIA Guidelines – Infant feeding and allergy prevention". *Australian Society of Clinical Immunology and Allergy*. https://www.allergy.org.au/hp/papers/infant-feeding-and-allergy-prevention. Accessed 1 June 2022.

[91] Barton A. "Homemade infant formulas dangerous, doctors warn". *The Globe and Mail*. Published Nov 26 2014. Updated May 12, 2018. https://www.theglobeandmail.com/life/health-and-fitness/health/homemade-infant-formulas-dangerous-doctors-warn/article21805683/. Accessed 1 June 2022.

[92] "Choosing an infant formula". *Center of Disease Control and Prevention (CDC)*. https://www.cdc.gov/nutrition/infantandtoddlernutrition/formula-feeding/choosing-an-infant-formula.html. Accessed 1 June 2022.

[93] "Calories in 100ml of infant formula". *Fatsecret*. https://www.fatsecret.com/calories-nutrition/generic/infant-formula?portionid=1136551&portionamount=100.000 Accessed 1 June 2022.

[94] Brizee LS. "Increasing energy density of infant formula". *Growing and Gaining: Assuring Nutritional Care of Preterm Babies. Children's Hospital and Regional*

Medical Center, Seattle, Washington. http://depts.washington.edu/growing/Nourish/Concform.htm. Accessed 1 June 2022.

[95] Kwok TC, Ojha S and Dorling J. "Feed thickeners in gastro-oesophageal reflux in infants". *British Medical journal Paediatrics Open.* 2018;2:e000262. doi: 10.1136/bmjpo-2018-000262 Accessed 1 June 2022.

[96] Holdy KE. "Fluid and electrolyte balance: A must with nutrition support". *The Oley Foundation.* https://oley.org/page/FluidElec_Balance. Accessed 1 June 2022. Taitz LS and Byers HD. "High calorie/osmolar feeding and hypertonic dehydration". *Archive of Diseases of Childhood.* 1972;47(252):257-260.

[97] Kwok TC, Ojha S, and Dorling J. "Feed thickener for infants up to six months of age with gastro-oesophageal reflux". *Cochrane Database Systems Review.* 2017;12:CD003211. doi: 10.1002/14651858.CD003211.pub2. Accessed 1 June 2022.

[98] Hall KD. "Pediatric Dysphagia: Resource Guide". *Albany, NY: Singular Publishing Group,* 2001. 119-150.

[99] Alper B and Manno C. "Dysphagia in infants and children with oral-motor deficits: assessment and management". *Seminars in Speech and Language.* 1996;17:283-310.

[100] LaBarre Millet M. "Thickener is not the answer in the NICU". *Ashawire,* https://leader.pubs.asha.org/doi/full/10.1044/leader.FMP.24062019.8 Accessed 1 June 2022.

[101] Carroll A, Garrison M and Christakis D. "A systematic review of non-pharmacological and non-surgical therapies for gastroesophageal reflux in babies". *Archives of Pediatrics and Adolescent Medicine.* 2002;156:109-113.

[102] Aggett P, Agostoni C, Goulet O, et al. "Antireflux or antiregurgitation milk products for babies and young children: a commentary by the ESPGHAN Committee on Nutrition". *Journal of Pediatric Gastroenterology and Nutrition.* 2002;34:496-498.

[103] Meunier L, Garthoff JA, Schaafsma A, et al. "Locust bean gum safety in neonates and young infants: An integrated review of the toxicological database and clinical evidence". *Regulatory Toxicology and Pharmacology.* 2014;70(1):155-169.

[104] Kwok TC, Ojha S and Dorling J. "Feed thickeners in gastro-oesophageal reflux in infants". *British Medical journal Paediatrics Open.* 2018;2:e000262. doi: 10.1136/bmjpo-2018-000262 Accessed 1 June 2022.

[105] Moukarzel AA, Abdelnour H and Akatcherian C. "Effects of a prethickened formula on esophageal pH and gastric emptying of babies with GER". *Journal of Clinical Gastroenterology.* 2007;41(9):823-829.

[106] Vandenplas Y, Lifshitz JZ, Orenstein S, et al. "Nutritional management of regurgitation in infants". *Journal of the American College of Nutrition.* 1998;17:308-316.

[107] As above

[108] Naimi S, Viennois E, Gewirtz AT and Chassaing B. "Direct impact of commonly used dietary emulsifiers on human gut microbiota". *Microbiome.* 2021;9:66. "Gums, thickeners, and emulsifiers in food: What you need to know". *Elmhurst.* https://elmhurst1925.com/blogs/news/gums-thickeners-and-emulsifiers-in-food-are-they-really-bad#references. Accessed 1June 2022.

[109] Theophilou IC, Neophytou CM, Kakas A, et al. "Carob and its components in the management of gastrointestinal disorders". *Journal of Hepatology & Gastroenterology Research Article* Open Access 2017 http://www.scientificoajournals.org/pdf/jhge.1005.pdf Accessed 1June 2022.

[110] Owens CJW, Labuschagne IL and Lombard MJ. "Infant formula for gastro-oesophageal reflux disease". *South African Family Practice.* 2012;54(2):106-110. Xinias I, Spiroglou K, Demertzidou V, et al. "An antiregurgitation milk formula in

the management of infants with mild to moderate gastroesophageal feflux". *Current Therapeutic Research, Clinical and Experimental.*
2003;64(4):270-278.

[111] "FAQs" *Gavison website.* https://www.gaviscon.ca/faqs#can-i-take-my-other-medications-while-using-gaviscon Accessed 1 June 2022.

[112] Owens CJW, Labuschagne IL and Lombard MJ. "Infant formula for gastro-oesophageal reflux disease". *South African Family Practice.* 2012;54(2):106-110.

[113] Zimlich R. "Impact of milk cereal drink on future obesity risk". *Contemporary Pediatrics.* 2019;36(3):41-42.

[114] Almquist-tangen G, Bergman S, Dahlgren J, et al. "Consuming milk cereal drinks at one year of age was associated with a twofold risk of being overweight at the age of five". *Acta Paediatricia,* First published:03 December 2018 https://onlinelibrary.wiley.com/doi/full/10.1111/apa.14666 Accessed 1 June 2022.

[115] American Academy of Pediatrics. "Cereal in bottles: solid food shortcuts to avoid". *Healthychildren.org.* https://www.healthychildren.org/English/ages-stages/baby/feeding-nutrition/Pages/Cereal-in-a-Bottle-Solid-Food-Shortcuts-to-Avoid.aspx. Accessed 1 June 2022.

[116] Owens CJW, Labuschagne IL and Lombard MJ. "Infant formula for gastro-oesophageal reflux disease". *South African Family Practice.* 2012;54(2):106-110.
Xinias I, Spiroglou K, Demertzidou V, et al. "An antiregurgitation milk formula in the management of infants with mild to moderate gastroesophageal reflux', *Current Therapeutic Research, Clinical and Experimental.*
2003;64(4):270-278.

[117] As above

[118] Boyles S. "Cereal may trigger Type 1 Diabetes". *WebMD* https://www.webmd.com/diabetes/news/20030930/cereal-may-trigger-type-1-diabetes#1. Accessed 1 June 2022.

[119] . "Constipation: Infant". *Nationwide Children's Hospital, USA.* https://www.nationwidechildrens.org/conditions/constipation-infant. Accessed 1 June 2022.

[120] García-Lara NR, Escuder-Vieco D, Garcia-Algar O, et al. "Effect of freezing time on macronutrients and energy content of breastmilk". *Breastfeeding Medicine.* 2012;7(4):295-301.

[121] "Temperature danger zone". *Food Safety Information Council.* https://foodsafety.asn.au/topic/temperature-danger-zone/. Accessed 1 June 2022.

[122] World Health Organization & Food and Agriculture Organization of the United Nations. 'Safe preparation, storage and handling of powdered infant formula: guidelines.' *World Health.* 2007. Pg 4. Retrieved from https://apps.who.int/iris/handle/10665/43659 (Accessed 1st June 2022.)

[123] Forsythe SJ. 'Enterobacter sakazakii and other bacteria in powdered infant milk formula.' *Maternal and Child Nutrition.* 2004;1:44-50.

[124] "Food and nutrition guidelines for healthy infants and toddlers (aged 0–2); A background paper". *Wellington: Ministry of Health, New Zealand,* 2008, p 39.

[125] World Health Organization & Food and Agriculture Organization of the United Nations. "Safe preparation, storage and handling of powdered infant formula: guidelines". *World Health Organization.* 2007. Pg 4. https://apps.who.int/iris/handle/10665/43659. Accessed 1 June 2022.

[126] "Fluoridation FAQs". *American Dental Association.* https://www.ada.org/resources/community-initiatives/fluoride-in-water/fluoridation-faqs. Accessed 1 June 2022.

[127] Li D, Shi Y, Yang L, et al. "Microplastic release from the degradation of polypropylene feeding bottles during infant formula preparation". *Nature Food.* 2020;1:746-754.
[128] As above.
[129] "Minimising microplastics release when preparing infant formula". *Hospital Healthcare.* https://www.hospitalhealth.com.au/content/clinical-services/article/minimising-microplastics-release-when-preparing-infant-formula-989613336. Accessed 1st June 2022.
[130] American Academy of Pediatrics. "Breastfeeding and the use of human milk". *Pediatrics.* 2010;129(3),827-841.
[131] Alghadir AH, Zafar H, Al-Sisa ES, et al. "Effect of posture on swallowing". *African Health Science.* 2017;17(1):133-137.
[132] Avital A, Donchin M, Springer C, et al. "Feeding young infants with their head in upright position reduces respiratory and ear morbidity". *Science Reports.* 2018;8(1):6588.
[133] "Ear infection—acute". *National Institutes of Health/National Library of Medicine.* 2014. https://medlineplus.gov/ency/article/000638.htm. Accessed 1June 2022.
[134] "The dangers of prop feeding". The Sydney Children's Hospitals Networks. https://www.schn.health.nsw.gov.au/news/articles/2019/01/the-dangers-of-prop-feeding. Accessed 1 June 2022.
[135] Avital A, Donchin M, Springer C, et al. "Feeding young infants with their head in upright position reduces respiratory and ear morbidity". *Science Reports.* 2018;8(1):6588.
[136] Britannica, The Editors of Encyclopaedia. "Intestinal gas". *Encyclopedia Britannica,* 12 Mar. 2014, https://www.britannica.com/science/intestinal-gas. Accessed 1 June 2022.
[137] Gellner C. "Do babies need burping after feeding?" *Health. University of Utah.* Jun 7, 2021, https://healthcare.utah.edu/the-scope/shows.php?shows=0_j8jqtr2m, Accessed 1 June 2022.
[138] As above
[139] Bryant-Waugh R, Markham L, Kreipe RE, et al. "Feeding and eating disorders in childhood". *International Journal of Eating Disorders.* 2010;43(2):98-111.
[140] Yang HR. "How to approach feeding difficulties in young children". *Korean Journal of Pediatrics.* 2017; 60(12):379-384.
[141] Bernard-Bonnin AC. "Feeding problems of infants and toddlers". *Canadian Family Physician.* 2006;52(10):1247-1251.
[142] Kim HY, Han Y, Pyun Y, et al. "Prolonged bedtime bottle feeding and respiratory symptoms in infants". *Asia Pacific Allergy.* 2011;1(1):30–35.
[143] Potter GDM, Skene DJ, Arendt J, et al. "Circadian rhythm and sleep disruption: causes, metabolic consequences, and countermeasures". *Endocrine Review.* 2016;37(6):584-608.
[144] Ong KK and Loos RJ. "Rapid infancy weight gain and subsequent obesity: systematic reviews and hopeful suggestions". *Acta Paediatricia.* 2006;95:904-908.
[145] Martin CR, Ling PR, and Blackburn GL. "Review of infant feeding: Key features of breast milk and infant formula". *Nutrients.* 2016;8(5):279
[146] Berg JM, Tymoczko JL and Stryer L. "Glycogen metabolism". 2002. Chapter 21. *Biochemistry.* 5th edition. New York: W H Freeman.

[147] Kim HY, Han Y, Pyun Y, et al. "Prolonged bedtime bottle feeding and respiratory symptoms in infants". *Asia Pacific Allergy.* 2011;1(1):30-35.
[148] American Academy of Pediatric Dentistry. "Policy on early childhood caries (ECC); classifications, consequences and preventive strategies." *Reference Manual.* 2016;38(6):16-17.
[149] American Academy of Pediatrics. "Discontinuing the bottle". Healthychildren.org. https://www.healthychildren.org/English/ages-stages/baby/feeding-nutrition/Pages/Discontinuing-the-Bottle.aspx. Accessed 1 June 2022.
[150] "The ultimate guide to transitioning from a bottle to a cup". *Speech Sisters.* April 8, 2020. https://speechsisters.com/bottle-to-cup/. Accessed 1 June 2022.
[151] Brotanek J, Halterman JS, Auinger P, et al. "Iron deficiency, prolonged bottle-feeding, and racial/ethnic disparities in young children". *Jama Pediatrics.* 2005:159(11):1004-1085.
[152] Li R, Magadia J, Fein SB, et al. "Risk of bottle-feeding for rapid weight gain during the first year of life".
Archive of Pediatric and Adolescent Medicine. 2012;166(5):431-436.
[153] American Dental Association. "Baby bottle tooth decay". *Mouth Healthy.* https://www.mouthhealthy.org/en/az-topics/b/baby-bottle-tooth-decay. Accessed 1 June 2022.
[154] Kong A. "Dental facts: Baby bottle rot". *A+ Dental clinic.* May 2018. https://aplusdental.net.au/dental-facts-baby-bottle-rot/. Accessed 1 June 2022.
[155] Meyers A and Hertzberg J. "Bottle feeding and malocclusions. Is there any association?" *American Journal of Orthodontics and Dentofacial Orthopedics.* 1988;93:149-152.
[156] Savolt J. "Sippy cup syndrome: Are sippy cups ruining your child's smile?" *Reflective Smiles website.* https://www.reflectivesmiles.com/sippy-cups. Accessed 1 June 2022.
[157] Keim SA, Fletcher EN, TePoel MR, et al. "Injuries associated with bottles, pacifiers, and sippy cups in the United States, 1991-2010". *Pediatrics.* 2012;129(6):1104-1110.
[158] Smith JL. "The role of gastric acid in preventing foodborne disease and how bacteria overcome acid conditions". *Journal of Food Protection.* 2003;66(7):1292-1303.
[159] Gupta RW, Tran L, Norori J, et al. "Histamine-2 receptor blockers alter the fecal microbiota in premature infants". *Journal of Pediatric Gastroenterology and Nutrition.* 2013;56:397-400. Levy EI, Hoang DM and Vandenplas Y. "The effects of proton pump inhibitors on the microbiome in young children". *Acta Paediatricia.* 2020;109:1531-1538.
[160] Eom CS, Jeon CY, Lim JW, et al. "Use of acid-suppressive drugs and risk of pneumonia: a systematic review and meta-analysis". *Canadian Medical Association Journal.* 2011;183(3):310-319.
[161] Yang YX. "Chronic PPI therapy and calcium metabolism". *Current Gastroenterology Reports.* 2012;14(6):473-479.
[162] Parkman HP, Urbain J-L C, Knight LC, et al. "Effect of gastric acid suppressants on human gastric motility". *Gut.* 1998;42(2):243-250.
[163] Sanaka M, Yamamoto T and Kuyama Y. "Effects of proton pump inhibitors on gastric emptying: a systematic review". *Digestive Diseases and Sciences.* 2010;55(9):2431-2440.

[164] Acosta A and Camilleri. "Prokinetics in gastroparesis". *Gastroenterology Clinics of North America.* 2015 Mar;44(1):97-111.
[165] Martin AJ, Pratt N, Kennedy JD, et al. "Natural history and familial relationships of infant spilling to 9 years of age". *Pediatrics.* 2002;109(6):1061-1067.
[166] Nelson SP, Chen EH, Syniar GM, et al. "Pediatric Practice Research Group. Prevalence of symptoms of gastroesophageal reflux during infancy. A pediatric practice-based survey". *Archive of Pediatric Adolescent Medicine.* 1997;151(6):569-572.
[167] Martin AJ, Pratt N, Kennedy JD, et al. "Natural history and familial relationships of infant spilling to 9 years of age". *Pediatrics.* 2002;109(6):1061-1067. Nelson SP, Chen EH, Syniar GM, et al. "Pediatric Practice Research Group. Prevalence of symptoms of gastroesophageal reflux during infancy. A pediatric practice-based survey". *Archive of Pediatric Adolescent Medicine.* 1997;151(6):569-572.
[168] Campanozzi A, Boccia G, Pensabene L,et al. "Prevalence and natural history of gastroesophageal reflux: pediatric prospective survey". *Pediatrics.* 2009;123(3):779–783.
[169] Helmenstein AM. "What is the acidity or pH of milk?" *Thought.co.* 12 Jan 2019. https://www.thoughtco.com/what-is-the-ph-of-milk-603652 Accessed 1 June 2022.
[170] Miller RA. "Observations on the gastric acidity during the first month of life". *Archive of Diseases in Childhood.* 1941;16:22.
[171] Omari TI and Davidson GP. "Multipoint measurement of intragastric pH in healthy preterm infants". *Archives of Disease in Childhood - Fetal and Neonatal Edition.* 2003;88;517-520.
[172] Helm JF, Dodds WJ, Hogan WJ, et al. "Acid neutralizing capacity of human saliva". *Gastroenterology.* 1982;83:69-74.
[173] Orenstein SR. "Crying in infant GERD: Acid or volume? Heartburn or dyspepsia?" *Current Gastroenterology Reports.* 2008;10:433-436.
[174] "Oversupply". *Le Leche League International.* https://www.llli.org/breastfeeding-info/oversupply/ Accessed 1 June 2022.
[175] Barr RG and Drummond KN. "Developing functional lactase sufficiency in the first five months". *Pediatric Research.* 1981;15;525.
[176] American Academy of Pediatrics. "Lactose intolerance in infants and children". *Healthychildren.org* https://www.healthychildren.org/English/healthy-living/nutrition/Pages/Lactose-Intolerance-in-Children.aspx. Accessed 1 June 2022.
[177] Mohrbacher N. "Fat Content of Breast milk – FAQs". *Le Leche League GB.* https://www.laleche.org.uk/health-professionals/fat-content-breast milk-faqs/#:~:text=Fat%20slows%20down%20the%20transit,(lactose)%20can%20be%20digested. Accessed 1 June 2022.
[178] Edwards CA and Parrett AM. "Intestinal flora during the first months of life: new perspectives". *British Journal of Nutrition.* 2002;88:11-18.
[179] Shao Y, Forster SC, Tsaliki E, et al. "Stunted microbiota and opportunistic pathogen colonization in caesarean-section birth". *Nature.* 2019;574:117-121.
[180] Ma J. Li Z, Zang W, et al. "Comparison of gut microbiota in exclusively breast-fed and formula-fed babies: a study of 91 term infants". *Scientific Reports.* 2020;10(1):15792.
[181] Jones RB, Berger PK, Plows JF, et al. "Lactose-reduced infant formula with added corn syrup solids is associated with a distinct gut microbiota in Hispanic infants". Gut Microbes. 2020;12(1):1813534. doi: 10.1080/19490976.2020.1813534.

[182] Amarri S, Benatti F, Callegari ML, et al. "Changes of gut microbiota and immune markers during the complementary feeding period in healthy breast-fed infants". *Journal of Pediatric Gastroenterology and Nutrition.* 2006;42(5):488-495.
[183] Gupta RW, Tran L, Norori J, et al. "Histamine-2 receptor blockers alter the fecal microbiota in premature infants". *Journal of Pediatric Gastroenterology and Nutrition.* 2013;56:397-400. Levy EI, Hoang DM and Vandenplas Y. "The effects of proton pump inhibitors on the microbiome in young children". *Acta Paediatricia.* 2020;109:1531-1538.
[184] Neuman H, Forsythe P, Uzan A. et al. "Antibiotics in early life: dysbiosis and the damage done". *FEMS Microbiology Reviews.* 2018;42(4):489–499.
[185] American Academy of Pediatics, Committee on Nutrition. "Hypoallergenic infant formulas". *Pediatrics.* 2000:106:*346-349. Kearney PJ, Malone AJ, Hayes T, et al.* "A trial of lactase in the management of infant colic". *Journal of Human Nutrition and Dietetics.* 1998;11:281-285. Kanabar D, Randhawa M and Clayton P. "Improvement of symptoms in infant colic following reduction of lactose load with lactase". *Journal of Human Nutrition and Dietetics.* 2001;14:359-363.
Infante D, Segarra O and Le Leyer B. "Dietary treatment of colic caused by excess gas in infants: Biochemical evidence". *World Journal of Gastroenterology.* 2011;17(16):2104-2108.
[186] Oak SJ and Jha R. "The effects of probiotics in lactose intolerance: A systematic review". *Critical Reviews in Food Science and Nutrition.* 2019;59(11):1675-1683.
[187] As above.
[188] Forsgard RA. "Lactose digestion in humans: intestinal lactase appears to be constitutive whereas the colonic microbiome is adaptable". *The American Journal of Clinical Nutrition.* 2019;110(2);273-279.
[189] Coelho AI, Berry GT and Rubio-Gozalbo ME. *Galactose Metabolism and Health.* Current Opinion. https://www.researchgate.net/publication/283726200_Galactose_metabolism_and_health; Fynn A. *Nutrition and Health: Galactosemia.* Reference Model in Food Science. 2016 https://www.sciencedirect.com/science/article/pii/B9780081005965009707
[190] Amstrong K, Previtera N, and McCallum R, "Medicalizing normality? Management of irritability in infants." *Journal of Pediatrics and Child Health.* 2000;36(4):301-5. Rautava P, Helenius H and Lehtonen L. "Psychosocial predisposing factors for infantile colic". *British Medical Journal.* 1993:307:600-604. Barr RG. "Colic and crying syndromes in infants". *Pediatrics.* 1998;1025:1282-1286. Poole SR. "The infant with acute, unexplained, excessive crying". *Pediatrics.* 1991;88:450-455.
[191] Hiscock H and Jordan B. "Problem crying in infancy". *Medical Journal of Australia.* 2004;181(9):507-12.
[192] Amstrong K, Previtera N, and McCallum R, "Medicalizing normality? Management of irritability in infants." *Journal of Pediatrics and Child Health.* 2000;36(4):301-5. Rautava P, Helenius H and Lehtonen L. "Psychosocial predisposing factors for infantile colic". *British Medical Journal.* 1993:307:600-604. Barr RG. "Colic and crying syndromes in infants". *Pediatrics.* 1998;1025:1282-1286. Poole SR. "The infant with acute, unexplained, excessive crying". *Pediatrics.* 1991;88:450-455.
[193] Jaffe AC. "Failure to thrive: Current clinical concepts". *Pediatrics in Review.* 2011;32(3):100-107. Panetta F, Magazzu D, Sferlazzas C, et al. "Diagnosis on a positive fashion of nonorganic failure to thrive". *Acta Paediatricia.* 2008;97(9):1281-1284.

[194] Behrman RE, Kliegman RM and Jenson HB. *Nelson Textbook of Pediatrics*, 16th ed, WB Saunders, Philadelphia, 2000, pp 1125-26.
[195] Campanozzi A, Bossia G, Pensabene L, et al "Prevalence and natural history of gastroesophageal reflux: pediatric prospective survey". *Pediatrics.* 2009;123:779-83.
[196] Untersmayr E and Jensen-Jarolim E. "The role of protein digestibility and antacids on food allergy outcomes". *Journal of Allergy and Clinical Immunology.* 2008;121(6):1301-1310. Merwat S and Spechler S. "Might the use of acid-suppressive medications predispose to the development of eosinophilic esophagitis?" *The American Journal of Gastroenterology.* 2009;104:1897-902.
[197] Rybk A, Pesce M, Thapar N, et.al. "Gastro-esophageal reflux in children". *International Journal of Molecular Science.* 2017;18(8):1671.
[198] Heidelbaugh JJ. "Proton pump inhibitors and risk of vitamin and mineral deficiency: evidence and clinical implications". *Therapeutic Advances in Drug Safety.* 2013;**4**(3)125-133.
[199] Sultan N, Nazareno J, and Gregor J. "Association between proton pump inhibitors and respiratory infections: A systematic review and meta-analysis of clinical trials". *Canadian Journal of Gastroenterology.* 2008;22(9):761–766.
[200] Mezoff EA. "Acid suppression and the risk of clostridium difficile Infection". *Journal of Pediatrics.* 2013;163(3):627-630.
[201] Cook GC. "Infective gastroenteritis and its relationship to reduced gastric acidity". *Scandinavian Journal of Gastroenterology Supplement.* 1985;111:17-23.
[202] "What is gut health? A brief review". *Australian Centre for Functional Medicine.* https://functionalmedicine.com.au/gut-health/. Accessed 1 June 2022
[203] Sanaka M, Yamamoto T and Kuyama Y. "Effects of proton pump inhibitors on gastric emptying: a systematic review". *Digestive Diseases and Science.* 2010;55(9):2431-40.
[204] Lødrup A, Reimer C and Bytzer P. "Systematic review: symptoms of rebound acid hypersecretion following proton pump inhibitor treatment". *Scandinavian Journal of Gastroenterology* 2013;48(5):515-22.
[205] Hassall E. "Over-prescription of acid-suppressing medications in infants: How it came about, why it's wrong, and what to do About it". *Journal of Pediatrics.* 2012:160(2):193-198.
[206] Elizur A, Cohen M, Goldberg MR, et al. "Mislabelled cow's milk allergy in infants: a prospective cohort study". *Archives of Disease in Childhood.* 2013;98:408-412.
[207] "Cow's milk (dairy) allergy". *Australasian Society of Clinical Immunology and Allergy.* https://www.allergy.org.au/patients/food-allergy/cows-milk-dairy-allergy. Accessed 1 June 2022.
[208] Høst A. "Frequency of cow's milk allergy in childhood". *Annuals of Allergy, Asthma and Immunology.* 2002;89(6):33-37.
[209] R Meyer. "New guidelines for managing cow's milk allergy in infants". *Journal of Family Health.* 2008;18(1):27–30.
[210] Høst A and Halken S," Cow's milk allergy: Where have we come from and where are we going?', *Endocrine, Metabolic Immune Disorders – Drug Targets*, 2014;14(1):2-8.
[211] Restani P. "Goat milk allergenicity". *Journal of Pediatric Gastroenterology and Nutrition.* 2004;39(4):323-324.

[212] "Cow's milk (dairy) allergy". *Australasian Society of Clinical Immunology and Allergy.* https://www.allergy.org.au/patients/food-allergy/cows-milk-dairy-allergy. Accessed 1 June 2022.

[213] Koplin JJ, Allen KJ, Gurrin LC, et al. "The Impact of Family History of Allergy on Risk of Food Allergy: A Population-Based Study of Infants". *International Journal of Environmental Research and Public Health.* 2013;10(11):5364-5377.

[214] As above.

[215] Olafsdottir E, Aksnes L, Fluge G, et al. "Faecal calprotectin levels in infants with infantile colic, healthy infants, children with inflammatory bowel disease, children with recurrent abdominal pain and healthy children". *Acta Paediatrica.* 2002:91(1):45-50.

[216] "Hypoallergenic infant formulas". *American Academy of Pediatrics Committee on Nutrition.* https://publications.aap.org/pediatrics/article-abstract/106/2/346/62820/Hypoallergenic-Infant-Formulas?redirectedFrom=PDF. Accessed 1 June 2022.

[217] Quigley EMM. "Prokinetics in the management of functional gastrointestinal disorders". *Journal of Neurogastroenterology Motility.* 2015;21(3):330-336.

[218] Sanaka M, Yamamoto T and Kuyama Y. "Effects of proton pump inhibitors on gastric emptying: a systematic review". *Digestive Disease and Science.* 2010;55(9):2431-2440.

[219] Dodrill P and Gosa MM. "Pediatric dysphagia; physiology, assessment, and management". *Annals of Nutrition and Metabolism.* 2015;66(suppl 5):24–31.

[220] "Laryngomalacia". *Children's Hospital of Philadelphia (USA).* https://www.chop.edu/conditions-diseases/laryngomalacia. Accessed 1 June 2022.

[221] Loening-Baucke V and Swidsinski A. "Observational study of children with aerophagia". *Clinical Pediatrics.* 2008;47(7):664-669.

Index

Made in the USA
Coppell, TX
02 February 2024